C000135374

RECOGNISING ACHIEVEMENT

G C S E
Mathematics

Graduated Assessment

Stages 7 & 8

Authors

Howard Baxter

Mike Handbury

John Jeskins

Jean Matthews

Mark Patmore

Contributor

Colin White

Series editor *Brian Seager*

Hodder & Stoughton
A MEMBER OF THE HODDER HEADLINE GROUP

Orders: please contact Bookpoint Ltd, 130 Milton Park, Abingdon, Oxon OX14 4SB.
Telephone: (44) 01235 827720, Fax: (44) 01235 400454. Lines are open from
9.00 – 6.00, Monday to Saturday, with a 24 hour message answering service.
Email address: orders@bookpoint.co.uk

British Library Cataloguing in Publication Data

A catalogue record for this title is available from The British Library.

ISBN 0 340 801913

First published 2001

Impression number   10 9 8 7 6

Year 2007 2006 2005 2004 2003

Cover illustration by Mike Stones.

Produced by Gecko Limited, Bicester, Oxon.

Printed in Dubai for Hodder & Stoughton Educational, a division of Hodder Headline
Plc, 338 Euston Road, London NW1 3BH.

Acknowledgements

The Publishers would like to thank the following individuals and companies for
permission to reproduce photographs in this book:

Bubbles Photo Library: Frans Rombout page 91 (right).
Paul Hart: page 6 (top).
Life File Photo Library: Ron Gregory page 6 (bottom), David Kampfner page 93
and Lionel Moss page 91 (left)
Robert Harding Picture library: pages 5, 20.
The Photographers Library: pages 22, 90, 92, 117, 122 and 205 (both).

Every effort has been made to trace ownership of copyright. The Publishers would
be happy to make arrangements with any copyright holder whom it has not been
possible to trace.

This book covers the last part of the specification for the Intermediate tier of GCSE Mathematics and also the first part for the Higher tier. It is particularly aimed at OCR Mathematics C (Graduated Assessment) but could be used for other GCSE Mathematics examinations.

The work in this book covers the criteria in stages M7 and M8, and aims to make the best of your performance in the module tests and the terminal examination:

- Each chapter is presented in a style intended to help you understand the mathematics, with straightforward explanations and worked examples.
- At the start of each chapter is a list of what you should already know before you begin.
- There are plenty of exercises for you to work through and practise the skills.
- At the end of each chapter there is a list of key ideas.
- After every four or five chapters there is a revision exercise.
- Some exercises are designed to be done without a calculator so that you can practise for the non-calculator sections of the papers.
- Many chapters contain Activities to help you develop the necessary skills to undertake coursework.
- At frequent intervals throughout the book there are exam tips, where the experienced examiners who have written this book offer advice and tips to improve your examination performance.
- Revision exercises and Module tests are provided in the Teacher's Resource.

Part of the examination is a calculator-free zone. You will have to do the first section of each paper without a calculator and the questions are designed appropriately.

The percentage of the marks for the Assessment Objectives on the module tests and terminal examination are:

- 10% AO1 Using and Applying Mathematics
- 40% AO2 Number and Algebra
- 20% AO3 Shape, Space and Measures
- 10% AO4 Handling Data

The remaining marks to balance AO1 (10%) and AO4 (10%) are awarded to the internal assessment (coursework).

Most of the marks given for Algebra in AO2 are for 'manipulative' algebra. This includes simplifying algebraic expressions, factorising, solving equations and changing formulae. Some questions are also being set which offer you little help to get started. These are called 'unstructured' or 'multi-step' questions. Instead of the question having several parts, each of which leads to the next, you have to work out the necessary steps to find the answer. There will be examples of this kind of question in the revision tests and past examination papers.

Top ten tips

Here are some general tips from the examiners to help you do well in your tests and examination.

Practise:

1 all aspects of **manipulative algebra** in the specification
2 answering questions **without** a calculator
3 answering questions which require **explanations**
4 answering **unstructured** questions
5 **accurate** drawing and construction
6 answering questions which **need a calculator**, trying to use it efficiently
7 **checking answers**, especially for reasonable size and degree of accuracy
8 making your work **concise** and well laid out
9 using the **formula sheet** before the examination
10 **rounding** numbers, but only at the appropriate stage.

Coursework

The GCSE Mathematics examinations will assess your ability to use your mathematics on longer problems than those normally found on timed written examination papers. Assessment of this type of work will account for 20% of your final mark. It will involve two tasks, each taking about three hours. One task will be an investigation, the other a statistics task.

Each type of task has its own mark scheme in which marks are awarded in three categories or 'strands'. The titles of these strands give you clues about the important aspects of this work.

For the investigation tasks the strands are:

● Making and monitoring decisions – what you are going to do and how you will do it
● Communicating mathematically – explaining and showing exactly what you have done
● Developing the skills of mathematical reasoning – using mathematics to analyse and prove your results.

The table below gives some idea of what you will have to do and show. Look at this table whenever you are doing some extended work and try to include what it suggests you do.

Mark	Making and monitoring decisions	Communicating mathematically	Developing the skills of mathematical reasoning
1	organising work, producing information and checking results	discussing work using symbols and diagrams	finding examples that match a general statement
2	beginning to plan work, choosing your methods	giving reasons for choice of presentation of results and information	searching for a pattern using at least three results
3	finding out necessary information and checking it	showing understanding of the task by using words, symbols, diagrams	explaining reasoning and making a statement about the results found

Mark	Making and monitoring decisions	Communicating mathematically	Developing the skills of mathematical reasoning
4	simplifying the task by breaking it down into smaller stages	explaining what the words, symbols and diagrams show	testing generalisations by checking further cases
5	introducing new questions leading to a fuller solution	justifying the means of presentation	justifying solutions explaining why the results occur
6	using a range of techniques and reflecting on lines of enquiry and methods used	using symbolisation consistently	explaining generalisations and making further progress with the task
7	analysing lines of approach and giving detailed reasons for choices	using symbols and language to produce a convincing and reasoned argument	report includes mathematical justifications and explanations of the solutions to the problem
8	exploring extensively an unfamiliar context or area of mathematics and applying a range of appropriate mathematical techniques to solve a complex task	using mathematical language and symbols efficiently in presenting a concise reasoned argument	providing a mathematically rigorous justification or proof of the solution considering the conditions under which it remains valid

For the statistical tasks the strands are:

- Specifying the problem and planning – choosing or defining a problem and outlining the approach to be followed
- Collecting, processing and representing data – explaining and showing what you have done
- Interpreting and discussing results – using mathematical and statistical knowledge and techniques to analyse, evaluate and interpret your results and findings.

The marks obtained from each task are added together to give a total out of 48.

The table below gives some idea of what you will have to do and show. Look at this table whenever you are doing some extended work and try to include what it suggests you do.

Mark	Specifying the problem and planning	Collecting, processing and representing data	Interpreting and discussing results
1–2	choosing a simple problem and outlining a plan	collecting some data; presenting information, calculations and results	making comments on the data and results
3–4	choosing a problem which allows you to use simple statistics and plan the collection of data	collecting data and then processing it using appropriate calculations involving appropriate techniques; explaining what the words, symbols and diagrams show	explaining and interpreting the graphs and calculations and any patterns in the data

Mark	Specifying the problem and planning	Collecting, processing and representing data	Interpreting and discussing results
5–6	considering a more complex problem and using a range of techniques and reflecting on the method used	collecting data in a form that ensures they can be used; explaining statistical meaning through the consistent use of accurate statistics and giving a reason for the choice of presentation; explaining features selected	commenting on, justifying and explaining results and calculations; commenting on the methods used
7–8	analysing the approach and giving reasons for the methods used; using a range of appropriate statistical techniques to solve the problem	using language and statistical concepts effectively in presenting a convincing reasoned argument; using an appropriate range of diagrams to summarise the data and show how variables are related	correctly summarising and interpreting graphs and calculations and making correct and detailed inferences from the data; appreciating the significance of results obtained and, where relevant, allowing for the nature and size of the sample and any possible bias; evaluating the effectiveness of the overall strategy and recognising limitations of the work done, making suggestions for improvement

Advice

Starting a task

Ask yourself:
- what does the task tell me?
- what does it ask me?
- what can I do to get started?
- what equipment and materials do I need?

Working on the task

- Make sure you explain your method and present your results as clearly as possible
- Break the task down into stages. For example in 'How many squares on a chessboard', begin by looking at 1 × 1 squares then 2 × 2 squares, then 3 × 3 squares. In a task asking for the design of a container, start with cuboids then nets, surface area, prisms … Or in statistics you might want to start with a pilot survey or questionnaire.
- Write down questions that occur to you, for example, *what happens if you change the size of a rectangle systematically?* They may help you find out more about the work. In a statistical task you might wish to include different age groups or widen the type of data.

- Explore as many aspects of the task as possible.
- Develop the task into new situations and explore these thoroughly.
  - What connections are possible?
  - Is there a result to help me?
  - Is there a pattern?
  - Can the problem be changed? If so, how?

Explain your work

- Use appropriate words and suitable tables, diagrams, graphs, calculations.
- Link as much of your work together as possible, explaining, for example, why you chose the tables and charts you used and rejected others, or why the median is more appropriate than the mean in a particular statistical analysis, or why a pie chart is not appropriate. Don't just include diagrams to show identical information in different ways.
- Use algebra or symbols to give clear and efficient explanations; in investigations, you must use algebra to progress beyond about 4 marks. You will get more credit for writing $T = 5N + 1$ than for writing 'the total is five times the pattern number, plus one'.
- Don't waffle or use irrelevant mathematics; present results and conclusions clearly.

State your findings

- Show how patterns have been used and test conclusions.
- State general results in words and explain what they mean.
- Write formulae and explain how they have been found from the situations explored.
- Prove the results using efficient mathematical methods.
- Develop new results from previous work and use clear reasoning to prove conclusions.
- Make sure your reasoning is accurate and draws upon the evidence you've presented.
- Show findings in clear, relevant diagrams.
- Check you've answered the question or hypothesis.

Review/conclusion/extension

- Is the solution acceptable?
- Can the task be extended?
- What can be learned from it?

Example task

On the next page there is a short investigative task for you to try, in both 'structured' and 'unstructured' form. The structured form shows the style of a question that might appear on a timed written paper. The unstructured form represents the usual style of a coursework task. The structured form leads you to an algebraic conclusion. Notice the appearance of algebra from question 4 onwards, through a series of structured questions. These mirror the sort of questions you would be expected to think of (and answer) if you were trying it as coursework.

Comments about the questions, linking the two forms of presentation, are also shown.

Although the task in both forms directs you to investigate trapezium numbers, you would be expected to extend the investigation into other forms of number, such as pentagon numbers, to achieve the higher marks.

ACTIVITY

| structured form | unstructured form |

Trapezium numbers

These diagrams represent the first three trapezium numbers.

Each diagram always starts with two dots on the top row.

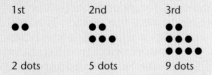

So the third trapezium number is 9 because nine dots can be arranged as a trapezium. There are two dots in the top row, three dots in the next row and four dots in the bottom row.

Trapezium numbers

These diagrams represent the first three trapezium numbers.

Each diagram starts with two dots on the top row.

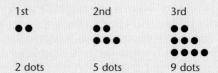

So the third trapezium number is 9 because nine dots can be arranged as a trapezium.

Investigate trapezium numbers

NB Although the task in this form asks you to investigate trapezium numbers, you have the freedom to – and are expected to – extend the investigation to consider other forms of number such as pentagon numbers.

Commentary

This question allows you to show understanding of the task, systematically obtaining information which **could** enable you to find an expression for trapezium numbers.

1 Write down the next two trapezium numbers

2 a) Draw a table, graph or chart of all the trapezium numbers, from the first to the tenth.
b) Work out the eleventh trapezium number.

This question provides a structure, using symbols, words and diagrams, from which you should be able to derive an expression from either a table or a graph. Part **b)** could be done as a 'predict and test'.

3 The 19th trapezium number is 209. Explain how you could work out the 20th trapezium number without drawing any diagrams.

In the unstructured form you would not normally answer a question like this.

4 Find an expression for the number of dots in the bottom row of the nth trapezium number.
Test your expression for a suitable value of n.

From here you are **directed** in the structured task, and **expected** in the unstructured task, to use algebra, testing the expression – the **generalisation**.

5 Find, giving an explanation, an expression for the number of dots in the bottom row of the diagram for the $(n + 1)$th trapezium number.

In the unstructured form this would represent the sort of 'new' question you might ask, to lead to a further solution and to demonstrate symbolic presentation and the ability to relate the work to the physical structure, rather than doing all the analysis from a table of values.

6 The nth trapezium number is x. Write down an expression in terms of x and n for the $(n + 1)$th trapezium number. Test your expression for a suitable value of n.

Stage 7

CONTENTS

1 Understanding and using ratios

Value for money

Most people think 'value for money' is very important. Although some supermarkets have realised this too, and give comparative prices, you often need to work out for yourself which item gives you better value for your money.

As an example, look at this special offer.

It is easy to spot that the large pack contains three times as much as the small one.

Cost of 1·5 kg = £4·99

Cost of three small packs (3 × 500 g) = 3 × £1·70 = £5·10

The large pack is better value.

If you can't see a quick method, here are two other methods you can use to make the comparison.

1 Price per unit

In this example, this is the price per kg.

	Large	Small
Price per kg	$\dfrac{£4·99}{1·5}$ = £3·33	£1·70 × 2 = £3·40

The unit price is lower for the large pack so this is better value.

2 Number of units per pence or pound (£)

	Large	Small
Number of grams for 1p	$\dfrac{1500}{499}$ = 3·01 to 2 d.p.	$\dfrac{500}{170}$ = 2·94 to 2 d.p.

The number of grams you buy for 1p is greater for the large pack, so this is better value.

Exam tip

There are different methods you can use for comparing prices. Take care with the units of what you have found and write them down clearly. This will help you to see whether a lower number is better or worse value! A question may also ask you to consider other factors that may influence a decision. For example a large pack may not be better value if the contents are not used by the 'best before' date.

Sharing

Other types of ratio problem that you may need to solve include questions about sharing. These examples cover two of them.

ACTIVITY 1

Go to your local shop. Choose something you like and find out the prices of different sizes of the same product. Are larger sizes cheaper in comparison?

EXAMPLE 1

Two families share a meal and the total cost is £77·91. They agree to pay in the ratio 3 to 4. How much should each family pay?

Number of shares = 3 + 4 = 7

Cost per share = £77·91 ÷ 7 = £11·13

One family pays £11·13 × 3 = £33·39

The other family pays £11·13 × 4 = £44·52

Check: £33·39 + £44·52 = £77·91 = total cost

EXAMPLE 2

Jenny and Mike share some prize money in the ratio 3 to 2. Jenny gets £12·60. How much does Mike get?

3 shares = £12·60

1 share = £12·60 ÷ 3 = £4·20

2 shares = £4·20 × 2 = £8·40

Mike gets £8·40.

EXERCISE 1.1A

1 A 400 ml can of drink costs 38p. How many pence is this for 100 ml?

2 A 420 g bag of Mars bars costs £1·59. How many pence per gram is this?

3 A 325 g bag of Mars bars costs £1·09. How many grams for 1p is this?

4 A 400 g tin of tomatoes costs 28p. How many pence per gram is this?

5 Three litres of sunflower oil cost £2·19. How much is this per millilitre?

6 Show which is better value, 5 litres of spa water for £1·29 or 2 litres for 87p.

7 Here are the prices of some bottles of cola. Which size gives the best value?

3 litre £1·99   2 litre £1·35
1 litre 57p   500 ml 65p

Give a reason why you might want to buy another size rather than the best-value one.

8 Here are the prices of some packs of cans of cola. Which pack gives the most cola for your money?

12 × 150 ml cans for £2·95
6 × 330 ml cans for £1·59
12 × 330 ml cans for £2·99

9 Three families share the cost of a holiday in the ratio 4 to 3 to 2. The total cost of the holiday is £2790. How much does each family pay?

10 Petra and Sam took part in a sponsored swim. The amounts they raised were in the ratio 5 to 3. Petra raised £75·50. How much did Sam raise?

EXERCISE 1.1B

1 A 100 ml tube of toothpaste costs £1·79. How much does 1 ml cost?

2 A tin of baked beans and sausages costs 75p for the 420 g size. How many grams is this for 1p?

3 A 680 g pack of mild cheese costs £2·59. Find the cost per gram.

4 A 500 g pack of mild cheese costs £1·99. Find the cost per gram.

5 A brand of shaving gel costs £1·19 for the 75 ml bottle and £2·89 for the 200 ml bottle. Show which is the better value.

Exercise 1.1B cont'd

6 Here are some comparisons for a brand of toothpaste.

Cost of tube	£1·19	£2·05
Amount	50 ml	100 ml
Cost of 1 ml	2·38p	2·05p

a) Which size is the better buy?

b) For each size, find how many millilitres you get for 1p.

7 Here are some special offers at two record stores.

Explain which is the better offer if you want to buy

a) three CDs **b)** four CDs.

8 Jo and Karen want to go out for a meal on a Wednesday. Their two local restaurants have special offers.

Buy a meal for £8.50 and get the second half-price

Monday to Thursday evenings – meals only £6.99

Which offer would be cheaper for them?

9 Jeff and his mother find that their ages are in the ratio 3 to 7. Jeff is 15 years old. How old is his mother?

10 The price of adults' and children's tickets for a theatre are in the ratio 5 to 2. The total price of one adult's and one child's ticket is £17·50. How much does each of these tickets cost?

Multiplier method

Ratio problems can also be solved using a multiplier method. This is used in the next example.

Drawing up a table often helps to decide which parts you need to use.

> **Exam tip**
>
> Ratios may be written 'a to b' or 'a : b'.

EXAMPLE 3

Adrian made a fruit drink with 9 parts orange juice, 4 parts lemon juice and 2 parts grapefruit juice. He made 2 litres of fruit drink. How much orange juice did he need?

	orange	: lemon	: grapefruit	Total
Parts	9	4	2	15
Quantity	x			2000 ml

Using ratios, $x : 9 = 2000 : 15$

$$x = \frac{2000}{15} \times 9 = 1200 \text{ ml}$$

This example could have been worked out without a calculator, and you may be able to do so.

In these exercises you will get some practice in solving ratio problems without a calculator. In some of the questions where you do use a calculator, you will need to round your answers.

Exam tip

A common error, when using a calculator, is to round at too early a stage. In Example 3, if the answer is rounded after dividing by 15 to give 133 and this is then multiplied by 9, the answer comes out as 1197 instead of 1200.

EXERCISE 1.2A

Answer the first five questions without using a calculator.

1 Split £100 in the ratio $2:3:5$.

2 The angles of a triangle are in the ratio $1:2:3$. What are the sizes of the angles?

3 John and Qasim share £20 in the ratio 2 to 3. How much does John get?

4 Paint is mixed as 3 parts red to 5 parts white. How much of this paint can be made with 2 litres of white?

5 Susan and Chika invest £4000 and £6000 in a business venture and agree to share the profits in the ratio of their investment. They make a profit of £250 in the first year. How much does Chika receive?

For the rest of the questions you can use a calculator.

6 Maureen and Sheena's earnings are in the ratio $3:5$. They earn £352 all together. How much does Sheena earn?

7 At Carterknowle Church Autumn Bazaar £875 was raised. It was agreed to share the profits between the church and the local charity for the homeless in the ratio 5 to 1. How much did the charity receive? Give the answer to the nearest pound.

Exercise 1.2A cont'd

8 To make her own breakfast cereal, Sally mixes bran, currants and wheatgerm in the ratio 8 to 3 to 1 by mass. How much bran, to the nearest 10 grams, does she use to make 500 grams of cereal?

9 David, Michael and Iain employed a gardener and agreed to pay him in the ratio of the time he spent on each garden. He spent 2 hours 20 minutes in David's garden, 3 hours 30 minutes in Michael's garden and 4 hours 10 minutes in Iain's garden. David paid £12·60. How much did the other two pay?

10 In a local election the votes were Labour 1200, Conservative 5312, Lib-Dems 878. Write this ratio in the form $1:n:m$. Correct n and m to three significant figures.

EXERCISE 1.2B

Do not use a calculator for the first five questions.

1 Share £75 in the ratio 8 to 7.

2 A firm uses first and second class stamps in the ratio 9 to 1. During a week they used 250 stamps altogether. How many first class stamps did they use?

3 A metal alloy is made up of copper, iron and nickel in the ratio $3:4:2$. How much copper is there in 450 g of the alloy?

4 Vicki and Inderjit share the winnings from a raffle in the ratio 2 to 3. Vicki received £15. How much did they win altogether?

5 Old 2-stroke scooters used to mix petrol with oil in the ratio 25 to 1. How much oil had to be mixed with 5 litres of petrol?

Use a calculator for the rest of the questions.

Exercise 1.2B cont'd

6 In a school there are 875 pupils and 41 teachers. Write the pupil : teacher ratio in the form $n:1$. Express n correct to three significant figures.

7 Shahida spends her pocket money on sweets, magazines and savings in the ratio $2:3:7$. She receives £15 a week. How much does she spend on sweets?

8 Doreen and Joan invested £5000 and £7500 respectively in a firm. They shared the profits in the ratio of their investment. Doreen received £320. How much did Joan receive?

9 Alec and Pat share a house. They agree to share the rent (to the nearest pound) in the ratio of the area of their bedrooms. The area of Alec's floor is $17\,m^2$ and the area of Pat's is $21\,m^2$. The rent is £320 a week. How much do they each pay?

10 In a questionnaire the three possible answers are 'Yes', 'No' and 'Don't know'. The answers from a group of 456 people are in the ratio $10:6:3$. How many 'Don't knows' are there?

Key ideas

- Best buy – compare the price per unit or the number of units you get for £1 or 1p. Sometimes, you might be able to see a quicker method.

- Ratios – think how many shares there are. Often, you need to find the value of one share.

2 Using the four operations with fractions

You should already know

- how to add and subtract simple fractions.

Mixed numbers

Look at this calculation.

$$\frac{2}{3} + \frac{2}{3} = \frac{4}{3}$$

As you can see the result of this addition is a fraction which is 'top-heavy'.

It is usual to write fractions like this as **mixed numbers.**

$$\frac{4}{3} = 1\frac{1}{3}$$

To change a top-heavy fraction to a mixed number, divide the denominator into the numerator and write the remainder as a fraction over the denominator.

EXAMPLE 1

Change these fractions to mixed numbers.

a) $\frac{7}{4}$ b) $\frac{11}{5}$ c) $\frac{24}{7}$

a) $\frac{7}{4} = 1\frac{3}{4}$ 7 ÷ 4 = 1 with 3 left over.

b) $\frac{11}{5} = 2\frac{1}{5}$ 11 ÷ 5 = 2 with 1 left over.

c) $\frac{24}{7} = 3\frac{3}{7}$ 24 ÷ 7 = 3 with 3 left over.

Exam tip

The most common error is to put the remainder over the numerator rather than over the denominator.

Mixed numbers can be changed to top-heavy fractions. Just reverse the process.

EXAMPLE 2

Change these mixed numbers to top-heavy fractions.

a) $3\frac{1}{4}$ **b)** $2\frac{3}{5}$ **c)** $3\frac{5}{6}$

a) $3\frac{1}{4} = 3 + \frac{1}{4} = \frac{12}{4} + \frac{1}{4} = \frac{13}{4}$

Change the whole number to quarters and then add. Another way to think of it is to multiply the whole number by the denominator and add on the numerator $(3 \times 4 + 1 = 13)$.

b) $2\frac{3}{5} = \frac{13}{5}$

$2 \times 5 + 3 = 13$

c) $3\frac{5}{6} = \frac{23}{6}$

$3 \times 6 + 5 = 23$

To add or subtract mixed numbers deal with the whole numbers first.

EXAMPLE 3

Work these out.

a) $1\frac{1}{6} + 2\frac{1}{3}$ **b)** $2\frac{3}{4} + \frac{3}{5}$ **c)** $3\frac{2}{3} - 1\frac{1}{6}$ **d)** $4\frac{1}{5} - 1\frac{1}{2}$

a) $1\frac{1}{6} + 2\frac{1}{3} = 3 + \frac{1}{6} + \frac{1}{3}$

$= 3 + \frac{1}{6} + \frac{2}{6}$

$= 3\frac{3}{6} = 3\frac{1}{2}$

Add the whole numbers, then deal with the fractions in the normal way.

b) $2\frac{3}{4} + \frac{3}{5} = 2 + \frac{15}{20} + \frac{12}{20}$

$= 2 + \frac{27}{20}$

$= 2 + 1 + \frac{7}{20}$

$= 3\frac{7}{20}$

You end up with a top-heavy fraction which you have to change to a mixed number, and then add the whole numbers.

c) $3\frac{2}{3} - 1\frac{1}{6} = 3 - 1 + \frac{2}{3} - \frac{1}{6}$

$= 2 + \frac{4}{6} - \frac{1}{6}$

$= 2\frac{3}{6} = 2\frac{1}{2}$

Subtract the numbers and then the fractions.

d) $4\frac{1}{5} - 1\frac{1}{2} = 3 + \frac{2}{10} - \frac{5}{10}$

$= 2 + \frac{10}{10} + \frac{2}{10} - \frac{5}{10}$

$= 2\frac{7}{10}$

Working out $\frac{2}{10} - \frac{5}{10}$ gives a negative answer of $\frac{-3}{10}$. Change one of the whole numbers into $\frac{10}{10}$, then subtract.

EXERCISE 2.1A

1 Change these top-heavy fractions to mixed numbers.

   a) $\frac{7}{4}$ **b)** $\frac{12}{5}$ **c)** $\frac{17}{3}$ **d)** $\frac{15}{4}$ **e)** $\frac{25}{2}$

2 Change these mixed numbers to top-heavy fractions.

   a) $1\frac{1}{2}$ **b)** $2\frac{3}{5}$ **c)** $5\frac{3}{8}$ **d)** $2\frac{4}{7}$ **e)** $9\frac{1}{4}$

3 Add. Write your answers as simply as possible.

   a) $1\frac{1}{3} + 3\frac{1}{4}$ **b)** $3\frac{1}{5} + \frac{7}{10}$

   c) $1\frac{3}{4} + 4\frac{2}{5}$ **d)** $2\frac{5}{6} + 7\frac{4}{9}$

   e) $\frac{2}{7} + \frac{1}{2} + \frac{5}{14}$ **f)** $1\frac{1}{2} + \frac{3}{4} + 2\frac{3}{8}$

4 Subtract. Write your answers as simply as possible.

   a) $2\frac{4}{5} - 1\frac{3}{5}$ **b)** $5\frac{3}{8} - 2\frac{1}{4}$

   c) $3\frac{2}{3} - \frac{1}{2}$ **d)** $3\frac{2}{5} - 1\frac{3}{4}$

   e) $5\frac{1}{6} - 3\frac{2}{3}$ **f)** $5\frac{1}{5} - \frac{2}{3}$

5 Work these out. Write the answers as simply as possible.

   a) $\frac{1}{4} + \frac{2}{3} + \frac{1}{2}$ **b)** $2\frac{1}{3} + 2\frac{1}{4} - 1\frac{5}{6}$

   c) $3\frac{3}{5} - \frac{1}{4} + \frac{1}{2}$ **d)** $2\frac{3}{8} - \frac{1}{2} + 3\frac{1}{4}$

   e) $4\frac{1}{5} + 1\frac{3}{10} - \frac{4}{5}$ **f)** $2\frac{3}{7} - \frac{1}{2} - 1\frac{2}{7}$

6 Faisal cut two pieces of wood $3\frac{3}{8}$ inches and $5\frac{1}{4}$ inches long from a piece 10 inches long. How long was the piece that was left?

7 A table $31\frac{5}{8}$ inches high was raised by putting its legs on blocks each $1\frac{3}{4}$ inches high. What was the new height of the table?

EXERCISE 2.1B

1 Change these top-heavy fractions to mixed numbers.

   a) $\frac{9}{2}$ **b)** $\frac{14}{3}$ **c)** $\frac{17}{4}$ **d)** $\frac{23}{6}$ **e)** $\frac{35}{8}$

2 Change these mixed numbers to top-heavy fractions.

   a) $5\frac{1}{2}$ **b)** $2\frac{3}{10}$ **c)** $2\frac{3}{7}$

   d) $4\frac{2}{3}$ **e)** $4\frac{5}{6}$

3 Add. Write your answers as simply as possible.

   a) $1\frac{1}{2} + 2\frac{1}{6}$ **b)** $1\frac{4}{5} + 2\frac{1}{10}$

   c) $6\frac{1}{6} + 1\frac{4}{9}$ **d)** $2\frac{4}{7} + 1\frac{2}{3}$

   e) $\frac{4}{5} + 1\frac{3}{4} + 2\frac{1}{2}$ **f)** $6\frac{1}{3} + 1\frac{4}{9} + 1\frac{2}{9}$

4 Subtract. Write your answers as simply as possible.

   a) $2\frac{2}{3} - 1\frac{1}{6}$ **b)** $3\frac{5}{8} - 1\frac{1}{4}$

   c) $2\frac{4}{5} - \frac{1}{2}$ **d)** $4\frac{2}{5} - 1\frac{1}{4}$

   e) $8\frac{1}{6} - 5\frac{3}{8}$ **f)** $1\frac{1}{4} - \frac{5}{8}$

5 Work these out. Write the answers as simply as possible.

   a) $2\frac{1}{3} + 3\frac{1}{2} - \frac{5}{6}$ **b)** $1\frac{3}{4} - \frac{5}{6} + 2\frac{1}{2}$

   c) $3\frac{1}{6} - 2\frac{1}{8} + \frac{3}{4}$ **d)** $4\frac{1}{3} - \frac{4}{5} + \frac{2}{5}$

   e) $3\frac{3}{4} - 2\frac{1}{2} + 1\frac{5}{8}$ **f)** $4\frac{1}{3} - 1\frac{5}{6} - 2\frac{1}{2}$

Exercise 2.1B cont'd

6 Caroline bought a piece of ribbon 24 inches long. She cut off two pieces, each $5\frac{5}{8}$ inches long. How long was the piece she had left?

7 Sam had a piece of wood $28\frac{1}{2}$ inches long. After using some, $9\frac{5}{8}$ inches were left. What length did he use?

Multiplying fractions

To multiply fractions, multiply the numerators and multiply the denominators, then simplify if possible. If the fractions are mixed numbers, change them to top-heavy fractions and then multiply.

EXAMPLE 4

Work these out.

a) $\frac{3}{5} \times \frac{1}{2}$ **b)** $\frac{3}{8} \times \frac{4}{9}$ **c)** $1\frac{3}{5} \times 3\frac{3}{4}$

a) $\frac{3}{5} \times \frac{1}{2} = \frac{3}{10}$

Multiply the numerators and multiply the denominators. The answer is already in its lowest terms.

b) $\frac{3}{8} \times \frac{4}{9} = \frac{12}{72} = \frac{1}{6}$

The answer simplifies to $\frac{1}{6}$ but you could divide by the common factors (cancel) first, for example $\frac{{}^1\cancel{3}}{{}_2\cancel{8}} \times \frac{\cancel{4}^1}{\cancel{9}_3} = \frac{1}{2} \times \frac{1}{3} = \frac{1}{6}$

as 3 divides into 3 and 9; 4 divides into 4 and 8.

c) $1\frac{3}{5} \times 3\frac{3}{4} = \frac{8}{5} \times \frac{15}{4}$

$= \frac{2}{1} \times \frac{3}{1} = 6$

5 divides into 5 and 15; 4 divides into 4 and 8.

> **Exam tip**
>
> Note: $\frac{1}{2} \times \frac{1}{3} = \frac{1}{6}$
> A common error is to multiply 1×1 and get 2.

> **Exam tip**
>
> When 'cancelling', divide a term in the numerator and a term in the denominator.

Remember that, when simplifying or 'cancelling', you can just cross out the numbers you are cancelling and write in the quotients, for example,

$\frac{3}{8} \times \frac{4}{9} = \frac{{}^1\cancel{3}}{{}_2\cancel{8}} \times \frac{\cancel{4}^1}{\cancel{9}_3} = \frac{1}{2} \times \frac{1}{3}$

Dividing fractions

Multiplying by $\frac{1}{2}$ is the same as dividing by 2, so dividing by $\frac{1}{2}$ is the same as multiplying by 2.

This can be extended, for example $4 \div \frac{2}{3} = 4 \times \frac{3}{2} = \frac{12}{2} = 6$

When dividing fractions, turn the second fraction upside-down and then multiply.

EXAMPLE 5

Work these out.

a) $\frac{4}{5} \div \frac{3}{10}$ **b)** $\frac{9}{10} \div \frac{3}{4}$ **c)** $2\frac{1}{4} \div 1\frac{1}{2}$

a) $\frac{4}{5} \div \frac{3}{10} = \frac{4}{5} \times \frac{10}{3}$
$\qquad = \frac{4}{1} \times \frac{2}{3} = \frac{8}{3} = 2\frac{2}{3}$

Turn the second fraction upside-down and multiply. Divide 10 and 5 by 5, multiply and change to a mixed number.

b) $\frac{9}{10} \div \frac{3}{4} = \frac{9}{10} \times \frac{4}{3}$
$\qquad = \frac{3}{5} \times \frac{2}{1} = \frac{6}{5} = 1\frac{1}{5}$

Divide 9 and 3 by 3, 4 and 10 by 2.

c) $2\frac{1}{4} \div 1\frac{1}{2} = \frac{9}{4} \div \frac{3}{2}$
$\qquad = \frac{9}{4} \times \frac{2}{3} = \frac{3}{2} \times \frac{1}{1}$
$\qquad = \frac{3}{2} = 1\frac{1}{2}$

Change to top-heavy fractions.
Divide 9 and 3 by 3, 2 and 4 by 2.

EXERCISE 2.2A

1 a) $\frac{1}{4} \times \frac{2}{3}$ **b)** $\frac{2}{3} \times \frac{3}{5}$ **c)** $\frac{4}{9} \times \frac{1}{2}$

2 a) $\frac{1}{3} \times \frac{2}{3}$ **b)** $\frac{5}{6} \times \frac{3}{5}$ **c)** $\frac{3}{7} \times \frac{7}{9}$

3 a) $\frac{4}{5} \div \frac{3}{10}$ **b)** $\frac{1}{4} \div \frac{3}{8}$ **c)** $\frac{3}{4} \div \frac{5}{6}$

4 a) $\frac{2}{5} \div \frac{1}{15}$ **b)** $\frac{2}{5} \div \frac{7}{10}$ **c)** $\frac{1}{6} \div \frac{3}{4}$

5 a) $4\frac{1}{2} \times 2\frac{1}{6}$ **b)** $1\frac{1}{2} \times 3\frac{2}{3}$ **c)** $4\frac{1}{5} \times 1\frac{2}{3}$

6 a) $2\frac{1}{3} \div 1\frac{1}{3}$ **b)** $2\frac{2}{5} \div 1\frac{1}{2}$ **c)** $3\frac{1}{5} \div \frac{4}{15}$

7 a) $2\frac{1}{2} \times 1\frac{1}{3} \times \frac{3}{8}$ **b)** $1\frac{1}{2} \times 2\frac{2}{3} \div 1\frac{3}{5}$ **c)** $1\frac{1}{4} \times 3\frac{1}{5} \div 1\frac{1}{2}$

EXERCISE 2.2B

1 **a)** $\frac{1}{2} \times \frac{5}{6}$ **b)** $\frac{5}{6} \times \frac{3}{5}$ **c)** $\frac{2}{3} \times \frac{5}{8}$

2 **a)** $\frac{3}{5} \times \frac{5}{12}$ **b)** $\frac{1}{6} \times \frac{3}{8}$ **c)** $\frac{3}{5} \times \frac{10}{9}$

3 **a)** $\frac{3}{8} \div \frac{1}{4}$ **b)** $\frac{2}{3} \div \frac{5}{8}$ **c)** $\frac{3}{4} \div \frac{3}{8}$

4 **a)** $\frac{2}{3} \div \frac{4}{15}$ **b)** $\frac{3}{5} \div \frac{9}{10}$ **c)** $\frac{1}{8} \div \frac{5}{12}$

5 **a)** $3\frac{1}{3} \times 2\frac{2}{5}$ **b)** $2\frac{2}{5} \times \frac{3}{4}$ **c)** $3\frac{1}{5} \times 1\frac{2}{3}$

6 **a)** $3\frac{1}{8} \div 1\frac{1}{4}$ **b)** $2\frac{1}{4} \div 3\frac{1}{2}$ **c)** $1\frac{1}{5} \div \frac{4}{15}$

7 **a)** $3\frac{1}{2} \times 1\frac{2}{3} \times \frac{5}{7}$ **b)** $1\frac{1}{4} \times 1\frac{2}{3} \div 1\frac{1}{9}$ **c)** $3\frac{1}{3} \times 1\frac{1}{4} \div 2\frac{1}{2}$

Key ideas

- When adding or subtracting fractions, change both fractions to the same denominator and add or subtract the numerators.
- If mixed numbers are involved, deal with the whole numbers separately when adding or subtracting.
- When multiplying fractions, multiply the numerators and multiply the denominators and cancel down.
- When dividing fractions, invert the second fraction and multiply.
- If mixed numbers are involved, change to top-heavy fractions before multiplying or dividing.

3 Theoretical probabilities and relative frequency

You should already know

- probabilities can be expressed as fractions, decimals or percentages
- how to simplify fractions
- how to round to 1, 2 or 3 decimal places.

This section brings together much of the previous work you have done on probabilities.

We can often use a theoretical argument to work out probabilities. For example, when you toss a coin, it can land heads or tails. If the coin is not biased, these outcomes are equally likely. So the probability of getting a head is $\frac{1}{2}$.

This may be written more concisely as P(head) = $\frac{1}{2}$.

Where there is a set of equally likely outcomes,

the probability of an event occurring = $\dfrac{\text{number of ways the event can occur}}{\text{total number of possible outcomes}}$

EXAMPLE 1

What is the probability of drawing a red counter out of a box containing 3 blue, 8 red and 7 white counters?

Total number of counters = 18

Number of red counters = 8

Assuming all counters are equally likely to be chosen,

P(red) = $\frac{8}{18}$ = $\frac{4}{9}$

In this example we assumed all the counters were equally likely to be chosen. This may also be signalled by words in a question such as 'drawn out without looking' or 'drawn at random'. They are all ways of indicating that there is no special bias in the way the counter is drawn out.

You may also need to use the result, that all probabilities add up to 1. In Example 1, for instance, P(a counter is not red) = 1 − P(red) = $\frac{5}{9}$

P(not A) = 1 − P(A)

EXERCISE 3.1A

1 When a fair dice is thrown, what is the probability of getting

    a) a five   **b)** a prime number?

2 A fair pentagonal spinner labelled 1,2,3,4,5 is spun. What is the probability of getting

    a) a five   **b)** a prime number?

3 The probability that it will rain today is 0·85. What is the probability that it will not rain?

4 A penny and a 10p piece are tossed together. List all the possible outcomes and find the probability of getting two heads.

5 A set of ordinary playing cards contains 52 cards. What is the probability of drawing the ace of spades if one card is chosen at random?

6 A box of chocolates contains 9 plain, 5 milk and 6 white chocolates. One of these is taken at random. Find the probability of taking **a)** a plain chocolate **b)** a chocolate that is not white.

7 Sam's pencil case contains 3 red, 4 blue and 5 black pens. He takes a pen out without looking. What is the probability that it is **a)** blue **b)** green?

8 Alice, Banda, Chris and Deena have agreed that two of them will do a sponsored swim. To decide which, they put their names in a bag and draw them out. What is the probability that Banda and Chris are chosen?

9 A family has 3 children. What is the probability that there are 2 boys and a girl, assuming girls and boys are equally likely?

10 A fair dice is thrown 1200 times. Roughly how many times would you expect it to land on a six?

EXERCISE 3.1B

1 When a fair dice is thrown, what is the probability of getting
  a) an even number
  b) a number which is divisible by 3?

2 The faces of a fair dice are labelled 1, 1, 2, 3, 4, 5. What is the probability for this dice of getting
  a) an even number
  b) a number which is divisible by 3?

3 The probability of Cheryl winning a race is 0·2. What is the probability that she doesn't win?

4 Two dice are thrown together. List all the possible outcomes and calculate the probability of getting **a)** a double six
  b) a score with a total of 10.

5 A set of ordinary playing cards contains 52 cards. What is the probability of drawing a heart if one card is chosen at random?

6 A box contains 12 red, 20 green and 8 yellow sweets. One is taken at random. Find the probability that the sweet is **a)** green
  b) not red.

7 Tim's sock drawer has 6 pairs of black socks, 4 pairs of navy and 5 pairs of patterned. He takes a pair out without looking. What is the probability that the pair is
  a) navy   **b)** white?

8 Alice, Banda, Chris and Deena sit next to each other in the cinema. What is the probability that Alice is in the seat nearest the aisle and Deena is next to her?

9 A fair coin is tossed 3 times. What is the probability of getting all heads?

10 A card is chosen at random from an ordinary pack of cards. It is put back and this is repeated for 1000 trials. Roughly how many times would you expect a heart to be chosen?

Relative frequency and probability

It is not always possible to find probabilities from looking at equally likely outcomes. You may have to work out the probability of throwing a six with a die which may be biased, the probability of a young driver having an accident, the probability that a person will visit a certain supermarket.

For this type of event you need to set up some sort of experiment, carry out a survey or look at past results.

Take the example of throwing a six with a die which may be biased. For a fair die (unbiased), the probability of getting a six = $\frac{1}{6}$ = 0·166... = 0·17 approximately.

If you were to throw it ten times and get four sixes would this be evidence of bias?

The proportion of sixes is $\frac{4}{10}$ = 0·4 which is very different from 0·17, but in a small sample of trials there may be runs of non-typical results. So you would not conclude that it is biased.

What about ten times in 50 throws? Here the proportion is $\frac{10}{50}$ = 0·2 which is still quite a bit different from 0·17 but again you have not thrown it often enough.
So you still would not conclude that it was biased.

What about 108 times in 600 throws? You have thrown it a large number of times and the proportion of sixes is $\frac{108}{600}$ = 0·18. This is too close to 0·17 to conclude it was biased, now that you have thrown it so many times.

What about 100 times in 500 throws? Now you have thrown it a large number of times and the proportion = $\frac{100}{500}$ = 0·2 which is significantly different from 0·17, but not so much that you should conclude that the die is biased.

The important question is, how many trials are necessary to ensure a representative result?

There is no fixed answer to this, other than 'the more the better'.

As a general rule, any event being examined should occur at least 20 times, but even this is probably a bare minimum.

In the last of a six occurring 100 times in 500 throws, the proportion of sixes is $\frac{100}{500}$. This fraction is called the relative frequency.

$$\text{Relative frequency} = \frac{\text{number of times an outcome occurs}}{\text{total number of trials}}$$

This is a measure of the proportion of the trials in which the outcome occurs. It is not itself a measure of probability. If, however, the number of trials is large enough, relative frequency can be used as an estimate to probability.

Remember that, however many trials have taken place, relative frequency is still only an estimate, but in many cases it is the only method of estimating probability.

EXAMPLE 2

Ian carries out a survey on the colours of the cars passing his school. His results are shown in this table.

Colour	Black	Red	Blue	White	Green	Other	Total
Number of cars	51	85	64	55	71	90	416

Use these figures to estimate the probability that the next car that passes will be **a)** red **b)** not red.

Since the number of trials is large, use relative frequency as an estimate to probability.

a) Relative frequency of a red car = $\frac{85}{416}$

Estimate of probability = $\frac{85}{416}$ or 0·204 (to 3 d.p.)

b) $416 - 85 = 331$

Relative frequency = $\frac{331}{416}$

Estimate of probability = $\frac{331}{416}$ or 0·796 (to 3 d.p.)

ACTIVITY 1

Perform an experiment or conduct a survey to test one of these hypotheses.

1 Every dice is unbiased so that the probability of getting any number is $\frac{1}{6}$.

Hint: Select a die that you think has been very unfair to you, throw it as many times as you can and estimate the probabilities of getting a 1,2,3 …

2 The probability of a boy or girl being born is the same, $\frac{1}{2}$.

Hint: Gather your data from your school by asking each pupil to state the genders of the members of their family (or your local hospital may give you information from the recent birth records). Estimate the probability of a boy or a girl birth.

EXERCISE 3.2A

1 Using the figures in Ian's survey in Example 2, estimate the probability that the next car will be

a) blue **b)** black or white.

Give your answers correct to three decimal places.

Exercise 3.2A cont'd

2 Kim Lee tossed a coin ten times and it came down heads eight times. Kim Lee said that the coin was biased towards heads. Explain why she may not be right.

3 Solomon has a spinner in the shape of a pentagon. The sides are labelled 1, 2, 3, 4 and 5. Solomon spun the spinner 500 times. The results are shown in the table.

Number on spinner	1	2	3	4	5
Number of times	102	103	98	96	101

a) What is the relative frequency of scoring **(i)** 2 **(ii)** 4?
b) Do the results suggest that Solomon's spinner is fair? Explain your answer.

4 In an experiment, a drawing pin is thrown. It can land either point up or point down. It lands point up 87 times in 210 throws. Use these figures to estimate the probability that, the next time it is thrown, it will land **a)** point up **b)** point down. Give your answers correct to two decimal places.

5 Denise carried out a survey about crisps. She asked 400 people, in the town where she lived, which was their favourite flavour of crisps. The results are shown in this table.

Flavour	Ready salted	Salt and vinegar	Cheese and onion	Prawn cocktail	Other
Number of people	150	75	55	50	70

a) Explain why it is reasonable to use these figures to estimate the probability that the next person Denise asks chooses salt and vinegar.
b) Use the figure to estimate the probability that the next person Denise asks will choose **(i)** salt and vinegar **(ii)** ready salted.

Give your answers as fractions in their simplest form.

6 An insurance company finds that 203 drivers out of 572 in the age range 17–20 have an accident in the first year after passing their driving test. Use these figures to estimate the probability that a driver aged 17–20 will have an accident in the first year after passing their test.

7 A large bag contains thousands of red beads and white beads. Describe carefully how you would find the probability of picking out a red bead from the bag.

Chapter 3 *Theoretical probabilities and relative frequency*

1 When Tom is standing at the bus stop he notices that five out of the 20 cars he sees passing are Fords. He says that therefore the probability the next car passing will be a Ford is $\frac{1}{4}$. Explain why he is wrong.

2 Freya carries out a survey to find out how students in her school travel to school. She asks a random selection of 200 students. The results are in this table.

Method of travel	Bus	Car	Train	Cycle	Walk
Number of students	34	33	23	45	65

   a) Explain why it is reasonable to estimate the probabilities of students travelling by the various methods from this survey.

   b) Use these figures to estimate the probability that a student selected at random from the school **(i)** travels by bus **(ii)** cycles.

3 Noel has two coins which he suspects may be biased.

   a) He tosses the first 600 times and throws 312 heads. Is there evidence to suggest that this coin is biased? Give your reasons. If there is, estimate the probability that the next throw is a head.

   b) He tosses the second coin 600 times and throws 420 heads. Is there evidence to suggest that this coin is biased? Give your reasons. If there is, estimate the probability that the next throw is a head.

4 The table shows the results of a survey on the type of detergent households use to do their washing.

Type of detergent	Liquid	Powder	Tablet
Number of households	120	233	85

Use these figures to estimate, correct to two decimal places, the probability that the next household surveyed will use

   a) liquid   **b)** tablet.

Exercise 3.2B cont'd

5 Stewart made a five-sided spinner. Unfortunately he did not make the pentagon regular. In order to find the probabilities of getting each of the numbers he spun the spinner 400 times. His results are shown in this table.

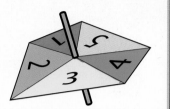

Number	1	2	3	4	5
Frequency	63	84	101	57	95

Use the figures in the table to estimate the probability of the spinner landing on

a) 1   **b)** 3   **c)** an even number.

6 A shopkeeper noticed from his till roll that, out of 430 customers that day, 82 had spent over £10. Use these figures to estimate the probability that his next customer will spend £10 or less.

7 Murphy's Law states that when you drop a piece of toast, it will land buttered side down nine times out of ten. Describe carefully an experiment you could carry out to test Murphy's Law.

Key ideas

- Where there is a set of equally likely outcomes.

    the probability of an event occurring = $\dfrac{\text{number of ways the event can occur}}{\text{total number of possible outcomes}}$.

- P(not A) = 1 – P(A).

- Relative frequency = $\dfrac{\text{number of times an event occurs}}{\text{total number of trials}}$.

- If the number of trials is large enough, relative frequency can be used as an estimate of probability.

4 Using and generating formulae

You should already know

- basic algebra (letters and simplifying)
- how to add, subtract, multiply and divide fractions and negative numbers.

Letters for unknowns

Imagine you had a job where you were paid by the hour. You would receive the same amount for each hour you worked.

How could you work out how much you will earn in a week?

You would need to work it out as:

> the number of hours worked multiplied by the amount you are paid for each hour

This is a formula in words.

If you work 35 hours at £4·50 an hour, it is easy to work out 35 × £4·50, but what if the numbers change?

The calculation '35 × £4·50' is only right if you work 35 hours.

Suppose you move to another job where you are paid more for each hour.

You need a simple formula that always works. You can use symbols to stand for the numbers that can change.

You could use ? or □, but it is less confusing to use letters.

Let: the number of hours be N
the amount you are paid each hour be P
the amount you earn in a week be W.

Then $W = N \times P$.

EXAMPLE 1

Find W when $N = 40$, $P = £5.00$

$W = 40 \times 5 = £200$

EXAMPLE 2

When you make a journey, S is the speed, d is the distance travelled and t is the time taken.

To find the speed, you divide the distance by the time, so the formula for S is:

$S = d \div t$

Exam tip

If you are not sure whether to multiply or divide, try an example with numbers first.

EXAMPLE 3

The cost (C) of hiring a car is a fixed charge (f), plus the number of days (n) multiplied by the daily rate (d), so:

$C = f + n \times d$

EXERCISE 4.1A

Write these formulae, using the letters given.

1 The cost (C) of x pencils at y pence each.

2 The area (A) of a rectangle m cm long and n cm wide.

3 The height (h) of a stack of n tins each t cm high.

4 The temperature (F) in °F is 32, plus 1·8 times the temperature in °C (C).

5 My gas bill (B) is a charge (s), plus the number (n) of units used multiplied by the cost (u) of each unit.

6 The mileage performance (number of miles per litre), (R), of a car is the number (m) of miles travelled divided by the number (p) of litres of petrol used.

7 The time (T) to cook a turkey is 30 minutes plus 40 minutes for each kilogram (k).

8 The area (A) of a triangle is half the base (b) times the height (h).

9 The number (d) of dollars is 1·65 times the number (p) of pounds.

10 The current in a circuit (i) is the voltage (V) divided by the resistance (r).

11 The cost (£C) of hiring a car for n days at a rate of £40 per day plus a basic charge of £12.

12 The cost (£C) of n units of electricity at 12p per unit, plus a standing charge of £6.

13 The hire charge £C for a car is £28 multiplied by the number of days (d), plus a charge of £15.

Exercise 4.1A cont'd

14 The area (A) of a semicircle is approximately 1·6 multiplied by the square of the radius (r).

15 The area (A) of an ellipse is π multiplied by its length (a) and its width (b).

EXERCISE 4.1B

Write these formulae, using the letters given.

1 The cost (c) of petrol is the number (n) of litres multiplied by the price (p) of petrol per litre.

2 The total of the wages (w) in a factory is the number (n) of workers multiplied by the weekly wage (q).

3 The perimeter (p) of a quadrilateral is the sum of the lengths of its sides (a, b, c, d).

4 The cost (P) of n books at q pounds each.

5 The number (N) of books that can fit on a shelf is the length (L) of the shelf divided by the thickness (t) of each book.

6 The time (t) for a journey is the distance (d) divided by the speed (s).

7 The number (F) of French francs is 9 times the number (P) of pounds.

8 The number (Q) of posts for a fence is the length (R) of the fence divided by 2, plus 1.

9 The number (n) of eggs in a box a eggs across, b eggs along and c eggs up.

10 The approximate circumference (c) of a circle is 6 multiplied by its radius (r).

11 The cost (£C) of n CDs at £7·50 each and v videos at £12 each.

12 The cost (£C) of n minutes of mobile phone use at 30p per minute, plus a rental charge of £14.

13 The area (A) of a kite is half the product of the width (w) and the length (m).

14 The density (d) of an object is its mass (m) divided by its volume (v).

15 The final velocity (v) of an object moving with constant acceleration (a) is the product of the time taken (t) and the acceleration, plus the start velocity (u).

Before you do these next exercises, check your answers to Exercises 4.1A and 4.1B.

EXERCISE 4.2A

Use the formulae in Exercise 4.1A to find:

1   C when $x = 15$, $y = 12$
2   A when $m = 7$, $n = 6$
3   h when $n = 20$, $t = 17$
4   F when $C = 40$
5   B when $s = 9.80$, $n = 234$, $u = 0.065$
6   R when $m = 320$, $p = 53.2$
7   T when $k = 9$
8   A when $b = 5$, $h = 6$
9   d when $p = 200$
10 i when $v = 13.6$, $r = 2.5$
11 C when $n = 5$
12 C when $n = 532$
13 C when $d = 5$
14 A when $r = 5$
15 A when $a = 3$ and $b = 2$

EXERCISE 4.2B

Use the formulae in Exercise 4.1B to find:

1   c when $n = 50$, $p = 70$
2   w when $n = 200$, $q = 150$
3   p when $a = 7$, $b = 5$, $c = 8$, $d = 2$
4   P when $n = 25$, $q = 7$
5   N when $L = 90$, $t = 3$
6   t when $d = 260$, $s = 40$
7   F when $P = 50$
8   Q when $R = 36$
9   n when $a = 12$, $b = 20$, $c = 6$
10 c when $r = 5$
11 C when $n = 2$ and $v = 3$
12 C when $n = 80$
13 A when $w = 40$ and $m = 60$
14 d when $m = 200$ and $v = 25$
15 v when $u = 6$, $a = 1.5$ and $t = 8$

Using harder numbers and formulae

Numbers that can be substituted in a formula may be positive, negative, decimals or fractions.

Exam tip

Take special care when negative numbers are involved.

EXAMPLE 4

If $W = 4p - 5q^2$, find W when:

a) $p = 2$, $q = {}^-3$ **b)** $p = 22 \cdot 5$, $q = 3 \cdot 4$

c) $p = \frac{3}{4}$, $q = \frac{2}{5}$.

a) $W = (4 \times 2) - (5 \times {}^-3 \times {}^-3)$

     $= 8 - (5 \times 9) = 8 - 45$

     $= {}^-37$

b) $W = (4 \times 22 \cdot 5) - (5 \times 3 \cdot 4 \times 3 \cdot 4)$

     $= 90 - 57 \cdot 8$

     $= 32 \cdot 2$

In part **b)** you would use a calculator.

c) $W = 4 \times \frac{3}{4} - 5 \times \frac{2}{5} \times \frac{2}{5}$

     $= 3 - \frac{4}{5}$

     $= 2\frac{1}{5}$

Exam tip

Remember $5b^2$ means $5 \times b \times b$ not $5 \times b \times 5 \times b$.

Exam tip

Work out each term separately and then collect together.

EXAMPLE 5

The formula for the surface area of a cylinder is $S = 2\pi rh + 2\pi r^2$.

Find the surface area when $r = 5 \cdot 7$ and $h = 4 \cdot 6$.

Give the answer to three significant figures.

$S = (2 \times \pi \times 5 \cdot 7 \times 4 \cdot 6) + (2 \times \pi \times 5 \cdot 7^2)$

     $= 164 \cdot 7 \ldots + 204 \cdot 1 \ldots = 368 \cdot 8 \ldots$

$S = 369$ (to 3 s.f.)

Exam tip

Use the π key on your calculator. Write down the intermediate values but leave them in your calculator to avoid making errors through rounding too early.

EXAMPLE 6

If $S = ut + \frac{1}{2}at^2$, find S when $u = 3$, $t = 4$, $a = {}^-5$.

$S = (3 \times 4) + (\frac{1}{2} \times {}^-5 \times 4^2) = 12 - 40 = {}^-28$

EXAMPLE 7

If $P = ab + 4b^2$, find P when $a = \frac{4}{5}$ and $b = \frac{3}{8}$, giving your answer as a fraction.

$P = (\frac{4}{5} \times \frac{3}{8}) + (4 \times \frac{3}{8} \times \frac{3}{8}) = \frac{3}{10} + \frac{9}{16} = \frac{24}{80} + \frac{45}{80} = \frac{69}{80}$

EXERCISE 4.3A

Work out each of the formulae in questions 1–7 for the values given, without using a calculator.

1 $V = ab - ac$ when $a = 3$, $b = {}^-2$, $c = 5$

2 $P = 2rv + 3r^2$ when $r = 5$, $v = {}^-2$

3 $T = 5s^2 - 2t^2$ when $s = {}^-2$, $t = 3$

4 $M = 2a(3b + 4c)$ when $a = 5$, $b = 3$, $c = {}^-2$

5 $R = \dfrac{2qv}{q + v}$ when $q = 3$, $v = {}^-4$

6 $L = 2n + m$ when $n = \frac{2}{3}$, $m = \frac{5}{6}$

7 $D = a^2 - 2b^2$ when $a = \frac{4}{5}$, $b = \frac{2}{5}$

8 Use a calculator to find the value of $M = \dfrac{ab}{2a + b^2}$ (correct to three significant figures) when $a = 2{\cdot}75$, $b = 3{\cdot}12$.

9 The distance S metres fallen by a pebble is given by the formula $S = \frac{1}{2}gt^2$, where t is in seconds.

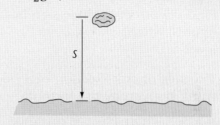

Find S when: **a)** $g = 10$, $t = 12$
b) $g = 9{\cdot}8$, $t = 2{\cdot}5$.

Use a calculator in part **b)** only.

10 The surface area of a cuboid with sides x, y and z is given by the formula $A = 2xy + 2yz + 2xz$.

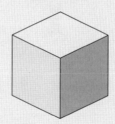

Find the surface area when $x = 5$, $y = 4{\cdot}5$, $z = 3{\cdot}5$.

EXERCISE 4.3B

Work out each of the formulae in questions 1–7 for the values given, without using a calculator.

1 $A = a^2 + b^2$ when $a = 5$, $b = {}^-3$

2 $P = 2c^2 - 3cd$ when $c = 2$, $d = {}^-5$

3 $B = p^2 - 3q^2$ when $p = {}^-4$, $q = {}^-2$

4 $T = (4a - 5b)^2$ when $a = {}^-2$, $b = {}^-1$

5 $Q = x(y^2 - z^2)$ when $x = {}^-2$, $y = 7$, $z = {}^-3$

6 $S = ab + 5b^2$ when $a = \frac{3}{4}$, $b = \frac{4}{5}$

7 $R = a + 2b$ when $a = 1\frac{5}{6}$, $b = \frac{2}{3}$

Chapter 4 *Using and generating formulae*

Exercise 4.3B cont'd

8 The elastic energy of an elastic string is given by the formula $E = \dfrac{\lambda x^2}{2a}$.

Find E (correct to three significant figures) when $\lambda = 3\cdot4$, $x = 5\cdot7$, $a = 2\cdot5$.

9 The area of cross-section of a tree trunk is given by the formula $A = \dfrac{P^2}{4\pi}$ where P is the distance round the trunk.

Find the area of cross-section when $P = 56\,\text{cm}$. Use $\pi = 3\cdot14$ and give the answer correct to three significant figures.

10 The focal length of a lens is given by the formula $f = \dfrac{uv}{u + v}$. Find the focal length when $u = 6$, $v = {}^{-}7$.

Key ideas

- When constructing a formula, if you are not sure what to do (for example whether to multiply or divide) try an example with easy numbers first.

- When you have substituted numbers in a formula and are working out the result, remember the order of operations – **b**rackets and powers, then **d**ivide and **m**ultiply, then **a**dd and **s**ubtract.

- Take special care when negative numbers are involved.

Exam tip

Remembering the word BODMAS may help.

Chapter 4 *Using and generating formulae*

5 Solving angle problems

You should already know

Regular polygons
- a regular polygon has equal angles and equal sides.

Symmetry properties of regular polygons
- a regular polygon has the same number of lines of symmetry as it has sides
- any regular polygon has the same order of rotation symmetry as its number of sides.

Some basic angle facts
- angles on a straight line add up to 180°
- angles round a point add up to 360°
- when two straight lines cross, the opposite angles are equal
- angles in a triangle add up to 180°
- angles in a quadrilateral add up to 360°
- in an isosceles triangle, the angles opposite the equal sides are themselves equal.

Angles with parallel lines
- thinking of a Z shape may help you remember that alternate angles are equal – or looking at the diagrams upside-down and seeing the same shapes
- thinking of an F shape or a translation may help you remember that corresponding angles are equal
- remembering a ⊏ shape or using facts about angles on a straight line may help you remember that allied angles add up to 180°; allied angles are sometimes called interior angles.

Here is some practice on solving problems using these facts.

EXERCISE 5.1A

1 How many lines of symmetry does a regular octagon have?

2 What is the order of rotational symmetry of this shape?

3 Sketch an isosceles triangle and show any symmetry it has.

4 An isosceles triangle has an angle of 40°. Find the sizes of the other angles in the triangle. There are two possible sets of answers – find both sets.

5 Three angles of a quadrilateral are 62°, 128° and 97°. Find the size of the other angle.

6 Find the sizes of the lettered angles, giving your reasons.

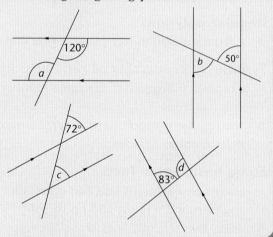

EXERCISE 5.1B

1 a) Name this shape.
b) State its order of rotational symmetry.

2 Draw a pentagon with just one line of symmetry.

3 a) How many axes of symmetry does a cuboid have, when none of its faces is a square?
b) How many planes of symmetry does a cube have?

4 An isosceles triangle has one angle of 108°. Calculate the size of the other two angles.

5 Three angles of a quadrilateral are 57°, 132° and 76°. Calculate the size of the other angle.

6 Find the sizes of the lettered angles, giving your reasons.

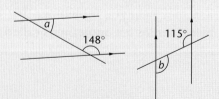

Angles in polygons

You should already have met angle facts for regular polygons. In this section you will find results for any polygons.

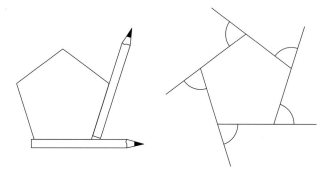

Put a pencil along the base of the pentagon, as shown, then slide it to the right until its end reaches the end of the base.

Now carefully rotate the pencil about its end until it is along the next side of the pentagon. Slide it up until its end reaches the top of that side. Continue in this way until you reach the base again, as shown. When you get back to the beginning, the pencil will have turned through 360°.

It will have turned through the angles shown in the diagram on the right, next to the first diagram. These angles are called **exterior angles**. You have shown that the sum of the exterior angles of the pentagon is 360°.

This method could have been used for any convex polygon.

> The sum of the exterior angles of any convex polygon is 360°.

At each vertex, the interior and exterior angles make a straight line.

> For any convex polygon, at any vertex:
> interior angle + exterior angle = 180°.

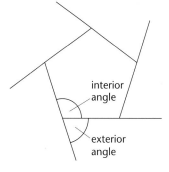

interior angle

exterior angle

EXAMPLE 1

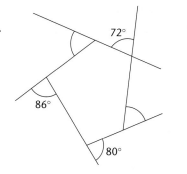

The two unlabelled exterior angles of this pentagon are equal. Find their size.

First, find the sum of the angles that are given:

72° + 80° + 86° = 238°.

The sum of all the exterior angles is 360°.

The sum of remaining two angles = 360° − 238° = 122°.

So each angle is 122 ÷ 2 = 61°.

In many problems about polygon angles, the easiest way to solve them is to use the fact that the sum of the exterior angles is 360°.

Sometimes, however, it is useful to find the sum of the interior angles.

At each vertex of a convex polygon:

interior angle + exterior angle = 180°.

Sum of (interior + exterior angles) for the polygon = 180° × number of angles
= 180° × number of sides.

But the sum of the exterior angles is 360°.

So the sum of the interior angles of the polygon = 180° × number of sides − 360°.

Putting this algebraically, for an *n*-sided convex polygon:

the sum of the interior angles = $(180n - 360)°$.

> ### ACTIVITY 1
>
> Some polygons have special names. For instance a pentagon is a 5-sided polygon. Make a list of as many of these special names as you can, with the corresponding number of sides.

EXAMPLE 2

Find the value of the missing angle in this pentagon.

For a pentagon:

the sum of the interior angles = $(180 \times 5 - 360)° = 540°$.

The sum of the four angles given = 437°.

So the missing angle = 540° − 437° = 103°.

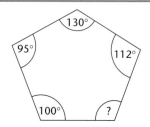

Finding angles in regular polygons

For regular polygons, each interior angle is the same, each exterior angle is the same. This is an easy way to work out the angles.

Another fact about regular polygons is that they may be divided, from their centre, into congruent isosceles triangles. This is often useful when you are asked to draw regular polygons accurately. For example, for a regular pentagon, the angle at the centre is 360° ÷ 5 = 72°.

> ### Exam tip
>
> For regular polygons:
> each exterior angle
> $$= \frac{360°}{\text{number of sides}}$$
> then use:
> interior angle
> = 180° − exterior angle.

The base angles of the triangle together equal 180° − 72° = 108°. So each base angle is 54°.

From the diagram, these base angles are each half of an interior angle, so this gives another way of working out interior angles, too.

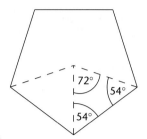

EXAMPLE 3

Find the interior angle of a regular octagon.

For a regular octagon, the exterior angle = 360° ÷ 8 = 45°.

So the interior angle = 180° − 45° = 135°.

EXAMPLE 4

Find the number of sides of a regular polygon with an interior angle of 144°.

If the interior angle = 144° the exterior angle = 36°.

The sum of the exterior angles = 360°.

Therefore the number of sides = 360° ÷ 36° = 10.

ACTIVITY 2

A shape will tessellate if a number of copies of the shape will fit together without any gaps.

Regular octagons do not tessellate, but as this picture of a tiled floor shows, regular octagons and squares may be combined to cover a surface.

Can you find:

1 which regular polygons tessellate?

2 which combinations of regular polygons will cover a surface?

You might make a display of your results…

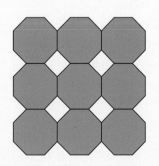

EXERCISE 5.2A

1 Three of the exterior angles of a quadrilateral are 90°, 52° and 87°. Find the size of the other exterior angle.

2 Four of the exterior angles of a pentagon are 70°, 59°, 83° and 90°. Find the size of the other exterior angle.

Chapter 5 *Solving angle problems*

Exercise 5.2A cont'd

3 Five of the exterior angles of a hexagon are 54°, 48°, 65°, 35° and 80°. Find the size of the other exterior angle.

4 Find the sizes of the interior angles of the pentagon in question 2.

5 Find the sizes of the interior angles of the hexagon in question 3.

6 A regular polygon has nine sides. Find the sizes of its exterior and interior angles.

7 Find the interior angle of a regular dodecagon (12 sides).

8 A regular polygon has an exterior angle of 24°. How many sides does it have?

9 What is the sum of the interior angles of:
   a) a hexagon
   b) a decagon?

10 Six of the angles of a heptagon are 122°, 141°, 137°, 103°, 164° and 126°. Calculate the size of the remaining angle.

EXERCISE 5.2B

1 Three of the exterior angles of a quadrilateral are 110°, 61° and 74°. Find the size of the other exterior angle.

2 Four of the exterior angles of a pentagon are 68°, 49°, 82° and 77°. Find the size of the other exterior angle.

3 Four of the exterior angles of a hexagon are 67°, 43°, 91° and 37°. Find the size of the other exterior angles, given that they are equal.

4 Find the sizes of the interior angles of the pentagon in question 2.

5 Find the sizes of the interior angles of the hexagon in question 3.

6 A regular polygon has 15 sides. Find the sizes of its exterior and interior angles.

7 Find the interior angle of a regular 20-sided polygon.

8 A regular polygon has an exterior angle of 30°. How many sides does it have?

9 What is the sum of the interior angles of:
   a) an octagon
   b) a nonagon?

10 A polygon has 11 sides. Ten of its interior angles add up to 1490°. Find the size of the remaining angle.

Exterior angle of a triangle

If one of the sides of a triangle is extended, to form an angle outside the triangle, this angle is called the exterior angle.

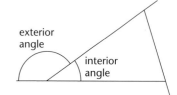

exterior angle

interior angle

ACTIVITY 3

Draw a large triangle with sides 10 cm, 12 cm and 14 cm. Extend the length of the base.

Cut off two of the corners, as shown by the shaded angles.

Try to fit them together, next to the remaining angle at the base.

What do you notice?

They should fit over the exterior angle.

exterior angle

Repeat for a different sized triangle with a different exterior angle.

Does the same thing happen?

You have demonstrated that:

the exterior angle of a triangle is equal to the sum of the interior opposite angles.

ACTIVITY 4

Try to write a proof of the result you have just found, using some or all of the statements given below. Give reasons if you can.

Note that there is more than one proof.

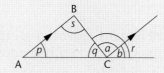

$a + b = r$

because angles on a straight line add up to 180°

$p = b$

because they are alternate angles

$p + s = r$

because they are vertically opposite angles

$s = a$

because they are corresponding angles

$p + s = a + b$

because angles in a triangle add up to 180°

Chapter 5   *Solving angle problems*

1 Calculate the sizes of all the angles marked with letters.

a)

b)

c)

d)

2 Write down as many different ways as you can to find the value of e once you have found the value of d.

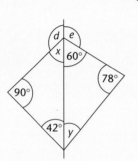

3 Calculate the sizes of all the angles marked with letters.

a)

b)

c)

d)

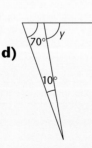

4 Calculate the sizes of all the angles marked with letters.

a)

b)

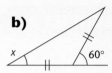

c)

d)

e)

5 Calculate the sizes of all the angles marked with letters.

a)

b)

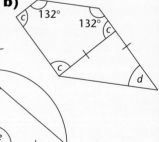

c)

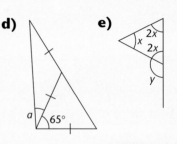

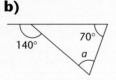

Exam tip

Remember all the angle properties you have met. There are several ways of calculating some of these angles.

EXERCISE 5.3B

1 Calculate the sizes of all the angles marked with letters.

a)

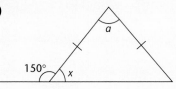

b)

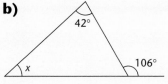

c)

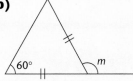

2 Calculate the sizes of all the angles marked with letters.

a)

b)

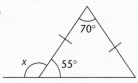

c)

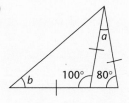

3 Calculate the sizes of all the angles marked with letters.

a)

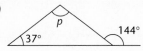

b)

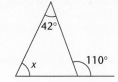

4 Calculate the sizes of all the angles marked with letters.

a)

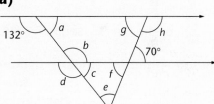

b)

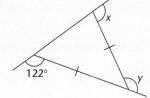

c)

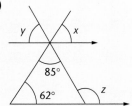

Exercise 5.3B cont'd

5 Calculate the sizes of all the angles marked with letters.

a)

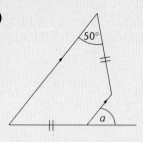

b)

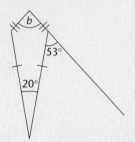

c)

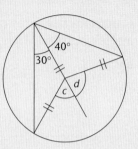

Key ideas

Angles in polygons

- The sum of the exterior angles of a convex polygon is 360°.

- Interior angle + exterior angle = 180°.

- For an *n*-sided polygon:
  sum of the interior angles = (180*n* – 360)°.

Finding angles in regular polygons

- Each exterior angle = $\dfrac{360}{\text{number of sides}}$.

- Then use: interior angle = 180° – exterior angle.

Exterior angle of a triangle

- The exterior angle of a triangle is equal to the sum of the interior opposite angles.

A1 **Revision exercise**

1 A 800 g white 'bloomer' loaf of bread costs 69p. How many grams do you buy for 1p?

2 A 500 ml pack of milk costs 27p. A 2 litre container of milk costs 75p. How much less do I pay if I buy 2 litres of milk in a container rather than in 500 ml packs?

3 Two friends shared the cost of a holiday in the ratio 3:2. The total cost of the holiday was £1060. How much did they each pay?

4 The distances travelled by Ravi and Sue to a party were in the ratio 5:2. Sue travelled 6·4 miles. How far did Ravi travel?

5 Kelly, Eileen and Susie share £1500 in the ratio 3:4:5. How much does Kelly receive?

6 To make 12 scones Maureen uses 5 ounces of flour. How many scones can she make using 8 ounces of flour? Answer to the nearest whole number.

7 The voting in an election was in the ratio 8:4:3 for Labour, Conservative and Others. If 6328 people voted Labour, how many voted altogether?

8 Work these out.

a) $\frac{1}{2} + \frac{2}{3}$ **b)** $1\frac{2}{5} + 3\frac{1}{4}$

c) $\frac{5}{9} - \frac{1}{6}$ **d)** $3\frac{1}{4} - 2\frac{2}{3}$

e) $\frac{2}{3} + 4\frac{1}{2} - 2\frac{5}{6}$ **f)** $\frac{2}{3} \times \frac{3}{5}$

g) $\frac{3}{8} \div \frac{1}{4}$ **h)** $2\frac{1}{2} \times 3\frac{1}{5}$

i) $3\frac{1}{5} \div 2\frac{2}{3}$ **j)** $4\frac{1}{3} \times 1\frac{1}{4} \div 2\frac{1}{6}$

9 To make a frame John uses four pieces of wood: two are $4\frac{1}{4}$ inches long and two are $6\frac{2}{3}$ inches long. He cut them all off a piece of wood 24 inches long. How much wood was left?

10 A fair octagonal spinner is numbered 1 to 8. When it is spun, what is the probability of getting
a) a number greater than 5
b) a multiple of 3?

11 A coin is tossed and a normal die is thrown. What is the probability of getting both a head and a six?

12 The probability that Jane wears red clothes is 0·3. What is the probability that she doesn't wear red?

13 A box contains 5 milk, 6 plain and 4 white chocolates. Chris picks one out at random. What is the probability that he gets a plain chocolate? Give your answer as a fraction in its lowest terms.

14 Over the last year Rebecca has been late for school 25 times in 190 days. Use these figures to estimate the probability that she will be on time the next school day. Give your answer correct to two decimal places.

15 The ages of the drivers of the last 250 cars to have crashes at an accident black spot are shown in the following table.

Age (years)	17–20	21–24	25–49	50–64	65 and over
No. of crashes	40	35	105	45	25

a) Use the table to estimate the probability that the next driver to have a crash at the black spot will be aged **(i)** 25–49 **(ii)** and over 65.

b) Explain why these figures do not necessarily mean that drivers aged 65 years and over are the safest.

16 Rachel has a four-sided spinner with the sides numbered 1, 2, 3 and 4. She wants to test whether the spinner is a fair one. Describe carefully how you would advise her to do this.

17 $P = a^2 + b^2$
  a) Find P when $a = 4$, $b = 7$
  b) Find P when $a = 3$, $b = 4$
  c) Find P when $a = {}^-3$, $b = {}^-4$

18 If $h = 7a - 2bc$, find h when
  a) $a = 2$, $b = 3$, $c = {}^-1$
  b) $a = \frac{1}{4}$, $b = \frac{1}{2}$, $c = \frac{3}{4}$
  c) $a = 3{\cdot}6$, $b = 7{\cdot}4$, $c = 2{\cdot}5$.

19 The formula for finding the area of the surface of a sphere is $A = 4\pi r^2$.

Find the area when $r = 4{\cdot}2$ cm, giving the answer correct to three significant figures.

20 Four of the exterior angles of a pentagon are 85°, 66°, 54° and 97°. Find the size of the other exterior angle.

21 Calculate the sum of the interior angles of a heptagon.

22 A regular polygon has ten sides. Find the size of its **a)** exterior **b)** interior angles.

23 An irregular polygon has eight sides. Seven of its interior angles add up to 940°. Calculate the size of its other interior angle.

24 Find the size of the angles marked with letters.

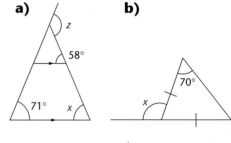

a) b)

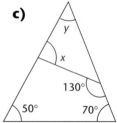

c)

25 Calculate the size of the interior angle of a regular polygon with 20 sides.

26 Calculate the number of sides of a regular polygon with an interior angle of 168°.

6 Direct proportion - calculating an unknown quantity

You should already know

● basic ideas about ratio and proportion.

When quantities are in direct proportion, multiplication patterns can be seen if the quantities are put in a table. Using these patterns is often the easiest way of calculating unknown values.

There are multiplying patterns horizontally in the table when x and y are proportional. When x is doubled, so is y. When x multiplied by 3, so is y.

	×2	×3
x	4	8	24
y	10	20	60
	×2	×3

There are also patterns vertically in the table. In this example, each y value is 2·5 times its corresponding x value. The equation connecting x and y is $y = 2·5x$.

x	4	8	24	
y	10	20	60	×2·5

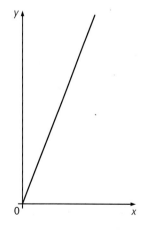

The graph of y against x is a straight line through the origin. This is so for any two quantities in direct proportion.

The statement 'y is directly proportional to x' is written in symbols as $y \propto x$.

EXAMPLE 1

Calculate the values of p and q in this table, where a and b are proportional.

a	3	p	12
b	18	54	q

$\frac{54}{18} = 3$, so $p = 3 \times 3 = 9$

$\frac{12}{3} = 4$, so $q = 18 \times 4 = 72$

EXERCISE 6.1A

1 Copy and complete this table, using multipliers.

$$y \propto x$$

x	6	12	30	
y	24			4

2 Copy and complete this table, using multipliers.

$$p \propto q$$

p	3	15		
q	18		12	30

3 Calculate the missing values in this table, where y is proportional to x.

x	4		20
y	10	30	

4 Calculate the missing value in this table, where y is proportional to x. Find also the equation connecting y and x.

x	6	12	
y	30	60	80

5 Calculate the missing values in this table, where A is proportional to x. Find also the equation connecting A and x.

x	4	12	
A	18		90

6 A is proportional to r. When $r = 4$, $A = 6$. Find the value of A when $r = 12$, and the value of r when $A = 30$.

7 C is proportional to x. When $x = 5$, $C = 8$. Find the value of C when $x = 15$, and the value of x when $C = 20$.

Exercise 6.1A cont'd

8 a and b are directly proportional. When $a = 5$, $b = 6$. Find the equation connecting a and b, and the value of a when $b = 15$.

9 Calculate the missing values in this table, where y is proportional to x.

x	12	⁻2	
y	18		6·9

10 $y \propto x$. When $x = 4$, $y = 6·4$. Find the equation connecting x and y and the value of x when $y = 56$.

11 Complete this table to show the rate of conversion between dollars and pounds.

Pounds	3	12	25	
Dollars	4·50			180·00

12 A 5 litre tin of paint covers 65 m², according to its label. Use a table or conversion graph to find how many litres of paint are required to cover the walls of a room with an area of **a)** 26 m², **b)** 47 m².

EXERCISE 6.1B

1 Copy and complete this table, using multipliers.

$y \propto x$

x	2	4	20	
y	14			56

2 Copy and complete this table, using multipliers.

$p \propto q$

p	4	20	1	
q	20			75

3 Calculate the missing values in this table, where y is proportional to x.

x	5		20
y	30	6	

4 Calculate the missing value in this table, where y is proportional to x. Find also the equation connecting y and x.

x	2	6	
y	15	45	90

5 Calculate the missing values in this table, where a is proportional to b. Find also the equation connecting a and b.

a	2	8	
b	7		105

6 $C \propto p$. When $p = 4$, $C = 18$. Find the value of C when $p = 20$, and the value of p when $C = 63$.

Exercise 6.1B cont'd

7 C is proportional to m. When $m = 5$, $C = 12$. Find the value of C when $m = 25$, and the value of m when $C = 18$.

8 a and b are directly proportional. When $a = 12$, $b = 15$. Find the equation connecting a and b, and the value of a when $b = 20$.

9 Calculate the missing values in this table, where y is proportional to x.

x	9	⁻3	
y	2·7		2·1

10 $y \propto x$. When $x = 5$, $y = 27$. Find the equation connecting x and y, and the value of x when $y = 18·9$.

11 A car goes 12·6 miles on 2 litres of petrol.
   a) How much petrol does it need to go 84 miles?
   b) How far can it go on 5 litres of petrol?

12 A 1500 g strawberry cheesecake to serve 8 people contains 210 g of strawberries. How many grams of strawberries should there be in a cheesecake to serve 12 people?

Key ideas

When two quantities x and y are in direct proportion:

- Multiplication patterns can be seen if the quantities are put in a table. Using these patterns is often the easiest way of calculating unknown values.

- There are multiplying patterns horizontally in the table when x and y are proportional. When x is doubled, so is y. When x is multiplied by 3, so is y.

- There are also patterns vertically in the table. Each y value is k times its corresponding x value, for some number k. The equation connecting x and y is $y = kx$.

- The graph of y against x is a straight line through the origin. This is so for any two quantities in direct proportion.

- The statement 'y is directly proportional to x' is written in symbols as $y \propto x$.

Checking solutions to calculations

7

You should already know

- basic numerical methods such as finding ratios and percentages
- how to round to 1 significant figure.

Checking your work

When you have solved a problem, how do you know if your answer is right? Sometimes, accuracy is vital. In the news recently there was a story of a doctor treating a baby. She put the decimal point in the wrong place in a calculation and prescribed 100 times as much drug as she intended.

Using common sense

Does your answer sound sensible in the context of the question? In practical problems, your own experience often gives you an idea of the size of the answer you expect. For example, in the case of a shopping bill, you would probably react and check if it came to more than you expected!

ACTIVITY 1

Multiplying

Starting with the number 400 multiply it by the numbers in each of the following sets:

A: 5   1·1   3·2   1·003   1·4   1·2

B: 0·5   0·999   0·6   0·9   0·7   0·95

What happens to the number 400? Does it get bigger or smaller? What conclusions can you come to? In particular what happens when any number is multiplied by a number which is **a)** greater than 1 **b)** less than 1 **c)** 1 itself?

Division

Repeat the activity but dividing instead of multiplying and write down your conclusions. In particular what happens when any number is divided by a number which is **a)** greater than 1 **b)** less than 1 **c)** 1 itself?

Multiplying and dividing by numbers greater or less than one

Look at the result to this calculation.

$752 \div 24 = 18\,048$

When 752 is divided by a number that is greater than 1, the result should be less than 752.

Instead, it is more. It looks as if the $\times$ button was pressed by mistake, instead of the $\div$ button. Checking whether the answer is sensible can help to spot errors like this.

Starting with any positive number:
- multiplying by a number greater than 1 makes the answer larger
- multiplying by a positive number smaller than 1 makes the answer smaller
- dividing by a number greater than 1 makes the answer smaller
- dividing by a positive number smaller than 1 makes the answer larger.

Using estimates

Look at this problem.

Kate has £25 birthday money to spend. She sees CDs at £7·99. How many of them can she buy?

Unless you take a calculator shopping, in this situation the easy way is to do a quick estimate.

Use £8 instead of £7·99.

$25 \div 8 = 3$ 'and a bit' $(3 \times 8 = 24)$

So Kate can buy three CDs.

Most people do this of mental check when they are shopping. You can extend it to your maths lessons, and any other subjects where you use calculations.

ACTIVITY 2

Which of these are correct and which are wrong? Show how you reached your answer.

1 $39·6 \times 18·1 = 716·76$

2 $175 \div 1·013 = 177·275$

3 $8400 \times 9 = 756\,000$

4 A lift takes 9 people so a party of 110 people will need 12 trips.

5 Henry has £100 birthday money to spend and reckons that he can afford 5 DVDs costing £17·99 each.

Using inverse operations

If neither of the above checks is easy to do, try doing the calculation another way. For instance, for a complex calculation you might use brackets instead of the memory. For a simpler one, using inverse operations is often useful.

For example using a calculator: $6.9 \div 750 = 0.0092$

Check using a calculator: $0.0092 \times 750 = 6.9$

You will need to use these methods in the rest of the chapter, but don't let it stop there.

Exam tip

Develop the habit of always checking whether your answer is about the right size.

EXERCISE 7.1A

Look at the calculations in questions 1–7. The answers are all wrong. For each one, show how you can quickly tell this without using a calculator to work it out. For some, your method may be different from the one shown in the answers!

1 $^-6.2 \div ^-2 = ^-3.1$

2 $12.4 \times 0.7 = 86.8$

3 $31.2 \times 40 = 124.8$

4 $\sqrt{72} = 9.49$ to 2 d.p.

5 $0.3^2 = 0.9$

6 $16.2 \div 8.1 = 20$

7 $125 \div 0.5 = 25$

In questions 8–12, use estimates to calculate rough values.

8 The cost of seven packs of crisps at 22p each.

9 The cost of nine CDs at £13·25 each.

10 $65.4 \div 3.9$

11 $\dfrac{194.4 + 16.7}{27.3}$

12 $\dfrac{49.7}{4.1 \times 7.9}$

EXERCISE 7.1B

Look at the calculations in questions 1–7. The answers are all wrong. For each one, show how you can quickly tell this without using a calculator to work it out. For some, your method may be different from the one shown in the answers!

1 $6.4 \times ^-4 = 25.6$

2 $24.7 + 6.2 = 30.8$

3 $76 \div 0.5 = 38$

4 $(^-0.9)^2 = ^-0.81$

5 $\sqrt{1000} = 10$

Chapter 7   *Checking solutions to calculations*

Exercise 7.1B cont'd

6 $1.56 \times 2.5 = 0.39$

7 $360 \div 15 = 2400$

In questions 8–12, use estimates to calculate rough values.

8 The cost of 39 theatre tickets at £7·20 each.

9 The cost of five CDs at £5·99 and two tapes at £1·99.

10 The cost of three meals at £5·70 and two drinks at 99p.

11 3.1×14.9

12 $47 \times (21.7 + 39.2)$

Checking answers by rounding to one significant figure

It is important to be able to check calculations quickly, without using a calculator. One way to do this is to round the numbers to one significant figure.

EXAMPLE 1

Find an approximate answer to the calculation 5.13×4.83.

$5.13 \times 4.83 \approx 5 \times 5$
$= 25$

Rounding 5·13 and 4·83 each to 1 s.f. to give a much simpler calculation.

Exam tip

In a calculation it may be possible to round one number up and another number down. This might give an answer closer to the exact answer.

EXERCISE 7.2A

1 Find approximate answers to these calculations by rounding each number to one significant figure.

a) $31.3 \div 4.85$
b) 113.5×2.99
c) $44.669 \div 8.77$
d) $3.6 \times 14.9 \times 21.5$

Now use a calculator to see how close your approximations are to the correct answers.

2 Find approximate answers to these calculations by rounding each number to one significant figure.

a) $\dfrac{14.56 \times 22.4}{59.78}$

b) $\dfrac{4.9^2 \times 49.3}{96.7}$

c) $\sqrt{4.9 \times 5.2}$

Now use a calculator to see how close your approximations are to the correct answers.

Exercise 7.2A cont'd

3 Find approximate answers to these calculations by rounding each number to one significant figure.

a) $(0.35 \times 86.3) \div 7.9$

b) $\sqrt{103.5} \div \sqrt{37.2}$

c) 9.87×0.0657

d) $0.95 \div 4.8$

4 Make up some multiplication and division calculations of your own to test this statement: 'In multiplication and division calculations, rounding each number to one significant figure will always give an answer which is correct to one significant figure'.

EXERCISE 7.2B

1 Find approximate answers to these calculations by rounding each number to one significant figure.

a) 48.67×12.69

b) 0.89×5.2

c) 61.33×11.79

d) $(1.8 \times 2.9) \div 3.2$

Now use a calculator to see how close your approximations are to the correct answers.

2 Find approximate answers to these calculations by rounding each number to one significant figure.

a) $\dfrac{3.99}{0.8 \times 1.64}$

b) $198.5 \times 63.1 \times 2.8$

c) $\dfrac{\sqrt{8.1 \times 1.9}}{1.9}$

Now use a calculator to see how close your approximations are to the correct answers.

3 Find approximate answers to these calculations by rounding each number to one significant figure.

a) $32 \times \sqrt{124}$

b) $\dfrac{62 \times 9.7}{10.12 \times 5.1}$

c) 0.246×0.789

d) $44.555 \div 0.086$

Key ideas

Check your work by doing at least one of these checks:

● Does the answer sound sensible in the context of the question?

● Do a quick estimate, for example round the numbers to 1 significant figure.

● Do the calculation another way to check.

● Work backwards from your answer.

Chapter 7 *Checking solutions to calculations*

8 Scatter graphs and correlation

You should already know

- how to plot graphs from tables of data
- basic ideas about correlation.

ACTIVITY 1

Do tall people have large feet?

Survey people in your class or in your year and record their height and foot size (measure might be better than shoe size but both could be done). Plot the height on the horizontal axis and the shoe size on the vertical axis. What do you notice? Try other year groups.

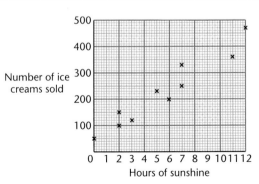

Correlation

The table shows the amount of ice-cream sold by an ice-cream seller in ten days last summer.

Number of hours of sunshine	3	6	11	2	0	7	2	12	7	5
Number of ice-creams sold	120	200	360	100	50	250	150	470	330	230

The graph shows this information plotted on a scatter diagram or scatter graph.

The number of hours of sunshine is plotted as the horizontal axis and the number of ice-creams sold is plotted as the vertical axis.

From the graph it can be seen that, in general, the **more** hours of sunshine there were, the **more** ice-creams were sold.

This is an example of **positive correlation**.

Although the points are not exactly in a straight line, nevertheless there is a trend that the further to the right on the graph the higher the point is.

In graphs such as these the nearer the graph is to a straight line, the better the correlation is.

Here are some examples of graphs showing positive correlation.

Perfect positive correlation

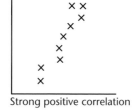
Strong positive correlation

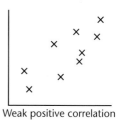
Weak positive correlation

If there is no correlation the scatter diagram looks like this.

A shopkeeper in the same town as the ice-cream seller noted how many umbrellas were sold in the same ten days. This is the table.

Number of hours of sunshine	3	6	11	2	0	7	2	12	7	5
Number of umbrellas sold	6	5	2	9	11	4	8	0	5	7

The scatter diagram for this information looks like this.

The number of hours of sunshine is plotted as the horizontal axis and the number of umbrellas sold is plotted as the vertical axis.

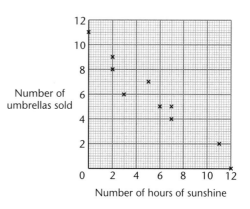

Number of umbrellas sold

Number of hours of sunshine

Exam tip

Always label the axes of graphs you draw.

Chapter 8 *Scatter graphs and correlation*

Here the trend is the other way round. In general, although the points are not exactly in a straight line, the **more** hours of sunshine there are the **fewer** umbrellas are sold.

This is an example of **negative correlation**.

Here are some examples of graphs showing negative correlation.

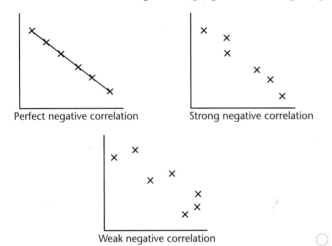

Perfect negative correlation   Strong negative correlation

Weak negative correlation

Exam tip

When commenting on a scatter diagram it is better (and quicker) to use the correct terms such as 'strong positive correlation' rather than using phrases like 'the more hours of sunshine, the more ice-creams are sold'.

Lines of best fit

Look again at the graph for ice-cream and hours of sunshine.

A straight line has been drawn on it, passing through the cluster of points. There are as many points above the line as there are below it. This is the 'best' straight line that can be drawn to show the trend of the points. It is called the **line of best fit**.

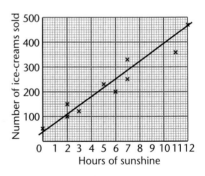

The line of best fit should reflect the slope of the points and have approximately the same number of points on either side.

It should ignore any points that obviously do not fit the trend. These are called **outliers**.

A line of best fit should **not** be attempted if there is little or no correlation.

The line of best fit can be used to estimate values that are not in the original table. For example, you could estimate that for 4·5 hours of sunshine 200 ice-creams would be sold.

If the line of best fit is used to estimate values it must be recognised that:

● if the correlation is not good the estimate will probably not be a very good one

● estimates should **not** be made too far beyond the range of the given points. For example, in the above case, estimates should not be made for 15 hours of sunshine.

Here are some examples of bad 'lines of best fit'.

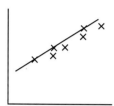

Fault: Slope about right but does not have the same number of points on either side.

Fault: Same number of points either side but slope wrong.

Exam tip

When drawing a line of best fit:
1 put your ruler on the graph at the right slope
2 slide the ruler, keeping it at the same slope, until you have approximately the same number of points on either side. Remember, lines of best fit do not necessarily go through the origin. It may be easier to hold your ruler on its edge, vertical to the page so you can see both sides of the line.

EXERCISE 8.1A

1 The scatter diagram shows the number of sun beds hired out and the hours of sunshine at Brightsea.

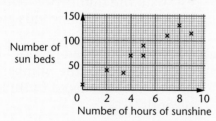

Comment on the results shown by the scatter graph.

2 A firm noted the number of days 'sick-leave' taken by its employees in a year, and their ages. The results are shown in the graph.

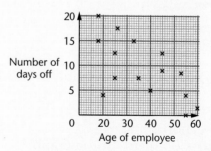

Comment on the results shown by the scatter graph.

Chapter 8 *Scatter graphs and correlation*

Exercise 8.1A cont'd

3 The table shows the Maths and Science marks of eight pupils in their last examination.

Pupil	A	B	C	D	E	F	G	H
Maths mark	10	20	96	50	80	70	26	58
Science mark	30	28	80	55	62	70	38	48

a) Draw a scatter graph to show this information, with the Maths score on the horizontal axis.

b) Comment on the graph.

c) Draw a line of best fit.

d) Use your line of best fit to estimate:
  (i)   the mark in Science of a pupil who scored 40 in Maths
  (ii) the mark in Maths of a pupil who scored 75 in Science.

4 The table shows the amount of petrol left in the fuel tank after the number of miles travelled.

Number of miles	50	100	150	200	250	300
Number of gallons	7	5·2	4·2	2·6	1·2	0·4

a) Draw a scatter graph to show this information, with the number of miles on the horizontal axis.

b) Comment on the graph.

c) Draw a line of best fit.

d) Use your line of best fit to estimate the number of gallons left after 170 miles.

5 In Kim's game 20 objects are placed on a table and you are given a certain time to look at them. They are removed or covered up and you then have to recall as many as possible. The table shows the amount of time given to nine people and the number of items they remembered.

Time in seconds	20	25	30	35	40	45	50	55	60
Number of items	9	8	12	10	12	15	13	16	18

a) Draw a scatter graph to show this information, with the amount of time on the horizontal axis.

b) Comment on the graph.

c) Draw a line of best fit.

d) Use your line of best fit to estimate the number of items remembered if 32 seconds are allowed.

e) Why should the graph not be used to estimate the number of items remembered in three seconds?

6 Sanjay thinks that the more time he spends on his school work, the less money he will spend. Sketch a scatter graph that shows this.

EXERCISE 8.1B

1 A teacher thinks that there is a correlation between how far back in class a pupil sits and how well they do at Maths. To test this she plotted their last Maths grade against the row they sit in. Here is the graph she drew.

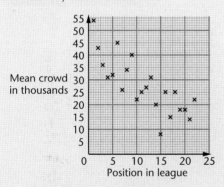

Was the teacher right? Give your reasons.

2 The scatter graph shows the positions of football teams in the league and their mean crowd numbers, in thousands.

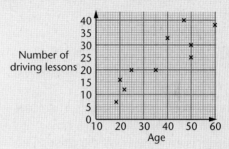

Comment on the graph.

3 The scatter graph shows the ages of people and the numbers of lessons they took before they passed their driving tests.

Comment on the graph.

4 In Jane's class a number of pupils have part-time jobs. Jane thinks that the more time they spend on their jobs, the worse they will do at school. She asked ten of them how many hours a week they spend on their jobs, and found their mean marks in the last examinations. Her results are shown in the table.

Pupil	A	B	C	D	E	F	G	H	I	J
Time on part-time job (hours)	9	19	13	3	15	20	5	17	6	22
Mean mark in examination	50	92	52	70	26	10	80	36	74	24

Exercise 8.1B cont'd

a) Plot a scatter graph to show Jane's results, with time in hours on the horizontal axis.

b) Do the results confirm Jane's views? Are there any exceptions?

c) Draw a line of best fit for the relevant points.

d) Estimate the mean score of a pupil who spent 12 hours on their part-time job.

5 In an experiment, Tom's reaction times are tested after he has undergone vigorous exercise. The table shows Tom's reaction times and the amounts of time spent in exercise.

Amount of exercise (minutes)	0	10	20	30	40	50
Reaction time (seconds)		0.34	0.46	0.52	0.67	0.82	0.91

a) Draw a scatter graph to show this information, with the number of minutes of exercise on the horizontal axis.

b) Comment on the graph.

c) Draw a line of best fit.

d) Use your line of best fit to estimate Tom's reaction time after 35 minutes' exercise.

6 Fiona thinks that the more she practises, the more goals she will score at hockey. Sketch a scatter graph to show this.

ACTIVITY 2 – EXTENSION

Investigate one of the following:

petrol consumption and the size of the car's engine

person's height and head circumference

prices of houses and the distance from the town centre

age of car and second-hand price.

Key ideas

- Scatter graphs show the correlation between two variables.

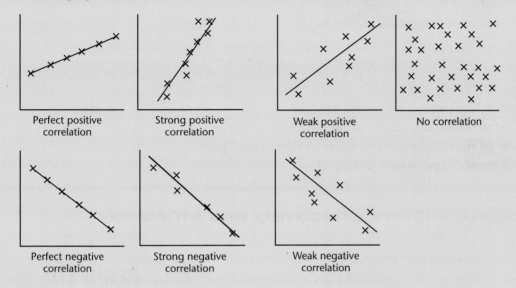

- If there is reasonable correlation, a line of best fit can be drawn.
- The line of best fit should reflect the slope of the points and should have approximately the same number of points on either side.
- The line of best fit can be used to estimate values of one variable if the other is known.
- The line of best fit can only be used to estimate values within the range of the given data.

Chapter 8   *Scatter graphs and correlation*

9 Calculators and accuracy

You should already know

- how to use powers and roots, brackets and the memory on your calculator
- how to round to a given number of decimal places
- how to round to a given number of significant figures
- the order of operations (BODMAS).

Using calculators effectively and efficiently

Buttons on your calculator such as powers and roots, brackets and the memory can be used in various different ways. Remind yourself now of the order in which you need to press buttons on your calculator to use these functions.

Exam tip

Get to know your calculator so you know how to use it to work out complicated calculations.

For example, to work out $\dfrac{61 \cdot 2}{4 \cdot 9 - 1 \cdot 05}$ you can use brackets or the memory.

The most efficient method is to use $\boxed{6}\ \boxed{1}\ \boxed{\cdot}$
$\boxed{2}\ \boxed{\div}\ \boxed{(}\ \boxed{4}\ \boxed{\cdot}\ \boxed{9}\ \boxed{-}\ \boxed{1}\ \boxed{\cdot}\ \boxed{0}\ \boxed{5}\ \boxed{)}\ \boxed{=}$

A two-stage calculation of $\boxed{4}\ \boxed{\cdot}\ \boxed{9}\ \boxed{-}\ \boxed{1}\ \boxed{\cdot}\ \boxed{0}\ \boxed{5}\ \boxed{=}\ \boxed{M_{in}}$
then $\boxed{6}\ \boxed{1}\ \boxed{\cdot}\ \boxed{2}\ \boxed{\div}\ \boxed{MR}\ \boxed{=}$ will also produce the correct answer.

Exam tip

If you are not sure how your calculator works, break the calculation down into simple steps and use the '$\boxed{=}$' key after each step. Better still, learn how to use your calculator efficiently!

Make sure you understand why these two methods work, but why $\boxed{6}\ \boxed{1}$
$\boxed{\cdot}\ \boxed{2}\ \boxed{\div}\ \boxed{4}\ \boxed{\cdot}\ \boxed{9}\ \boxed{-}\ \boxed{1}\ \boxed{\cdot}$
$\boxed{0}\ \boxed{5}\ \boxed{=}$ gives the wrong answer!

EXERCISE 9.1A

Make the following calculations using your calculator.

1 **a)** $\sqrt{4\cdot1^2 + 3\cdot7^2}$ **b)** $(67\cdot9 + 8\cdot34)^3$ **c)** $\left(\dfrac{4\cdot1}{2\cdot5}\right)^5$

2 **a)** $6\cdot3\sqrt{121}$ **b)** $\sqrt[3]{8}$ **c)** $(\sqrt{20} + \sqrt{50})^2$

3 **a)** $6\cdot3 + \dfrac{9\cdot4}{3\cdot6 + 8\cdot7}$ **b)** $\dfrac{21\cdot6 - 4\cdot9}{6\cdot8 + 5\cdot7}$ **c)** $\dfrac{4\cdot8}{6\cdot4 \times 3\cdot1}$

4 **a)** $\dfrac{8\cdot25 - 4\cdot4}{5\cdot5}$ **b)** $8\cdot25 - \dfrac{4\cdot4}{5\cdot5}$ **c)** $\dfrac{8\cdot25}{5\cdot5} - 4\cdot4$

5 **a)** $(4\cdot16 - 6\cdot98) \times (7\cdot3 - 2\cdot16)$ **b)** $\dfrac{7\cdot9}{6\cdot7 \times 5\cdot2} + 8\cdot92$ **c)** $\sqrt{\dfrac{9\cdot8}{28\cdot7}}$

EXERCISE 9.1B

Calculate:

1 **a)** $\sqrt{6\cdot7^2 - 2\cdot8^2}$ **b)** $(3\cdot5 + 6\cdot17)^4$ **c)** $\left(\dfrac{8\cdot1}{5\cdot2}\right)^{-1}$

2 **a)** $\sqrt[3]{216} + 2\cdot45$ **b)** $(\sqrt[3]{14})^2 \times 1\cdot73$ **c)** $\left(\dfrac{7}{1\cdot13 - 0\cdot989}\right)^2$

3 **a)** $12\cdot6 - \dfrac{7\cdot4}{8\cdot9 + 14\cdot7}$ **b)** $\dfrac{16\cdot3 - 12\cdot1}{5\cdot4 + 2\cdot6}$ **c)** $\dfrac{7\cdot5}{6\cdot8 \times 4\cdot7}$

4 **a)** $\dfrac{1}{3\cdot26 + 18\cdot45 - 11\cdot23}$ **b)** $\dfrac{17 - 6\cdot3}{4\cdot2 \times 5\cdot3}$ **c)** $\dfrac{4\cdot5^2 - 0\cdot75^2}{16 \times 1\cdot42}$

5 **a)** $(14\cdot2 - 8\cdot7) \div (7\cdot3 + 5\cdot2)$ **b)** $\dfrac{7\cdot4}{0\cdot6 \times 5\cdot8} + 12\cdot3$ **c)** $\sqrt{\dfrac{15\cdot8}{4\cdot7}}$

Working to a reasonable degree of accuracy

Measurements and calculations should always be expressed to a suitable degree of accuracy. For example, it would be silly to say that a car journey took 4 hours 46 minutes and 13 seconds, but reasonable to say that it took four and three-quarter hours, or about five hours. In the same way, saying that the distance the car travelled was 93 kilometres 484 metres and 78 centimetres would be giving the measurement to an unnecessary degree of accuracy. It would more sensibly be stated as 93 km.

As a general rule the answer you give after a calculation should not be given to a greater degree of accuracy than any of the values used in the calculation.

EXAMPLE 1

Ben measured the length and width of a table as 1·8 m and 1·3 m. He calculated the area as 1·8 × 1·3 = 2·34 m². How should he have given the answer?

Ben's answer has two places of decimals (2 d.p.) so it is more accurate than the measurements he took. His answer should be 2·3 m².

EXERCISE 9.2A

Write down sensible values for each of these measurements.

1   3 minutes 24·8 seconds to boil an egg.

2   2 weeks, 5 days, 3 hours and 13 minutes to paint a house.

Work these out and give the answers to a reasonable degree of accuracy.

3   Find the length of the side of a square field with area 33 m².

4   Three friends win £48·32. How much will each receive?

5   It takes 12 hours to fly between two cities, if the aeroplane is travelling at 554 km/h. How far apart are the cities?

6   The length of a strip of card is 2·36 cm and the width is 0·041 cm, each measured to two significant figures. Calculate the area.

EXERCISE 9.2B

Write down sensible values for each of these measurements.

1   A book weighing 2·853 kg.

2   The height of a door as 2 metres 12 centimetres and 54 millimetres.

Work these out and give the answers to a reasonable degree of accuracy.

3   The length of a field is 92 m correct to two significant figures and the width is 58·36 m correct to four significant figures. Calculate the area of the field.

4   A book has 228 pages and is 18 mm thick. How thick is Chapter 1 which has 35 pages?

5   The total weight of 13 people in a lift is 879 kg. What is their average weight?

6   Last year a delivery driver drove 23 876 miles. Her van travels an average of 27 miles to the gallon. Diesel costs 72p per litre. If one gallon equals 4·55 litres, calculate the cost of the fuel used.

Key ideas

- Get to know your calculator so that you know how to use it to work out complicated calculations.
- The degree of accuracy in measurement depends on the purpose of the measurement.

Revision exercise

1 £C is the cost of L m of piping. C is directly proportional to L.

a) Copy and complete the table.

L	1·3	5·2	
C	3·12		6·00

b) State the equation connecting C and L.

2 Find the equation connecting y and x if y is directly proportional to x and y = 10·8 when x = 6.

3 A is directly proportional to h. A is 5·6 when h = 4. Calculate the value of A when h = 5.

4 Estimate the cost of travelling 48 miles by car if the cost per mile is 31p.

5 Stephen has £25. Show a rough calculation to check whether he has enough money to buy six CDs at £3·98.

6 Estimate the answers to these.
a) 63·9 × 14·9
b) $\sqrt{143} \times \sqrt{170} \times \sqrt{80}$
c) $(6·32 + 5·72) \times (\sqrt{16·1} + \sqrt{48·9})$

7 The scatter graphs show the heights and weights of ten boys and ten girls in a class. Compare the two graphs, noting any differences and any similarities.

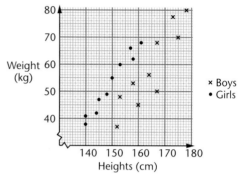

8 Brian thinks that the more he practises, the lower his golf score will be. State the type of correlation of which this is an example.

9 Two judges at a cat show marked eight cats for the quality of their coats. The marks are out of 30. The marks they gave are shown in the table.

Cat	A	B	C	D	E	F	G	H
Judge 1	17	23	15	28	22	18	27	14
Judge 2	7	23	9	27	13	15	25	4

a) Draw a scatter diagram to show the judges' scores, with Judge 1 on the horizontal axis.
b) Comment on the relationship between the two judges' scores.
c) Draw a line of best fit.
d) Judge 2 gave a ninth cat 18 marks. Estimate the marks that Judge 1 would give the same cat.

10 Market research predicts that the possible prices for replica shirts would lead to sales as shown in the table.

Price (£)	20	25	30	35	40	45	50
Number of shirts	7600	7400	6800	5600	5400	4500	3600

    a) Draw a scatter diagram to show this information.

    b) Comment on the relationship between price and predicted sales.

    c) Draw a line of best fit.

    d) Estimate the sales of shirts if the price were fixed at £33.

    e) Why would it be wrong to predict the sales if the price were fixed at £65?

11 A survey is carried out at the checkout of a supermarket. It investigates the total cost of bills and the number of items bought. Sketch what you think the scatter diagram would look like, with number of items on the horizontal axis and total cost of the bill on the vertical axis.

12 Calculate

    a) $\sqrt{1\cdot7^2 - 1\cdot5^2}$ **b)** $\dfrac{48\cdot7}{\pi \times 3\cdot6^2}$

    c) $\dfrac{9\cdot81 + 10\cdot97}{5\cdot42 - 3\cdot16}$

13 Calculate

    a) $(\sqrt{6} + \sqrt{8})^2$ **b)** $\dfrac{1}{0\cdot20 \times 40}$

    c) $\sqrt{\dfrac{9\cdot7 + 1\cdot8}{6\cdot4}}$

14 The diameter of a circle is 3·5 m correct to two significant figures. Calculate the circumference of the circle. Take π = 3·141 593.

15 Light travels at approximately 300 000 km/s. If light takes about 8 minutes to reach the Earth from the sun, how far is the Earth from the sun, in kilometres?

16 The mean weight of eight men is 78·7 kg. A ninth man joins them. His weight is 48·6 kg. What is the mean weight of all nine men?

10 Pythagoras' theorem

You should already know

- how to find the area of a triangle
- how to find squares and square roots on a calculator.

Pythagoras' theorem

This is a square drawn on dotty paper.
Its area is 4 square units.

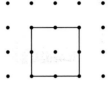

Here is a tilted square.
Calculating its area is more difficult.
There are two methods you could use.

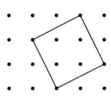

1   Calculate the area of the large square drawn round the outside and subtract the area of the shaded triangles:

9 – 1 – 1 – 1 – 1 = 5 square units

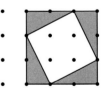

2   Add together the area of the four shaded triangles and the area of the middle square:

1 + 1 + 1 + 1 + 1 = 5 square units

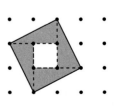

Chapter 10 *Pythagoras' theorem*

ACTIVITY 1

Using either method 1 or method 2 calculate the area of the squares in the diagram below.

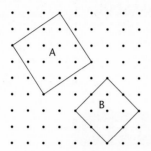

You should have found that the area of square A is 13 square units and the area of square B is 8 square units.

Draw some more tilted squares of your own on dotty paper and find their areas.

Look at all the tilted squares.

Code the tilt by drawing a triangle at the base and writing down the length of its sides, like this.

In this diagram the code is (2, 1). In the first diagram of the activity, square A has a code of (3, 2) and square B has a code of (2, 2).

Check that you agree.

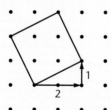

Code all the squares you have drawn and write the codes and the areas of the squares in a table. Include the square from the beginning of this chapter. Its code is (2, 0) and its area is 4 square units. Include all the other squares you have already studied in this chapter.

Look at the codes and their areas. See if you can find a rule linking them together

Code	Area
(2, 0)	4
(2, 1)	5
(3, 2)	13
(2, 2)	8

You will have found that squaring each code number and then adding the squares together gives the area:

$3^2 + 2^2 = 9 + 4 = 13$

$2^2 + 2^2 = 4 + 4 = 8$

$2^2 + 1^2 = 4 + 1 = 5$

The rule linking them together is called Pythagoras' theorem.

Squaring the numbers in the code and adding them is the same as squaring the lengths of the sides of the triangle.

Chapter 10 Pythagoras' theorem

Here is square A again.

Can you see that you can calculate the area of the largest square by adding together the areas of the smaller squares?

The largest square will always be on the longest side of the triangle – this is called the **hypotenuse** of the triangle.

Pythagoras' theorem can be stated as:

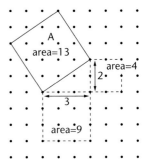

> The area of the square on the hypotenuse = the sum of the areas of the squares on the other two sides

Here is a shorter version:

> The square on the hypotenuse = the sum of the squares on the other two sides

ACTIVITY 2

Draw this diagram. Cut up the two smaller squares so that they fit together to make square A.

ACTIVITY 3

Calculate the missing area in each of these diagrams.

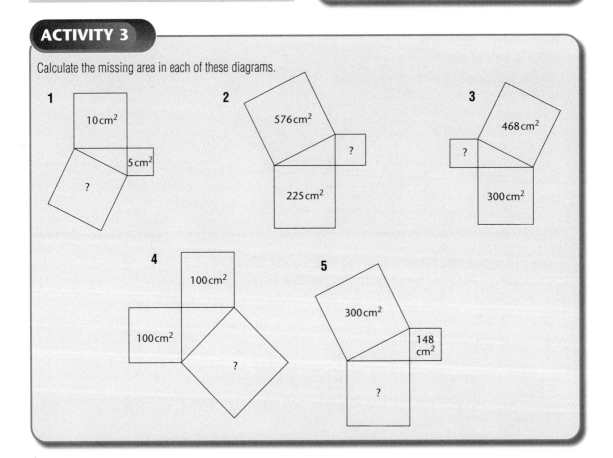

If you know the lengths of two sides of a right-angled triangle you can use Pythagoras' theorem to find length of the third side.

The unknown area = 64 + 36 = 100 cm²

This means that the length of the sides of the unknown square is 10 cm.

When using Pythagoras' theorem, you don't need to draw the squares – you can simply use the rule.

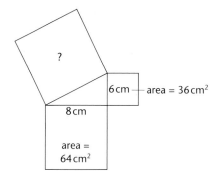

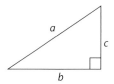 $a^2 = b^2 + c^2$

So, for this triangle:

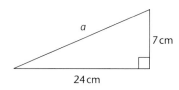

$$a^2 = 9^2 + 12^2$$
$$= 81 + 144$$
$$= 225$$
$$a = \sqrt{225}$$
$$= 15\,\text{cm}$$

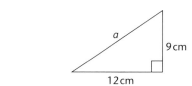

$$a^2 = 7^2 + 24^2$$
$$= 49 + 576$$
$$= 625$$
$$a = \sqrt{625}$$
$$= 25\,\text{cm}$$

ACTIVITY 4

Find the length of the hypotenuse in each of these triangles.

1

2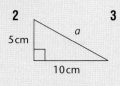

3

4

5

6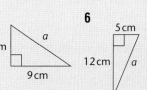

Chapter 10 *Pythagoras' theorem*

If you know the length of the hypotenuse and the length of one other side you can find the length of the third side.

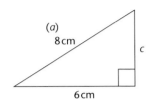

(a)

$a^2 = b^2 + c^2$

$8^2 = 6^2 + c^2$

$64 = 36 + c^2$

$c^2 = 64 - 36 = 28$

$c = \sqrt{28} = 5.29$ cm (to 2 d.p.)

ACTIVITY 5

Calculate the length of the third side in each of these triangles. Give your answers correct to two decimal places.

1 17 cm, 15 cm, b

2 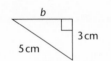 7 cm, 9 cm, b

3 20 cm, 12 cm, c

4 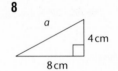 30 cm, 8 cm, b

5 5 cm, 169 cm, b

6 b, 5 cm, 3 cm

7 14 cm, 20 cm, c

8 a, 4 cm, 8 cm

Solve these problems.

1 A rectangular field is 225 m long and 110 m wide. Find the length of the diagonal path across it.

2 A rectangular field is 25 m long. A footpath 38·0 m long crosses the field diagonally. Find the width of the field.

3 A ladder is 7 m long. It is resting against a wall, with the top of the ladder 5 m above the ground. How far from the wall is the base of the ladder?

4 Harry is building a kite for his sister. This is his diagram of the kite. The kite is 30 cm wide. Harry needs to buy some cane to make the struts AC and DB. What length of cane does he need to buy?

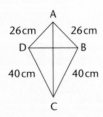

A 26 cm, 26 cm, D, B, 40 cm, 40 cm, C

5 This is the side view of a shed. Find the length of the sloping roof.

2·8 m, 1·9 m, 3·1 m

6 This is the cross-section of a roof space. The roof timbers AB and BC are each 6·5 m long. The floor joist AC is 12 m. What is the maximum height in the roof space?

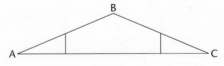

A, B, C

7 A tent pole is secured by guy ropes which are 2·4 m long. They reach the ground, which is horizontal, 1·6 m away from the base of the pole. How high up the pole are the guy ropes fastened?

ACTIVITY 6

Plot the points A(3, 1) and B (7, 4) on graph paper.

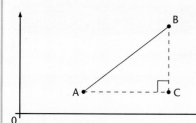

Complete the right-angled triangle ABC.

Find the length of AB.

$AB^2 = AC^2 + BC^2$

$AC = 7 - 3 = 4$ and $BC = 4 - 1 = 3$

$AB^2 = 4^2 + 3^2 = 25$

$AB = 5$

Now find the distances between these pairs of points.

1 (1, 1) and (5, 5)   **2** (6, 2) and (2, 1)

3 (3, 4) and (0, 0)   **4** (⁻2, ⁻1) and (4, 1)

Exam tip

It is a good idea to draw a sketch if a diagram isn't given. Try to draw it roughly to scale and mark on it any lengths you know. It may help you see any errors in your working.

Key ideas

- For a right-angled triangle, Pythagoras' theorem states that
$a^2 = b^2 + c^2$

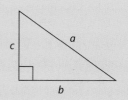

Quadratic graphs

You should already know

● how to draw the graph of a straight line, given its equation.

Quadratic graphs

Quadratic graphs are graphs of equations of the form $y = ax^2 + bx + c$, where a, b, c are constants and b and c may be zero, for example, $y = x^2 + 3$, $y = x^2 - 4x + 3$. When the graph is drawn, it produces a curve called a parabola.

In an examination you may be expected to complete a table of values to work out the points. Even if you are not given a table, it is still best to use one.

EXAMPLE 1

Draw the graph of $y = x^2 + 4$, for values of x from $^-3$ to 3. First draw a table of values.

x	$^-3$	$^-2$	$^-1$	0	1	2	3
x^2	9	4	1	0	1	4	9
$y = x^2 + 4$	13	8	5	4	5	8	13

Now label the axes. The values of x go from $^-3$ to 3 and the values of y go from 4 to 13. It is better to include 0 in the values of y, so let them go from 0 to 15.

> Always include the x-axis even when the y values are all positive.

On this graph the scale used is 1 square to 1 unit on the x-axis and 1 square to 5 units on the y-axis.

Plot the points and join them with a smooth curve. Label the curve.

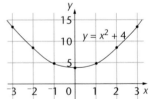

Exam tip

Practice drawing smooth curves. Keep your pencil on the paper. Make the curve a thin single line. Look ahead to the next point as you draw the line.

Exam tip

x^2 is always positive ($-x^2$ is always negative). If the equation involves $-x^2$, the parabola will be the opposite way up. In quadratic graphs, the values of y go down and then up again (or vice versa). If one point does not fit that pattern, check that point again.

EXAMPLE 2

Draw the graph of $y = x^2 + 3x$, for values of x from $^-5$ to 2.

Label the axes from $^-5$ to 2 for x and from $^-5$ to 10 for y.

x	$^-5$	$^-4$	$^-3$	$^-2$	$^-1$	0	1	2
x^2	25	16	9	4	1	0	1	4
$3x$	$^-15$	$^-12$	$^-9$	$^-6$	$^-3$	0	3	6
$y = x^2 + 3x$	10	4	0	$^-2$	$^-2$	0	4	10

Add the numbers in rows 2 and 3 to give the value of y.

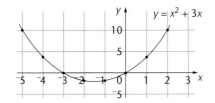

Here you can see that $x = ^-1$ and $x = ^-2$ both give $y = ^-2$, and the lowest value (called the minimum) will be *when x is between $^-1$ and $^-2$.*

It is useful to work out the value of y when $x = ^-1.5$. To do this, add some more values to your table:

$x = ^-1.5$, $x^2 = 2.25$, $3x = ^-4.5$, $y = ^-2.25$.

Plot ($^-1.5$, $^-2.25$), which is the lowest point of the graph.

> ### Exam tip
>
> A common error is to include the values of the x-row when adding to find y. So separate this row off clearly.

> ### Exam tip
>
> If you find that you have two equal lowest (or highest) values for y, the curve will go below (or above) the point. You will need to find the y-value between the two equal values. To do this, find the value of x halfway between the two points and substitute to find the corresponding value of y.

> ### Exam tip
>
> The y-scale for Examples 1 and 2 could be 1 cm to 5 units. This is satisfactory and does not take a lot of space, but if you do have enough space it will look better and be easier to plot if you use a scale of 2 cm to 5 units, as in Example 3.

Exam tip

Sometimes a table will be given with only the two rows for x- and y-values. You may find it useful to include all the rows and then just add the correct rows to get the value of y.

EXAMPLE 3

a) Draw the graph of $y = x^2 - 2x - 3$, for values of x from $^-2$ to 4. Label the axes from $^-2$ to 4 for x, and from $^-5$ to 5 for y.

b) Solve the equation $x^2 - 2x - 3 = 0$ from your graph.

a)

x	$^-2$	$^-1$	0	1	2	3	4
x^2	4	1	0	1	4	9	16
$-2x$	4	2	0	$^-2$	$^-4$	$^-6$	$^-8$
-3	$^-3$	$^-3$	$^-3$	$^-3$	$^-3$	$^-3$	$^-3$
$y = x^2 - 2x - 3$	5	0	$^-3$	$^-4$	$^-3$	0	5

To find the value of y, add together the values in rows 2, 3 and 4.

Use a scale of 1 square to 1 unit on the x-axis and 2 squares to 5 units on the y-axis.

Now plot the points $(^-2, 5)$, $(^-1, 0)$ and so on. Join them with a smooth curve. Label the curve.

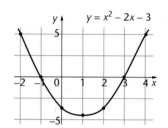

b) $x^2 - 2x - 3 = 0$ when $y = 0$, which is when the curve crosses the x-axis. This is when $x = ^-1$ or $x = 3$.

Sometimes questions will be put in context. They will be about a real-life situation, rather than just being about a graph in terms of x and y.

EXAMPLE 4

The cost C, in pounds, of circular plates is given by the formula $C = \dfrac{x^2}{10} + 2$, where x is the radius of the plate in centimetres.

a) Draw up a table of values and complete it.

b) (i) Draw the graph of C against x, for values of x from 0 to 20, and C from 0 to 45.

(ii) From your graph find the size of plate that would cost £16·40.

a)

x	0	5	8	10	15	20
x^2	0	25	64	100	225	400
$\dfrac{x^2}{10}$	0	2·5	6·4	10	22·5	40
$C = \dfrac{x^2}{10} + 2$	2	4·5	8·4	12	24·5	42

Example 4 cont'd

b) (i)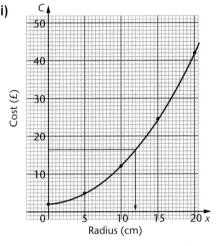

(ii) You can buy a plate with radius 12 cm for £16·40.

EXERCISE 11.1A

1 Copy the table for $y = x^2 + 5$ and complete it. Do not draw the graph.

x	$^-3$	$^-2$	$^-1$	0	1	2	3
x^2	9						
5	5						
$y = x^2 + 5$	14						

2 Copy the table of values for $y = x^2 + 3x - 7$ and complete it. Do not draw the graph. Notice the extra value at $x = ^-1·5$.

x	$^-4$	$^-3$	$^-2$	$^-1$	0	1	2	$^-1·5$
x^2			4					
$3x$			$^-6$					
$^-7$			$^-7$					
$y = x^2 + 3x - 7$			$^-9$					

Exercise 11.1A cont'd

3 Copy the table of values for $y = -x^2 - 5x + 6$ and complete it. Do not draw the graph. Remember $-x^2$ is always negative. Notice the extra value at $-2 \cdot 5$.

x	$^-6$	$^-5$	$^-4$	$^-3$	$^-2$	$^-1$	0	1	2	$^-2 \cdot 5$
x^2			$^-16$						$^-4$	
^-5x			20						$^-10$	
6			6						6	
$y = -x^2 - 5x + 6$			10						$^-8$	

4 Draw up a table of values for $y = x^2 - 3x + 1$, for $x = {^-2}$ to 4. Do not draw the graph.

Use 2 mm graph paper for these questions.

5 a) Copy the table of values for $y = x^2 - 2$ and complete it.

x	$^-3$	$^-2$	$^-1$	0	1	2	3
x^2							
$^-2$							
$y = x^2 - 2$							

b) Draw the graph of $y = x^2 - 2$ for $x = {^-3}$ to 3. Label the x-axis from $^-3$ to $+3$ and the y-axis from $^-5$ to 10. Use a scale of 1 cm to 1 unit on the x-axis and 2 cm to 5 units on the y-axis.

6 Draw the graph of $y = -x^2 + 4$ for $x = {^-3}$ to 3. Label the x-axis from $^-3$ to $+3$ and the y-axis from 0 to 15. Use a scale of 1 cm to 1 unit on the x-axis and 2 cm to 5 units on the y-axis.

7 a) Copy this table of values for $y = x^2 - 3x$ and complete it.

x	$^-1$	0	1	2	3	4	5	$1 \cdot 5$
x^2								
^-3x								
$y = x^2 - 3x$								

Exercise 11.1A cont'd

b) Draw the graph of $y = x^2 - 3x$, for $x = {}^-1$ to 5. Label the x-axis from $^-1$ to $+5$ and the y-axis from $^-5$ to 10.
Use a scale of 1 cm to 1 unit on the x-axis and 2 cm to 5 units on the y-axis.

8 Draw the graph of $y = x^2 - 4x + 3$, for $x = {}^-1$ to 5.

9 **a)** Draw the graph of $y = x^2 - 5x + 2$, for $x = {}^-1$ to 6.
b) Find the values of x on your graph when $y = 0$. Give your answers correct to one decimal place.

10 When a stone is dropped from the edge of a cliff, the distance, d metres, it falls is given by the formula $d = 5t^2$, where t is the time in seconds.

a) Work out the values of d for $t = 0$ to 5.
b) Draw the graph for $t = 0$ to 5.
c) The cliff is 65 metres high. How long does it take the stone to reach the bottom of the cliff? Give the answer correct to one decimal place.

EXERCISE 11.1B

1 Copy the table of values for $y = x^2 + 6$ and complete it.
Do not draw the graph.

x	$^-3$	$^-2$	$^-1$	0	1	2	3
x^2		4					
6		6					
$y = x^2 + 6$		10					

2 Copy the table of values for $y = 2x^2 - 8$ and complete it.
Do not draw the graph.

x	$^-3$	$^-2$	$^-1$	0	1	2	3
x^2	9						
$2x^2$	18						
$^-8$	$^-8$						
$y = 2x^2 - 8$	10						

To find the value of y rows 3 and 4 are added. Some people do not include the x^2 row but it can help.

3 Draw up a table of values for $y = x^2 - 5x + 8$, for $x = {}^-2$ to 4. Do not draw the graph.

Exercise 11.1B cont'd

4 Draw the graph of $y = x^2 + 4x$, for $x = {}^-6$ to 2. Label the x-axis from $^-6$ to 2 and the y-axis from $^-5$ to 15.

Use a scale of 1 cm to 1 unit on the x-axis and 1 cm to 5 units on the y-axis.

5 Draw the graph of $y = {}^-x^2 + 2x + 6$, for $x = {}^-2$ to 4. Label the x-axis from $^-2$ to 4 and the y-axis from $^-5$ to 10.

> An extra point at $x = 2{\cdot}5$ might be useful.

Use a scale of 1 cm to 1 unit on the x-axis and 1 cm to 5 units on the y-axis.

6 Draw the graph of $y = x^2 - 6x + 5$, for $x = {}^-1$ to 6.

7 Draw the graph of $y = {}^-x^2 + 4x - 3$, for $x = {}^-1$ to 5.

8 a) Draw the graph of $y = 2x^2 - 5x + 1$, for $x = {}^-2$ to 4.

> Note that in this case the values of y are not symmetrical.

b) Find the value of x on your graph where $y = 0$.

Give your answers correct to one decimal place.

9 a) Draw the graph of $y = 2x^2 - 12x$ for values of x from $^-1$ to 7.
b) Write down the values of x where the curve crosses $y = 5$.

10 The surface area (S) of a cube is given by the formula $S = 6x^2$, where x is the length of an edge of the cube.

a) Copy this table of values and complete it to find S.

x	0	1	2	3	4	5	6
x^2				9			
$S = 6x^2$				54			

b) Draw the graph of $S = 6x^2$ for values of x from 0 to 6.
c) From your graph, find the length of the edge of a cube with surface area 140 cm².

Graphical methods of solving equations

One way of finding solutions to quadratic equations is to draw and use a graph.

EXAMPLE 5

a) Draw the graph of $y = x^2 - 2x - 8$ for values of x from $^-3$ to 5.

b) Solve the equation $x^2 - 2x - 8 = 0$.

c) Solve the equation $x^2 - 2x - 8 = 5$.

a)

x	$^-3$	$^-2$	$^-1$	0	1	2	3	4	5
x^2	9	4	1	0	1	4	9	16	25
^-2x	6	4	2	0	$^-2$	$^-4$	$^-6$	$^-8$	$^-10$
$^-8$	$^-8$	$^-8$	$^-8$	$^-8$	$^-8$	$^-8$	$^-8$	$^-8$	$^-8$
$y = x^2 - 2x - 8$	7	0	$^-5$	$^-8$	$^-9$	$^-8$	$^-5$	0	7

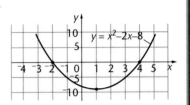

b) The solution of $x^2 - 2x - 8 = 0$ is when $y = 0$, where the curve cuts the x-axis.

The solution is $x = ^-2$ or $x = 4$.

c) The solution of $x^2 - 2x - 8 = 5$ is when $y = 5$.

The solution is $x = ^-2 \cdot 7$ or $x = 4 \cdot 7$, to 1 d.p.

EXERCISE 11.2A

1 a) Draw the graph of $y = x^2 - 7x + 10$ for values of x from 0 to 7.

b) Solve the equation $x^2 - 7x + 10 = 0$.

2 a) Draw the graph of $y = x^2 - x - 2$ for values of x from $^-2$ to 3.

b) Solve the equation $x^2 - x - 2 = 0$.

3 a) Draw the graph of $y = x^2 - 8$ for values of x from $^-4$ to 4.

b) Solve the equation $x^2 - 8 = 0$.

c) Solve the equation $x^2 - 8 = 3$.

4 a) Draw the graph of $y = x^2 + x - 3$ for values of x from $^-3$ to 2.

b) Solve the equation $x^2 + x - 3 = 0$.

c) Solve the equation $x^2 + x - 3 = ^-2$.

EXERCISE 11.2B

1 **a)** Draw the graph of $y = x^2 - 4x + 3$ for values of x from ⁻1 to 5.
   b) Solve the equation $x^2 - 4x + 3 = 0$.

2 **a)** Draw the graph of $y = x^2 - 3x$ for values of x from ⁻2 to 5.
   b) Solve the equation $x^2 - 3x = 0$.

3 **a)** Draw the graph of $y = x^2 - 5$ for values of x from ⁻3 to 3.
   b) Solve the equation $x^2 - 5 = 0$.
   c) Solve the equation $x^2 - 5 = 2$.

4 **a)** Draw the graph of $y = x^2 - 3x - 2$ for values of x from ⁻2 to 5.
   b) Solve the equation $x^2 - 3x - 2 = 0$.
   c) Solve the equation $x^2 - 3x - 2 = 6$.

Key ideas

● Quadratic equations have the form $y = ax^2 + bx + c$, where a, b and c are constants and b and c may be zero.

● The graph of a quadratic equation is a parabola. It has the following shape:

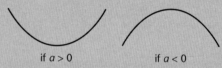

if $a > 0$ if $a < 0$

● To solve the quadratic equation $ax^2 + bx + c = k$ graphically, find the values of x where the graph of $y = ax^2 + bx + c$ crosses the line $y = k$.

12 *Finding the mean of grouped data*

You should already know

- how to find the mean of non-grouped data
- how to construct and interpret frequency polygons and bar graphs.

Grouped discrete data

It is often easier to see the pattern of the data if they are grouped.
For example, this is a list of goals scored in 20 matches.

1 1 3 2 0 0 1 4 0 2
2 0 6 3 4 1 1 3 2 1

Instead, the information could be set out like this.

Number of goals	Frequency
0	4
1	6
2	4
3	3
4	2
5	0
6	1

ACTIVITY 1

1 Collect some data such as points, goals or runs scored in last week's matches or the number of coins each person has in their purse or pocket.

2 Organise the data and work out the mean.

Mode

From the table, it is easy to identify the number of goals with the greatest frequency. This is the mode of the data. Here the mode is 1 goal.

Mean

The table can also be used to calculate the mean.

There are: four matches with 0 goals $4 \times 0 = 0$ goals
six matches with 1 goal $6 \times 1 = 6$ goals
four matches with 2 goals $4 \times 2 = 8$ goals

and so on.

To find the total number of goals scored altogether, multiply each number of goals by its frequency and then add the results.

Then dividing by the total number of matches (20) gives the mean.

The working for this is shown in the table.

Number of goals	Frequency	Number of goals × frequency
0	4	0
1	6	6
2	4	8
3	3	9
4	2	8
5	0	0
6	1	6
Totals	20	37

Exam tip

When given a table of grouped data, add an extra column if necessary to help you work out the values multiplied by their frequencies.

Mean = 37 ÷ 20 = 1·85 goals.

In this example you have been given the original data.
Check the answer by adding up the list of goals scored and dividing them by 20!

EXAMPLE 1

Work out the mean, mode and range for the number of children in the houses in Berry Road, listed in this table.

Number of children (c)	Frequency (number of houses)	c × frequency
0	6	0
1	4	4
2	5	10
3	7	21
4	1	4
5	2	10
Totals	25	49

Mean = 49 ÷ 25 = 1·96 children
Mode = 3 children
Range = 5 − 0 = 5 children

EXERCISE 12.1A

1 Ben has counted the number of sweets in ten packets. Here are the results.

12   11   10   10   12   13   12   11   12   11

   a) Make a frequency table for Ben's results.
   b) What is the mode of his results?
   c) Use the frequency table to calculate the mean number of sweets.
   d) Use the original list to calculate the mean, to check your results.

2 Here are some results for the number of crisps in a bag.

Number of crisps	25	26	27	28	29
Frequency	4	9	16	7	4

   a) How many bags of crisps were counted?
   b) What was the total number of crisps in these bags?
   c) What was the mean number of crisps in these bags?

3 a) What is the mode for the data in question 2?
   b) What is the range for these data?

4 Find the mean value of x in these data.

x	7	8	9	10	11	12
Frequency	6	0	12	23	8	16

5 Here are the numbers of letters a postman delivered to the houses in Selly Road one morning.

Number of letters	0	1	2	3	4	5	6
Number of houses	4	5	7	2	6	0	2

   a) How many houses are there in Selly Road?
   b) What was the mode of the number of letters delivered there?
   c) What was the mean number of letters delivered there? Give your answer correct to one decimal place.

Chapter 12 *Finding the mean of grouped data*

EXERCISE 12.1B

1 Jenny counted the numbers of peas in ten pods. Here are the results.

   5   6   4   5   6   5   4   4   3   5

   a) Make a frequency table for Jenny's results.

   b) What is the mode of her results?

   c) Use your frequency table to calculate the mean number of peas.

   d) Use the original list to calculate the mean, to check your results.

2 Here are some results for the number of matches in a box.

Number of matches	43	44	45	46	47
Frequency	6	8	17	15	4

   a) How many boxes of matches were counted?

   b) What was the total number of matches in these boxes?

   c) What was the mean number of matches in these boxes?

3 **a)** What is the mode for the data in question 2?

   b) What is the range for these data?

4 Find the mean value of x in these data.

x	5	6	7	8	9	10
Frequency	13	9	0	13	24	3

5 In a game, scores from 1 to 10 are possible. Dipta had 60 goes and obtained these scores.

Score	1	2	3	4	5	6	7	8	9	10
Frequency	3	4	8	7	11	9	1	4	5	8

   a) What was Dipta's modal score?

   b) Calculate Dipta's mean score.

Finding the mean with grouped continuous data

When working out the mean of grouped data in a table, you do not know the exact value for each item of data, so the midpoint value is chosen to represent each group, and this is used to calculate an estimate of the mean. The midpoint is multiplied by the frequency of the group, as in calculating the mean of grouped discrete data.

ACTIVITY 2

1 Collect some continuous data such as the 'weights' of school bags for people in your class.

2 Group the data and represent them on a frequency polygon or bar chart. Calculate the mean of these data.

EXAMPLE 2

Calculate an estimate of the mean height of the students in year 11 at Sandish School.

Height (h cm)	Frequency	Midpoint	Midpoint × frequency
$155 \leqslant h < 160$	2	157·5	315
$160 \leqslant h < 165$	6	162·5	975
$165 \leqslant h < 170$	18	167·5	3015
$170 \leqslant h < 175$	25	172·5	4312·5
$175 \leqslant h < 180$	9	177·5	1597·5
$180 \leqslant h < 185$	4	182·5	730
$185 \leqslant h < 190$	1	187·5	187·5
Totals	65		11 132·5

Mean = 11 132·5 ÷ 65 = 171·3 cm, correct to one decimal place.

Exam tip

Add two columns to the frequency table to help you work out the mean – one column for the midpoints of each group and one for the midpoints multiplied by their frequencies.

EXERCISE 12.2A

1 State the boundaries of these intervals.

  a) 18 cm, to the nearest cm   b) 35 m, to the nearest m
  c) masses to the nearest gram: 5–9, 10–14
  d) times to the nearest second: 2–3, 4–5

2 State the midpoints of these intervals.

  a) 10 cm < length ⩽ 20 cm   b) 2·0 m ⩽ length ⩽ 2·5 m
  c) 80 kg ⩽ mass < 85 kg
  d) masses to the nearest kg: 81–85, 86–90
  e) times to the nearest second: 31–40, 41–50

Exercise 12.2A cont'd

3 Calculate an estimate of the mean of these times.

Time (seconds)	0–2	2–4	4–6	6–8	8–10
Frequency	4	6	3	2	7

4 Calculate an estimate of the mean of these heights.

Height (cm)	50–60	60–70	70–80	80–90	90–100
Frequency	15	23	38	17	7

5 Calculate an estimate of the mean of these lengths.

Length (m)	1·0–1·2	1·2–1·4	1·4–1·6	1·6–1·8	1·8–2·0
Frequency	2	7	13	5	3

6 Calculate an estimate of the mean length for this distribution.

Length (y cm)	Frequency
$10 \leqslant y < 20$	2
$20 \leqslant y < 30$	6
$30 \leqslant y < 40$	9
$40 \leqslant y < 50$	5
$50 \leqslant y < 60$	3

7 Calculate an estimate of the mean mass of these tomatoes.

Mass of tomato (t g)	Frequency
$35 < t \leqslant 40$	7
$40 < t \leqslant 45$	13
$45 < t \leqslant 50$	20
$50 < t \leqslant 55$	16
$55 < t \leqslant 60$	4

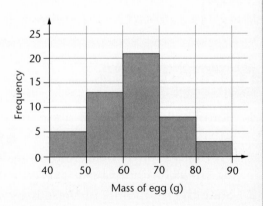

8 The bar graph shows the masses of a sample of 50 eggs.

   a) Make a frequency table for this information.

   b) Calculate an estimate of the mean mass of these eggs.

EXERCISE 12.2B

1 State the boundaries of these intervals.

   a) 20 cm, to the nearest cm
   b) 41 m, to the nearest m
   c) masses to the nearest gram: 15–16, 17–18
   d) times to the nearest second: 11–15, 16–20

2 State the midpoints of these intervals.

   a) 15 cm < length ⩽ 20 cm
   b) 12·0 cm ⩽ length < 12·5 cm
   c) 100 kg ⩽ mass < 105 kg
   d) masses to the nearest kg: 100–104, 105–109
   e) times to the nearest second: 24–26, 27–29

3 Calculate an estimate of the mean of these times.

Time (seconds)	0–20	20–40	40–60	60–80	80–100
Frequency	4	9	13	8	6

4 Calculate an estimate of the mean of these heights.

Height (m)	0–2	2–4	4–6	6–8	8–10
Frequency	12	26	34	23	5

5 Calculate an estimate of the mean of these lengths.

Length (cm)	3·0–3·2	3·2–3·4	3·4–3·6	3·6–3·8	3·8–4·0
Frequency	3	8	11	5	3

6 Calculate an estimate of the mean of these masses.

Mass (w kg)	Frequency
$30 \leqslant w < 40$	5
$40 \leqslant w < 50$	8
$50 \leqslant w < 60$	2
$60 \leqslant w < 70$	4
$70 \leqslant w < 80$	1

7 Calculate an estimate of the mean of these lengths.

Length (x cm)	Frequency
$0 < x \leqslant 5$	8
$5 < x \leqslant 10$	6
$10 < x \leqslant 15$	2
$15 < x \leqslant 20$	5
$20 < x \leqslant 25$	1

Chapter 12 *Finding the mean of grouped data*

Exercise 12.2B cont'd

8   The bar graph shows the heights
    of students in year 9.

    a) Make a frequency table for this
    information.

    b) Calculate an estimate of the
    mean height.

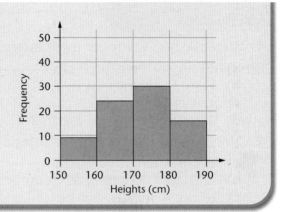

Key ideas

- To find the mean of grouped data, multiply each value by its frequency, add the
  results, and divide by the sum of their frequencies.

- For finding the mean of grouped continuous data, use the midpoint of each group
  as the value for the group.

13 Forming and solving equations and inequalities

You should already know

- how to write a simple formula in letters
- how to collect together simple algebraic terms
- how to multiply out expressions such as 3 (2x −5)
- how to solve linear equations.

Inequalities

$a < b$ means a is less than b

$a \leq b$ means a is less than or equal to b

$a > b$ means a is greater than b

$a \geq b$ means a is greater than or equal to b

Expressions involving these signs are called inequalities.

In equations, if you always do the same thing to both sides the equality is still valid.

The same is true for in equalities, except in one case.

Consider the inequality $5 < 7$.

Add 2 to each side:	$7 < 9$	Still true
Subtract 5 from each side:	$2 < 4$	Still true
Multiply each side by 3:	$6 < 12$	Still true
Divide each side by 2:	$3 < 6$	Still true
Multiply each side by ⁻2:	$^-6 < {}^-12$	No longer true
But reverse the inequality sign:	$^-6 > {}^-12$	Now true

EXAMPLE 1

Find the integer (whole number) values of x when

a) $^-3 < x \leq {}^-1$ **b)** $1 \leq x < 4$.

a) If $^-3 < x \leq {}^-1$, then $x = {}^-2$ or $^-1$.

Note that ⁻3 is not included but ⁻1 is.

b) If $1 \leq x < 4$, then $x = 1, 2$ or 3.

Note that 1 is included but 4 is not.

If an inequality is multiplied or divided by a negative number, the inequality sign must be reversed.

Otherwise inequalities can be treated in the same way as equations.

EXAMPLE 2

Solve these inequalities.

a) $3x + 4 < 10$ **b)** $2x - 5 \leqslant 4 - 3x$ **c)** $x + 4 > 3x - 2$

a) $3x + 4 < 10$

$3x < 6$	Subtract 4 from each side
$x < 2$	Divide each side by 2

b) $2x - 5 \leqslant 4 - 3x$

$2x \leqslant 9 - 3x$	Add 5 to each side
$5x \leqslant 9$	Add $3x$ to each side
$x \leqslant 1.8$	Divide each side by 5

c) $x + 4 < 3x - 2$

$x < 3x - 6$	Subtract 4 from both sides
$^-2x < {}^-6$	Subtract $3x$ from both sides
$x > 3$	Divide each side by $^-2$ and change the $<$ to $>$ (when dividing by $^-2$)

These solutions may be shown on a number line.

a)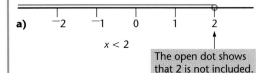

$x < 2$

The open dot shows that 2 is not included.

b)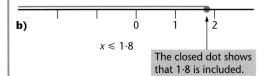

$x \leqslant 1.8$

The closed dot shows that 1·8 is included.

c)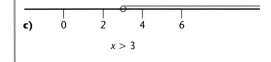

$x > 3$

> **Exam tip**
>
> To avoid dealing with negative numbers, use a solution like this for part c):
> $x + 4 < 3x - 2$
> $x + 6 < 3x$ Add 2 to both sides.
> $6 < 2x$ Subtract x from both sides.
> $3 < x$ Divide both sides by 2.
> $x > 3$ Rewriting with x as subject.

EXERCISE 13.1A

1 Write down the integer values of x when:

   a) $^-4 \leqslant x < 0$
   b) $1 < x \leqslant 5$.

Solve these inequalities. For numbers 2 to 5, represent your solutions on a number line.

2 $x - 3 \leqslant 4$

3 $x + 7 > 9$

4 $2x - 3 < 5$

5 $3x + 4 \leqslant 7$

6 $2x \geqslant x + 5$

7 $5x > 3 - x$

8 $2x + 1 < 7$

9 $4x > 2x + 5$

10 $3x - 6 \geqslant x + 2$

EXERCISE 13.1B

1 Write down two possible values of x for the inequality $x < {}^-2$.

2 Write down the integer values of x when

   a) $1 < x \leqslant 4$
   b) $^-5 < x \leqslant {}^-1$.

Solve these inequalities. For numbers 3 to 6, represent your solutions on a number line.

3 $x - 2 < 5$

4 $2x + 3 > 6$

5 $3x - 4 \leqslant 8$

6 $3x \geqslant x - 2$

7 $4x + 2 < 3$

8 $5a - 3 > 2a$

9 $2x - 3 < x + 1$

10 $3x + 2 \geqslant x - 1$

Forming equations and inequalities

Everyday problems can often be solved by forming equations or inequalities and solving them.

EXAMPLE 3

The length of a rectangle is 4 cm longer than its width, which is x cm.

a) Write down an expression in terms of x for the perimeter of the rectangle.

b) The perimeter is 32 cm.
   (i) Write down an equation in x and solve it.
   (ii) What are the length and width of the rectangle?

a) The length is 4 cm longer than the width, so it is $x + 4$ cm.

Perimeter $= x + x + 4 + x + x + 4 = 4x + 8$

b) (i) The perimeter is 32 cm, so:

$$4x + 8 = 32$$
$$4x = 24$$
$$x = 6$$

(ii) The width is $x = 6$ cm.
   The length is $x + 4 = 10$ cm.

EXAMPLE 4

John is having a party but he has only £60 to spend on it. He has to pay £10 to hire the room and £4 for every person at the party. How many people can he invite to his party?

Let the number of people be n. Write down an inequality involving n and solve it to find the largest number that can go to the party.

Cost of party $\leqslant$ £60
Therefore $10 + 4n \leqslant 60$
$$4n \leqslant 50$$
$$n \leqslant 12 \cdot 5$$

So the largest number of people that can go to the party is 12.

Exam tip

Always think whether an answer is sensible. In this example, the final answer must be a whole number!

Exam tip

In these questions you can sometimes work out the answer without writing down the equation or inequality, but you must do so when asked in an exam, otherwise you will lose marks.

Chapter 13 *Forming and solving equations and inequalities*

EXERCISE 13.2A

1 Erica is x years old and Jayne is three years older than Erica. Their ages add up to 23. Write down an equation in x and solve it to find out their ages.

2 Two angles of a triangle are the same and the other is 15° bigger. Call the two equal angles a. Write down an equation and solve it to find the angles.

3 A man is papering a room. It takes him 30 minutes to prepare his paste and 20 minutes to cut and hang a length of paper. He is working for 4 hours and hangs x lengths.

Write down an inequality in x and solve it to find the largest number of lengths he can hang in the time.

4 In Devonshire School there are 28 more girls than boys. There are 616 pupils in the school. Let the number of boys be x. Write down an equation in x and solve it. Write down the number of boys and girls in the school.

5 To hire a bus the charge is £60 and £2 a mile. The bus company will only hire the bus if they take at least £225. Let the number of miles be x.

a) Write down an inequality and solve it for x.

b) What is the smallest distance that the bus can be hired to go?

6 It costs £x to hire a bike for an adult, and it is £2 cheaper for a child's bike. Mr Newton hires bikes for two adults and three children.

a) Write down an expression in x for the cost of the bikes.

b) The cost is £19.

    (i) Write down an equation and solve it to find x.

    (ii) How much did each bike cost?

7 Ameer has 40 metres of fencing, in one-metre lengths that cannot be split. He wants to use as much of it as he can to mark out a rectangle that is twice as long as it is wide.

Chapter 13 *Forming and solving equations and inequalities*

Exercise 13.2A cont'd

a) Call the width of the rectangle x metres and write down an inequality.

b) Solve it to find the length and width of the biggest rectangle that he can make.

8 Mark, Patrick and Iain all collect matchbox cars. Mark has four more than Patrick. Iain has three more than Mark. They have 41 altogether. Set up an equation and solve it to find how many matchbox cars each boy has.

EXERCISE 13.2B

1 Mrs Pippard and her daughter go shopping. Mrs Pippard spends £x and her daughter spends twice as much. They spend £45 altogether. Set up an equation and solve it to find how much each spends.

2 A pentagon has two angles of 150°, two of x° and one of $(x + 30)$°. The sum of the angles in a pentagon is 540°.

a) Write down an equation in x and solve it.

b) State the size of each of the angles.

3 Sara is x years old; Mary is ten years older than Sara. The sum of their ages is less than 50.

a) Write down an inequality and solve it.

b) What is the oldest Sara can be?

4 On a school trip to France, there are 15 more girls than boys. Altogether 53 pupils go.

a) If the number of boys is x, write down an equation in x and solve it.

b) How many boys and how many girls go on the trip?

Exercise 13.2B cont'd

5 Paul goes to the shop and buys two chocolate bars at 30p each and *x* cans of cola at 45p each. He has £2 and wants to buy as many cans as possible.

a) Write down an inequality in *x* and solve it.

b) What is the largest number of cans he can buy?

6 In the Oasis café a cup of tea costs *x* pence; a cup of coffee costs 10 pence more than tea. David bought three teas and two coffees and spent £1·20.

a) Write down an equation in *x* and solve it.

b) What do tea and coffee cost at the Oasis café?

7 A firm employs 140 people, of whom *x* are men. There are ten fewer women than men. Use algebra to find how many men and women work for the firm.

8 It costs £5 for each person to go skating. Skates can be hired for £2. Ten friends went skating and *n* of them hired skates.

a) Write down an expression in pounds for the amount they spent.

b) They spent £62. Write down an equation in *n* and solve it to find how many hired skates.

Key ideas

- To solve inequalities, treat them like equations, except when multiplying or dividing by a negative number, when you must reverse the inequality sign.

- To solve a problem using algebra, set up an equation for the unknown quantity, then solve it.

Revision exercise

1 Calculate the value of x in each triangle.

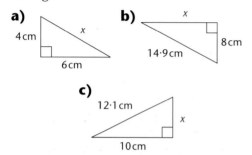

a)
4 cm, x, 6 cm

b)
x, 8 cm, 14·9 cm

c)
12·1 cm, x, 10 cm

2 Calculate the length of the diagonal of a rectangle with length 22 cm and width 12 cm.

3 A ship sails 20 km due North and then 30 km due West. How far is it from its starting point?

4 a) Draw the graph of
$y = x^2 – 6x + 3$, for $x = {}^-1$ to 7.
Label the x-axis from $^-1$ to 7 and the y-axis from $^-10$ to 10.

b) Use the graph to find solutions to the equation $x^2 – 6x + 3 = 0$.

5 a) Draw the graph of
$y = –x^2 – x + 12$, for $x = {}^-5$ to 4.
Label the x-axis from $^-5$ to 4 and the y-axis from $^-10$ to 15.

b) Use the graph to solve the equation $x^2 + x – 12 = 0$.

6 The height h, in metres, of a ball thrown upwards at 40 metres per second is given by the formula $h = 40t – 5t^2$, where t is the time in seconds.

a) Copy this table of values and complete it.

t	0	1	2	3	4	5	6	7	8
t^2									
$40t$									
$^-5t^2$									
$h = 40t – 5t^2$									

b) Draw the graph of $h = 40t – 5t^2$, for values of t from 0 to 8.

c) Find the times when the ball is 70 metres above the ground. Give your answers correct to one decimal place.

7 a) Draw the graph of $y = x^2 + 2x$ for values of x from $^-4$ to 2.

b) Solve the equation $x^2 + 2x = 0$ from your graph.

8 a) Draw the graph of $y = x^2 – 5x + 5$ for values of x from 0 to 5.

b) Solve the equation $x^2 – 5x + 5 = 0$ from your graph.

9 Harry picked and measured some runner beans. These were their lengths.

Length (L cm)	Frequency
$10 < L \leqslant 15$	3
$15 < L \leqslant 20$	7
$20 < L \leqslant 25$	11
$25 < L \leqslant 30$	8
$30 < L \leqslant 35$	1

Calculate an estimate of the mean length of the runner beans.

10 Lisa timed her little brother when he was playing with his new toys over Christmas:

Time (*t* minutes)	Frequency
$0 < t \leqslant 10$	2
$10 < t \leqslant 20$	5
$20 < t \leqslant 30$	7
$30 < t \leqslant 40$	10
$40 < t \leqslant 50$	4

Calculate an estimate of the mean of these times.

11 Kim and Petra asked their class, 'How much exercise have you had this week?' These were the results.

Time of exercise (*h* hours)	Number of people
$0 \leqslant h < 1$	3
$1 \leqslant h < 2$	8
$2 \leqslant h < 5$	12
$5 \leqslant h < 10$	5
$h \geqslant 10$	0

a) How many people were in the survey?
b) What are the midpoints of the classes
   (i) $2 \leqslant h < 5$ **(ii)** $5 \leqslant h < 10$?
c) Calculate an estimate of the mean time of exercise.

12 Some batteries were tested to see how long they lasted. Here are the results.

Time (hours)	0–2	2–4	4–6	6–8	8–10
Frequency	4	5	12	16	3

Calculate an estimate of the mean time these batteries lasted.

13 Solve the inequalities.
   a) $2x > 5$
   b) $x + 3 \leqslant 5$
   c) $2x - 4 \geqslant x + 2$
   d) $4x - 3 < 7 - x$
   e) $4x - 9 \leqslant 2x + 7$

14 David has two brothers. One brother is two years younger than him and the other brother is five years older than him.
   a) Let David be x years old and write down an expression for the sum of their ages.
   b) The sum of their ages is 39. Write down an equation and solve it to find x.
   c) What are their ages?

15 Angela has £5 to spend. She spends £3·20 on her lunch and decides to buy as many packets of crisps as possible at 24p each with the rest.
   a) If the number of packets she buys is x, write down an inequality in x and solve it.
   b) How many packets of crisps does she buy?

16 A quadrilateral has angles $x°$, $3x°$, $90°$ and $(x + 20)°$.
   a) Write down an equation in x and solve it.
   b) What are the sizes of the angles?

14 Interpreting graphs

You should already know

- how to draw straight line graphs
- how to draw curved graphs.

Some graphs tell a story – they show what happened in an event. To find out what is happening, first look at the labels on the axes. They tell you what the graph is about.

Exam tip

When drawing a graph, don't forget to label the axes.

Look for important features on the graph. For instance, does it increase or decrease at a steady rate (a straight line) or is it curved?

ACTIVITY 1

Think of some labels for the axes and an appropriate 'story' description to fit this shape graph.

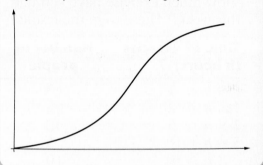

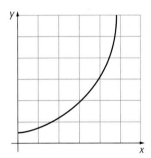

The rate of change is increasing

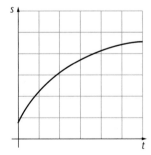

The rate of change is decreasing

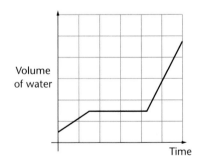

A flat part of the graph – no change for the variable on the vertical axis.

EXAMPLE 1

This graph shows the noise levels at a football stadium one afternoon.

The boxes describe what may have caused the change in shape of the graph at certain points.

Gradual increase in the sound level as the crowd builds up towards the 3pm start.

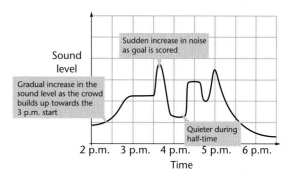

EXAMPLE 2

John ran the first two miles to school at a speed of 8 mph. He then waited 5 minutes for his friend. They walked the last mile to school together, taking 20 minutes.

The graph for this story has been started. Finish the graph. (The different colour on the graph shows where this has been done.)

The first part of this graph is steeper than the last part. This shows that John went faster in the first 15 minutes than he did in the last 20 minutes. The flat part of the graph shows where John stayed in the same place for 5 minutes.

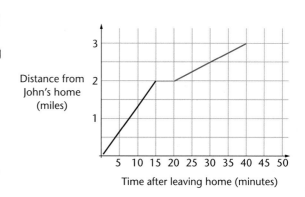

EXERCISE 14.1A

1 This graph shows the volume of water in a bath.

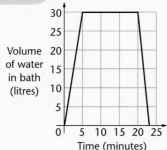

a) How long did the bath take to fill?

b) How much water was in the bath when the taps were turned off?

c) How many litres per minute went down the plughole when the bath was emptied?

97

Chapter 14 *Interpreting graphs*

Exercise 14.1A cont'd

2 This graph shows the number of people at a theme park one bank holiday.

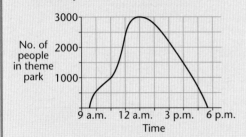

No. of people in theme park / Time
3000, 2000, 1000
9 a.m. 12 a.m. 3 p.m. 6 p.m.

a) When did the park open?
b) During which hour did most people go into the park?

3 At a rock concert, the gates opened at 5 p.m. People came in fairly slowly at first, but then quite steadily from 5.45 p.m. until the start at 7 p.m. There were then 50 000 people in the stadium. The concert lasted until 10 p.m. At the end people left quickly and the stadium was almost empty by 10.30 p.m.

Sketch a graph to show how the number of people in the stadium for this rock concert changed.

4 This graph shows the cost of hiring a car for a day.

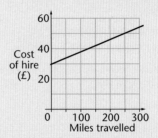

Cost of hire (£)
60, 40, 20
0 100 200 300
Miles travelled

a) Pedro travelled 150 miles. How much did he pay for his car hire?
b) Jane paid £48 for her car hire. How many miles did she travel?
c) What was
(i) the basic hire charge
(ii) the charge per mile?

5 Water is poured at a steady rate into this conical glass until it is full. Sketch a graph to show how the depth of water in the glass changes with time.

EXERCISE 14.1B

1 This graph shows the amount of fuel in a car's petrol tank.

a) How many litres were used between 6 and 7 p.m?
b) Describe what happened between 7.30 and 8 p.m.

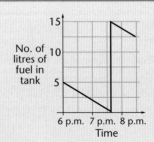

No. of litres of fuel in tank
15, 10, 5
6 p.m. 7 p.m. 8 p.m.
Time

Exercise 14.1B cont'd

2 The speed of a car at the start of a journey is shown on this graph.

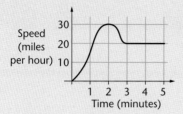

a) What is happening on the flat portion of the graph?
b) Between which times is the car slowing down?

3 Jane ran hot water into a bath for 4 minutes at a rate of 15 litres per minute. She then turned on the cold tap too so that the bath filled at 20 litres a minute for another 2 minutes.

a) Draw a graph to show how the volume of water in the bath changed.
b) How much water was there in the bath at the end of this time?

4 This graph shows the monthly bill for a mobile phone for different amounts of minutes used.

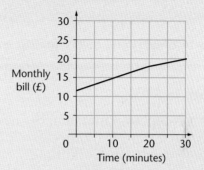

a) How many minutes have been used if the bill is £15?
b) There are two line segments on the graph. What do they show?

5 A water company charges £8 each quarter for a water meter, then 50p per cubic metre for the first 100 cubic metres used, and 70p per cubic metre for water used above this amount.

Draw a graph to show the total bill for different amounts of water used, up to 200 cubic metres.

Key ideas

● The labels on the axes tell you what a graph is about.

● Each feature on the graph is part of the story. For instance, does it increase or decrease at a steady rate (a straight line) or is it curved?

Exam tip

If you are asked to describe a story graph, try to include numerical information. For example, instead of 'stopped' write 'stopped at 10:14 p.m. for 6 minutes'.

Compound measures

You should already know

- how to convert one metric unit to another.

Speed

Speed is a compound measure, because it is calculated from two other measurements: distance and time.

$$\text{average speed} = \frac{\text{total distance travelled}}{\text{total time taken}}$$

The units of your answer will depend on the units you begin with. Speed has units 'distance per time' such as km/h.

EXAMPLE 1

Find the average speed of an athlete who runs 100 m in 20 s.

$$\text{average speed} = \frac{100\,\text{m}}{20\,\text{s}} = 5\,\text{m/s}$$

The formula for speed can be rearranged to find the distance travelled or the time taken for a journey.

$$\text{distance} = \text{speed} \times \text{time} \qquad \text{time} = \frac{\text{distance}}{\text{speed}}$$

EXAMPLE 2

How many minutes does it take to walk 2 km at 5 km/h?

$$\text{time} = \frac{\text{distance}}{\text{speed}} = \frac{2}{5}\,\text{h} = \frac{2}{5} \times 60 \text{ minutes} = 24 \text{ minutes}$$

Exam tip

You may find the d.s.t triangle helpful. Cover up the one you are trying to find.

ACTIVITY 1

Discuss some everyday situations in which you use speeds. Use appropriate numbers and units.

EXAMPLE 3

Find the average speed of a delivery driver who travelled 45 km in 30 minutes.

$$\text{The average speed} = \frac{45\,\text{km}}{30\,\text{minutes}} = 1.5\,\text{km/minute}$$

However, the speed here is more likely to be needed in kilometres per hour. To find this, first change the time into hours.

$$\text{So the average speed} = \frac{45\,\text{km}}{0.5\,\text{h}} = 90\,\text{km/h}$$

You may also be able to see other ways of obtaining the results in Examples 2 and 3.

Density

Another example of a compound measure is density, which is linked to mass and volume.

density of a substance = $\dfrac{\text{mass}}{\text{volume}}$

It is measured in units such as grams per cubic centimetre (g/cm^3).

EXAMPLE 4

The density of gold is $19.3\,g/cm^3$. Calculate the mass of a gold bar with a volume of $30\,cm^3$.

density = $\dfrac{\text{mass}}{\text{volume}}$

so mass = density × volume

The mass of the gold bar = density × volume = $19.3 \times 30 = 579\,g$

Population density

Population density is another example of a compound measure. It gives an idea of how heavily populated an area is. It is measured as the number of people per square kilometre.

EXERCISE 15.1A

1 Find the average speed of a car which travels 75 miles in one and a half hours.

2 Find the average speed of a runner who covers $180\,m$ in $40\,s$.

3 Calculate the density of a stone of mass $350\,g$ and volume $40\,cm^3$.

4 Waring has a population of $60\,000$ in an area of 8 square kilometres. Calculate its population density.

5 A motorbike travels 1 mile in 3 minutes. Calculate its average speed, in miles per hour.

6 A bus travels at $5\,m/s$ on average. How many kilometres per hour is this?

7 A foam plastic ball with volume $20\,cm^3$ has density $0.3\,g/cm^3$. What is its mass?

8 A town has a population of $200\,000$. Its population density is $10\,000$ people per square mile. What is the area of the town?

Chapter 15 *Compound measures*

Exercise 15.1A cont'd

9 A runner's average speed in a 80 m race is 7 m/s. Find the time he takes for the race, to the nearest 0·1 seconds.

10 A car travels 15 km in 12 minutes. What is the average speed in km/h?

EXERCISE 15.1B

1 Find the average speed of a car which travels 63 miles in one and a half hours.

2 Find the average speed of a runner who goes 180 m in 48 s.

3 Calculate the density of a stone of mass 690 g and volume 74 cm^3. Give your answer to a suitable degree of accuracy.

4 Trenton has a population of 65 000 in an area of 5·8 square kilometres. Calculate its population density, correct to two significant figures.

5 A cyclist rides 0·6 mile in 3 minutes. Calculate her average speed, in miles per hour.

6 A bus travels at 6·1 m/s on average. How many kilometres per hour is this?

7 A rubber ball with volume 28·3 cm^3 has density 0·7 g/cm^3. What is its mass?

8 A town has a population of 276 300. Its population density is 9800 people per square mile. What is the area of the town?

9 A runner's average speed in a 200 m race is 5·3 m/s. Find the time he takes for the race, to the nearest 0·1 seconds.

10 A car travels 15 km in 14 minutes. What is the average speed, in km/h?

Key ideas

- Some compound measures are:

  average speed (units such as m/s)

  density (units such as g/cm^3)

  population density (units such as population/km^2).

16 Reciprocals, factors and multiples

You should already know

- the meaning of factor and multiple
- how to convert fractions to decimals.

Reciprocals

The reciprocal of a number is $\dfrac{1}{\text{the number}}$.

Using the rules of fractions gives these results.

the reciprocal of n is $\dfrac{1}{n}$

the reciprocal of $\dfrac{1}{n}$ is n

the reciprocal of $\dfrac{a}{b}$ is $\dfrac{b}{a}$.

To find reciprocals on a calculator, use the $\boxed{1/x}$ button.

ACTIVITY 1

What are the reciprocals of **a)** 2 **b)** 5 **c)** 10 **d)** 0·01 **e)** $\frac{3}{5}$ **f)** $1\frac{1}{2}$?

What do reciprocals do? Multiply each number above by its reciprocal. What do you get?

Now try these products on your calculator and see what you get. Don't forget to press $\boxed{=}$ after each sum.

55×2 (press $\boxed{=}$) $\times \dfrac{1}{2}$ (press $\boxed{=}$))

55×4 $\qquad \times \dfrac{1}{4}$

7×8 $\qquad\ \ \times \dfrac{1}{8}$

Try some more out until you are sure what is happening.

EXAMPLE 1

Find the reciprocals of **a)** 1·25, giving your answer as a decimal, **b)** $\frac{3}{5}$, giving your answer as a mixed number, **c)** $1\frac{3}{4}$, giving your answer as a fraction.

a) using the calculator, the reciprocal of $1·25 = \dfrac{1}{1·25} = 0·8$

b) the reciprocal of $\frac{3}{5} = \frac{5}{3} = 1\frac{2}{3}$.

c) $1\frac{3}{4} = \frac{7}{4}$ so its reciprocal is $\frac{4}{7}$.

EXERCISE 16.1A

1 Write down the reciprocal of each of these numbers.

   a) 3   **b)** 6   **c)** 49

   d) 100   **e)** 640

2 Write down the numbers of which these are the reciprocals.

   a) $\frac{1}{16}$ **b)** $\frac{1}{9}$ **c)** $\frac{1}{52}$

   d) $\frac{1}{67}$ **e)** $\frac{1}{1000}$

3 Calculate the reciprocals of these numbers, giving your answers in decimal form.

   a) 2·5   **b)** 3·2   **c)** 0·5

   d) 125   **e)** 0·8

4 Calculate the reciprocals of these numbers, giving your answers as fractions or mixed numbers.

   a) $\frac{4}{5}$ **b)** $\frac{3}{8}$ **c)** $1\frac{3}{5}$

   d) $3\frac{1}{3}$ **e)** $\frac{2}{25}$

EXERCISE 16.1B

1 Write down the reciprocal of each of these numbers.

   a) 4   **b)** 9   **c)** 65

   d) 10   **e)** 4·5

2 Write down the numbers of which these are the reciprocals.

   a) $\frac{1}{3}$ **b)** $\frac{1}{10}$ **c)** $\frac{1}{25}$

   d) $\frac{1}{71}$ **e)** $\frac{1}{100}$

3 Calculate the reciprocals of these numbers, giving your answers in decimal form.

   a) 25   **b)** 6·4   **c)** 0·2

   d) 625   **e)** 0·16

4 Calculate the reciprocals of these numbers, giving your answers as fractions or mixed numbers.

   a) $\frac{3}{5}$ **b)** $\frac{4}{9}$ **c)** $2\frac{2}{5}$

   d) $5\frac{1}{3}$ **e)** $\frac{3}{100}$

Prime factors

A prime number has as factors only 1 and itself.
The first prime numbers are 2, 3, 5, 7, 11, 13, 17, 19, ...
Note that 1 is not a prime number.

To express a number in prime factor form, first divide by 2 until you get an odd number then try to divide by 3 and then 5, and so on.

The divisors are always prime numbers.

Example: $2\,\overline{)36}$

$2\,\overline{)18}$

$3\,\overline{)\ 9}$

$3\,\overline{)\ 3}$

1

So 36 written as a product of its prime factors is $2 \times 2 \times 3 \times 3$ which can be written as $2^2 \times 3^2$.

ACTIVITY 2

Copy and complete the following table up to $n = 36$, writing the prime factors in index form.

Number n	Prime factors in index form
2	2^1
3	3^1
4	2^2
5	5^1
6	$2^1 \times 3^1$
⋮	⋮
36	$2^2 \times 3^2$

The complete list of factors for 36 is:
1, 2, 3, 4, 6, 9, 12, 18, 36
This can be written as F(36) = 9 because there are nine factors.

But 36 is also equal to $2^2 \times 3^2$. Adding 1 to each of the powers gives $(2 + 1)$ and $(2 + 1)$.

Multiplying these numbers gives
$(2 + 1) \times (2 + 1) = 3 \times 3 = 9$ which is the same value as F(36).

1 Investigate prime factors and the number of factors for numbers up to 36.

You might want to add a column to the table you have just completed.

Number n	Prime factors in index form	Number of factors
2	2^1	2
3	3^1	2
4	2^2	3
5	5^1	
6	$2^1 \times 3^1$	
⋮	⋮	
36	$2^2 \times 3^2$	

Check to see if there is a link between the indices or powers of the prime factors and the number of factors.

2 What do you notice about numbers with only two factors?

3 Which numbers have an odd number of factors?

Factor tree method for finding prime factors

Rather than systematic division by primes, you may prefer to use the factor tree method. In this method, you split the number into any two factors you spot, then split those factors, continuing until all the factors are prime.

For example, here is a factor tree for the number 126.

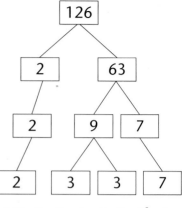

$$126 = 2 \times 3 \times 3 \times 7 = 2 \times 3^2 \times 7$$

ACTIVITY 3

Use this method to find the prime factors of 64, 100, 144, 350, 540, 72.

Highest common factor and lowest common multiple

When two or more numbers have been decomposed into their prime factors, these prime factors can be used to find the highest common factor and the lowest common multiple.

> The highest common factor (HCF) of two numbers is the highest number that is a factor of both numbers.
>
> The lowest common multiple (LCM) of two numbers is the lowest number that is a multiple of both numbers.

EXAMPLE 2

Find the highest common factor (HCF) and lowest common multiple (LCM) of 96 and 180.

Finding the prime factors of each of the numbers, we can obtain

$96 = 2^5 \times 3$ $96 = 2 \times 2 \times 2 \times 2 \times 2 \times 3$

$180 = 2^2 \times 3^2 \times 5$ $180 = 2 \times 2$ $\times 3 \times 3 \times 5$

so the HCF is $2 \times 2 \times 3$

The HCF of 96 and 180 is $2^2 \times 3 = 12$.

     $96 = 2 \times 2 \times 2 \times 2 \times 2 \times 3$

    $180 = 2 \times 2$ $\times 3 \times 3 \times 5$

so the LCM is $2 \times 2 \times 2 \times 2 \times 2 \times 3 \times 3 \times 5$

The LCM of 96 and 180 is $2^5 \times 3^2 \times 5 = 1440$.

This means that 12 is the highest number that is a factor of both 96 and 180. 1440 is the lowest number that has both 96 and 80 as factors. It is the lowest number that is a multiple of both 96 and 180.

Exam tip

To find the HCF, use the prime numbers that appear in both lists and use the lower power for each prime.

Exam tip

To find the LCM, use all the prime numbers that appear in either or both lists and use the higher power for each prime.

ACTIVITY 4

Find the prime factors of these numbers and use this to write down the HCF and LCM of each pair.

64 and 100
18 and 24
50 and 350
72 and 126

EXERCISE 16.2A

1 Express as a product of their prime factors.

   a) 48   **b)** 72   **c)** 210   **d)** 350

2 Decompose into their prime factors.

   a) 495   **b)** 260
   c) 2700   **d)** 1078

3 Use your results from question 1 to find **a)** the HCF of 48 and 72 **b)** the LCM of 210 and 350.

4 Use your results from question 2 to find **a)** the HCF of 495 and 2700 **b)** the LCM of 495 and 2700.

5 Find **a)** the HCF **b)** the LCM of 5544 and 2268.

EXERCISE 16.2B

1 Express as a product of their prime factors.

   a) 75   **b)** 120   **c)** 275   **d)** 198

2 Decompose into their prime factors.

   a) 420   **b)** 1125
   c) 112   **d)** 1960

3 Use your results from question 1 to find **a)** the HCF of 75 and 275 **b)** the LCM of 120 and 198.

4 Use your results from question 2 to find **a)** the HCF of 420 and 112 **b)** the LCM of 420 and 1960.

5 Find **a)** the HCF **b)** the LCM of 2016 and 10 584.

ACTIVITY 5 – EXTENSION

Co-primes

Two numbers are co-prime if the only integer which goes into, or is a factor of, or is a divisor of both of them is 1.

For example:

- 3 and 7 are co-prime because the only factor they have in common is 1
- 4 and 6 are not co-prime because they share a common factor of 2
- 14 and 21 are not co-prime because they share a common factor of 7
- 5 and 23 are co-prime because they have no common factor except 1

1 Try to find four pairs of numbers that are co-prime and four pairs of numbers that are not co-prime.

2 Write down all the positive integers less than 10:

1 2 3 4 5 6 7 8 9

Of these, 2, 4, 6 and 8 share a common factor of 2 with 10, and 5 divides into 10 so is also a factor.

Therefore there are four numbers:

1 3 7 9

that are less than 10 and also co-prime with 10.

3 Copy this table and complete it for the integers up to 24.

Integer	Integers less than and co-prime with it	Number of these integers
2	1	1
3	1, 2	2
4	1, 3	2
5	1, 2, 3, 4	4
6	1, 5	2
7	1, 2, 3, 4, 5, 6	6
⋮		⋮
24	1, 5, 7, 11, 13, 17, 19, 23	8

What do you notice about the numbers in the right-hand column?

Denote the number of integers which are less than n and co-prime with n by $\Psi(n)$.

So $\Psi(10) = 4$

a) Does $\Psi(3) \times \Psi(4) = \Psi(12)$?

b) Does $\Psi(2) \times \Psi(6) = \Psi(12)$?

c) Investigate $\Psi(m) \times \Psi(n) = \Psi(mn)$.

Key ideas

Reciprocals

- The reciprocal of n is $\dfrac{1}{n}$.

- The reciprocal of $\dfrac{1}{n}$ is n.

- The reciprocal of $\dfrac{a}{b}$ is $\dfrac{b}{a}$.

Factors

- All positive integers can be decomposed into their prime factors.

- The highest common factor of two numbers is the highest number that is a factor of both numbers.

- The lowest common multiple of two numbers is the lowest number that is a multiple of both numbers.

17 Circles and tangents

You should already know

- basic circle language such as chord, tangent, diameter
- angle facts about triangles
- symmetry facts about triangles
- the meaning of congruency.

Angle in a semicircle

ACTIVITY 1

Draw a circle of radius 6 cm.
On the circumference, mark three points that can be joined up to form a right-angled triangle.
Repeat for circles with different radii.
What do you notice? Write down your idea.
Now test your idea by drawing a right-angled triangle with sides 6 cm, 8 cm and 10 cm.
Use a protractor or angle measurer to draw the angles as accurately as you can.
Draw a circle that passes through the three vertices of the triangle.
Was your idea correct?
Check by drawing a different right-angled triangle and then drawing a circle round it.

An alternative approach is to use a set-square or a piece of card with a right-angled corner, and two nails. You could use two points marked on the paper if you prefer to.
Place the set-square between the two nails so that the edges of the set-square which form the right angle touch the nails.

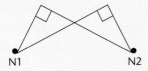

Mark a point to represent the position of the tip of the right angle, when the edges of the set-square are firmly against the nails.

Repeat for different positions of the set-square.

a) What shape are the marks forming?
b) What can you say about the line joining the two nails (or points)?
c) What would happen if the angle at the corner were
   (i) acute? **(ii)** obtuse?
   In each case, state what shape would be formed.

Notes

a) If you repeat the activity enough times, the pencil marks at the right-angled corner will trace a circle.
b) The line joining the two nails (or points) is a diameter.
c) If the angle is acute, the points form the major part of a circle.

   If the process is continued below the imaginary line joining N1 and N2 the shape formed makes two parts of two equal circles which join but do not make a complete circle.

   If the angle is obtuse then a similar result is obtained but from the smaller part of a circle.

The angle in a semicircle is 90°
You have just demonstrated an important fact!

Activity 1 cont'd

Now you can prove it.
First study the diagram.

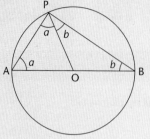

Now copy and complete statements **1–4**.

1 The lines OA, OP and OB are equal because …

2 The angles marked *a* are equal because …

3 The angles marked *b* are equal because …

4 In triangle APB, $a + a + b + b = 180°$ because …

In other words $2(a + b) = 180°$

So angle APB = $a + b = 90°$

Now use a cylindrical tin, or something similar, to draw a circle.

Use the fact that the angle in the semicircle is 90° to think of a method for finding the centre of the circle which you have drawn.

Explain your method.

EXERCISE 17.1A

In questions **1–3**, points A and B are at opposite ends of a diameter of the circle with its centre at O.

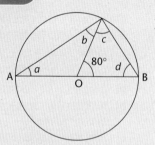

1 a) Without calculating their values, write down a fact that is true about *a* and *b*, and also about *c* and *d*.

b) Now write down their values, explaining how you worked them out.

c) Write down another angle fact that you could use to check that your answer to part **b)** is correct.

2 Find *a*, when $d = 46°$.

3 a) Calculate the sizes of the angles marked with letters in this diagram.

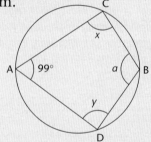

b) Why can't the straight line joining C and D be a diameter?

4 APQBRS is a regular hexagon. Prove that AB is a diameter.

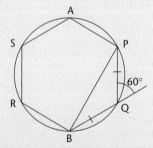

EXERCISE 17.1B

1 These three diagrams show semicircles. Find the sizes of all the angles marked with letters.

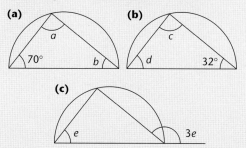

(a) 70°, a, b

(b) c, d, 32°

(c) e, 3e

2 Find the sizes of all the angles marked with letters in this diagram, if O is the centre of the circle.

C, b, a, A, d, c, x, O, B

3 A, B, C and D are points on a circle. AC is a diameter. Prove that angle A + angle C = 180°.

Angles in circles

ACTIVITY 2

1 Draw a circle, radius 6 cm. Mark the centre O.
Mark three points, A, B and C.
Join AO, BO, BC.
Measure angle AOB and angle ACB. What do you notice?
Try with other points on the circle.
Suggest two general results.

2 Now draw a straight line to touch the circle at A.
This is a tangent.
Measure the angle between the tangent and the radius at A.
Try this at other points. Suggest a general result.

3 Draw another circle.
Mark four points round the circumference, A, B, C and D. Join them in order.
Measure angles ABC and CDA. Add them.
Measure angles BCD and DAB. Add them.
Try this for another circle and quadrilateral.
Suggest a general result.

General results

- The angle subtended by an arc (or chord) at the centre of a circle is twice the angle subtended by the same arc at the circumference.
- Angles subtended at the circumference by the same arc (or chord) are equal.
- The angle between a tangent and the radius at the point of contact is 90°.
- The opposite angles of a cyclic quadrilateral add up to 180°.

Definitions

- 'Subtended by' means made, or based on.
- A cyclic quadrilateral has all its vertices on the circumference of a circle.

EXERCISE 17.2A

Work out the sizes of all the angles marked with letters.
In each case, O is the centre of the circle.

1

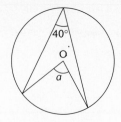 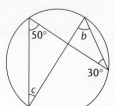 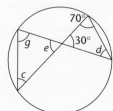

2

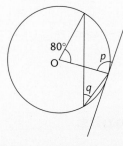 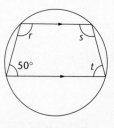 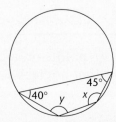

EXERCISE 17.2B

Work out the sizes of all the angles marked with letters.
In each case, O is the centre of the circle.

1

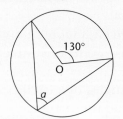 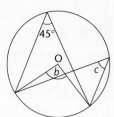 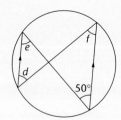

2

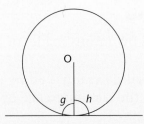 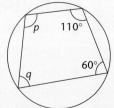 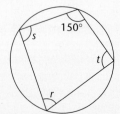

Chapter 17 *Circles and tangents*

ACTIVITY 3

1 Make up 5 questions using facts about circles or triangles that you know already.

2 Work out the answers to your questions.

3 Swap your questions with a neighbour and answer each other's.

The diagram shows some important facts to remember about circles and tangents.

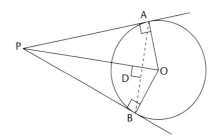

The angle between a tangent and radius at point of contact is 90°.

The two tangents from any point to a circle are equal in length.

The line OP bisects the chord AB at right angles.

Triangles APO and BPO are congruent.

Triangles AOD and BOD are congruent.

Triangles APD and BPD are congruent.

EXAMPLE 1

In the diagram above, angle APO = 35°. Calculate angle AOB.

angle AOP = 55° (angle sum of triangle = 180°)

angle BOP = 55° (by symmetry)

So angle AOB = 110°

EXERCISE 17.3A

In this exercise, the letters refer to a circle diagram like the one at the beginning of this chapter.

1 Find angle PAD when angle APO = 65°.

2 What shape is quadrilateral APBO?

3 Calculate angle AOB when angle APB = 46°.

4 Calculate angle OBD when angle BPO = 28°.

5 Explain how you can tell that angles DAO and APO are always equal.

Extension questions

6 A circle centre O has radius 5 cm. The length of a tangent from a point P to the circle is 12 cm. Find **a)** the distance OP **b)** the shortest distance from P to the circle.

Exercise 17.3A cont'd

7 A circle of radius 8 cm has a chord of length 12·8 cm. What is the perpendicular distance of this chord from the centre of the circle?

Exam tip

With right-angled triangles, you may need to use Pythagoras' Theorem too!

EXERCISE 17.3B

In this exercise, the letters refer to a circle diagram like the one at the beginning of the chapter.

1 Find angle AOP when angle APO = 65°.

2 Name three other angles in the diagram that are equal to angle PAD.

3 Calculate angle APB when angle AOB = 124°.

4 Calculate angle OBD when angle BPO = 28°.

5 Calculate angle ABP when angle APB = 108°.

Extension questions

6 A point P is 17 cm from the centre O of a circle of radius 5 cm. A tangent from P meets the circle at A. Calculate the distance AP.

7 A chord in a circle of radius 7 cm is 3·5 cm from the centre of the circle. Find, to the nearest millimetre, the length of this chord.

Key ideas

- The angle in a semicircle is 90°.
- The angle at the centre is twice the angle at the circumference.
- Angles at the same arc (or chord) are equal.
- Opposite angles of a cyclic quadrilateral add up to 180°.
- The angle between a tangent and radius at the point of contact is 90°.
- The two tangents from any point P to a circle centre O are equal in length.
- When the tangents meet the circle at A and B, then the line OP bisects the chord AB perpendicularly (at right angles).
- Triangles AOP and BOP are congruent.

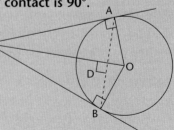

Chapter 17 *Circles and tangents*

Revision exercise

1 The distance travelled by a train between two stations is shown on this graph.

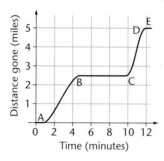

a) How far is it between stations?
b) What was happening on section BC of the graph?
c) What was happening on section DE of the graph?
d) On which section did the train travel at the greatest speed?

2 A kite was launched and gained height, slowly at first but then more quickly, until it was 30 m up after about 10 s. It flew at this height for 30 s, then came down 20 m very quickly. It descended the remaining 10 m more gently, landing 50 s after it started. Draw a graph to show this.

3 Find the reciprocals of these numbers.
   a) 5   b) $\frac{4}{5}$ c) $2\frac{1}{4}$ d) 0·4

4 a) Express 84 and 540 as products of their prime factors.
   b) Find the highest common factor of 84 and 540.

5 Find the lowest common multiple of 24 and 78.

6 Buses to Shenley leave the bus station every 40 minutes. Buses to Winley leave every 15 minutes. At 8·15 am buses to both Shenley and Winley leave the bus station. When is the next time that buses to both places leave at the same time?

7 A cyclist travels 5 km in 20 minutes. Calculate her speed in kilometres per hour.

8 A metal weight has mass 200 g and density 25 g/cm³. What is its volume?

You will need a calculator for questions 9 and 10.

9 Sasha runs a 100 m race in 13·58 s. Calculate her average speed. Give your answer to a suitable degree of accuracy.

10 Winkton has a population density of 5720 people/km². Its population is 47 500. What is the area of Winkton?

11

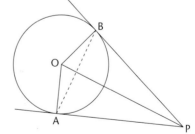

a) If angle BPO is 32°, calculate
   (i) angle POB   **(ii)** angle OAB.
b) If angle OAB is 25°, calculate angle APB.
c) If angle ABP is 75°, calculate angle AOB.

18 Changing the subject of a formula

You should already know

- how to simplify and solve linear equations.

Rearranging formulae

Formulae can be treated in the same way as equations.
This means they can be rearranged to change the subject.

EXAMPLE 1

Rearrange these formulae to make the letter in brackets the subject.

a) $a = b + c$ (b)

b) $a = bx + c$ (b)

c) $n = m - 3s$ (s)

d) $p = \dfrac{q + r}{s}$ (r)

e) $s = 3(a + b)$ (b)

> **Exam tip**
>
> If you have difficulty in rearranging a formula, practise by replacing some of the letters with numbers.

a) $a = b + c$

$a - c = b$ Subtract c from both sides.

$b = a - c$ Reverse to get b on the left.

b) $a = bx + c$

$a - c = bx$ Subtract c from both sides.

$\dfrac{a - c}{x} = b$ Divide both sides by x.

$b = \dfrac{a - c}{x}$ Reverse to get b on the left.

c) $n = m - 3s$

$n + 3s = m$ Add $3s$ to both sides.

$3s = m - n$ Subtract n from both sides.

$s = \dfrac{m - n}{3}$ Divide both sides by 3.

d) $p = \dfrac{q + r}{s}$

$sp = q + r$ Multiply both sides by s.

$sp - q = r$ Subtract q from both sides.

$r = sp - q$ Reverse to get r on the left.

e) $s = 3(a + b)$

$s = 3a + 4b$ Multiply out the bracket.

$s - 3a = 4b$ Subtract $3a$ from both sides.

$\dfrac{s - 3a}{4} = b$ Divide both sides by 4.

$b = \dfrac{s - 3a}{4}$ Reverse to get b on the left.

EXERCISE 18.1A

Rearrange each formula to make the letter in the brackets the subject.

1 $a = b - c$ (b)

2 $3a = wx + y$ (x)

3 $v = u + at$ (t)

4 $A = \dfrac{T}{H}$ (T)

5 $C = P - 3T$ (T)

6 $P = \dfrac{u + v}{2}$ (u)

7 $C = 2\pi r$ (r)

8 $A = p(q + r)$ (q)

9 The formula for finding the perimeter P of a rectangle with sides of length x and y is $P = 2(x + y)$.

Rearrange the formula to make x the subject.

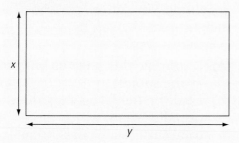

10 The cost (£C) of catering for a wedding reception is given by the formula $C = A + 32n$, where A is the cost of the room and n is the number of guests.

  a) Rearrange the formula to make n the subject.

  b) Work out the number of guests when A is £120 and the total cost C is £1912.

11 The cooking time T minutes for w kg of meat is given by $T = 45w + 40$.

  a) Make w the subject of this formula.

  b) What is the value of w when the cooking time is 2h 28min?

12 The curved surface area (S cm^2) of a cylinder of radius r cm and height h cm is given by $S = 2\pi rh$.

  a) Rearrange this formula with r as the subject.

  b) Find the radius of a cylinder of height 4 cm, which has a curved surface area of 60·3 cm^2.

EXERCISE 18.1B

Rearrange each formula to make the letter in the brackets the subject.

1 $p = q + 2r$ (q)

2 $B = s + 5r$ (r)

3 $s = 2u - t$ (t)

4 $m = \dfrac{pqr}{s}$ (q)

5 $L = 2G - 2F$ (G)

6 $F = \dfrac{m + 4n}{t}$ (n)

7 $T = \dfrac{S}{2a}$ (S)

8 $A = t(x - 2y)$ (y)

9 The formula for the volume V of a cone of height h and base radius r is $V = \frac{1}{3}\pi r^2 h$.

Rearrange the formula to make h the subject.

10 The cost (£C) of a minibus to the airport is given by the formula

$$C = 20 + \frac{d}{2}$$ where d is the distance

in miles.

a) Rearrange the formula to make d the subject.

b) Work out the distance when its costs £65 to go to the airport.

11 The cost (£C) of booking a coach for a party of n people is $C = 40 + 5n$.

Make n the subject of this formula.

Find the number of people when the cost is £235.

12 The total surface area (S cm^2 of a cylinder) of radius r cm and height h cm is given by $S = 2\pi r h + 2\pi r^2$.

a) Rearrange this formula with h as the subject.

b) Find the height of a cylinder of radius 6 cm, which has a total surface area of 500 cm^2.

Key ideas

- Rearrange a formula using the same steps as you would if it were an equation with numbers instead of letters.

The equations of straight-line graphs

You should already know

- how to draw straight-line graphs when given coordinates
- how to work out the coordinates of points on a graph given its equation.

Gradient

The gradient of a graph is the mathematical way of measuring its steepness or rate of change.

$$\text{gradient} = \frac{\text{increase in } y}{\text{increase in } x}$$

To find the gradient of a line, mark two points on the graph, then draw in the horizontal and the vertical to form a triangle as shown.

$$\text{gradient} = \frac{6}{2} = 3$$

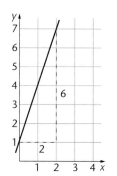

Exam tip

Choose two points far apart on the graph, so that the x-distance between them is an integer. If possible choose points where the graph crosses gridlines. This makes reading values and dividing easier.

Here the gradient $= \dfrac{^-8}{2}$ or $\dfrac{8}{^-2}$.

Both give the answer $^-4$.

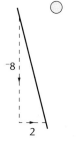

Exam tip

Check you have the correct sign, positive or negative, for the slope of the line.

Lines with a positive gradient slope forwards /.

Lines with a negative gradient slope backwards \.

Flat lines – have a gradient of zero.

EXAMPLE 1

Find the gradient of the line joining the points (3, 5) and (8, 7).

Increase in $x = 5$ Subtract $8 - 3 = 5$

Increase in $y = 2$ Subtract $7 - 5 = 2$. Remember to subtract in the same order.

Gradient $= \dfrac{2}{5} = 0 \cdot 4$

You can do this type of example without drawing a diagram, but do draw one if you prefer, so that you can see the triangle.

When interpreting graphs about physical situations, the gradient tells you the rate of change.

Exam tip

When calculating gradients from a graph, count the number of units on the axes, not the number of squares on the grid.

EXAMPLE 2

For a distance-time graph the gradient gives the speed.

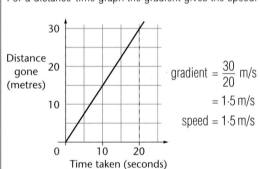

gradient $= \dfrac{30}{20}$ m/s

$= 1 \cdot 5$ m/s

speed $= 1 \cdot 5$ m/s

Exam tip

Use the units on the axes to help you to recognise what the rate of change represents.

EXERCISE 19.1A

1 Find the gradient of each of these lines.

a)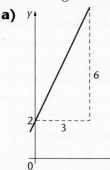

b)

c)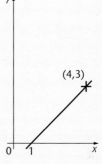

2 Find the gradient of each of these lines.

a)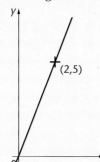

b)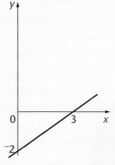

c)

3 Calculate the gradients of the lines joining each of these pairs of points.

a) (3, 2) and (4, 8)
b) (5, 3) and (7, 3)
c) (0, 4) and (2, ⁻6)
d) (⁻1, 1) and (3, 2)

4 Calculate the gradients of the lines joining each of these pairs of points.

a) (1, 8) and (5, 6)
b) (⁻3, 0) and (⁻1, 5)
c) (3, ⁻1) and (⁻1, ⁻5)
d) (2·5, 4) and (3·7, 4·9)

5 A ball bearing rolls in a straight groove. The graph shows its distance from a point P in the groove. Find the gradient of the line in this graph. What information does it give?

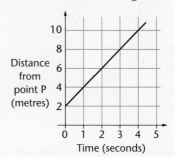

Chapter 19 *The equations of straight-line graphs*

Exercise 19.1A cont'd

6 Find the gradient of each of the sides of triangle ABC.

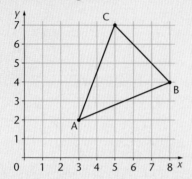

7 The table shows the cost of x minutes of calls on a mobile phone.

Number of minutes (x)	5	12	20	23
Cost (£C)	1·30	3·12	5·20	5·98

Find the gradient of the graph of C against x, and say what this gradient represents.

8 Draw, on the same diagram, the graph of
   a) $y = 3x$
   b) $y = 3x + 2$ and find their gradients.

9 Draw a graph for each of these straight lines and find their gradients.
   a) $y = 2x + 1$
   b) $y = 5x - 2$
   c) $y = 4x + 3$

10 Draw a graph for each of these straight lines and find the gradients.
   a) $y = {}^-2x + 1$
   b) $y = {}^-3x + 2$
   c) $y = {}^-x$

Chapter 19 *The equations of straight-line graphs*

EXERCISE 19.1B

1 Find the gradient of each of these lines.

a)

b)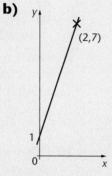

c)

2 Find the gradient of each of these lines.

a)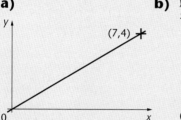

b)

c)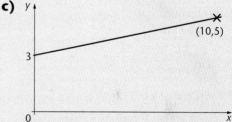

3 Calculate the gradient of the lines joining each of these pairs of points.

a) (4, 0) and (6, 8)
b) (⁻1, 4) and (7, 2)
c) (1, 5) and (3, 5)
d) (⁻2, 6) and (0, 4)

4 Calculate the gradients of the lines joining each of these pairs of points.

a) (2, 10) and (10, 30)
b) (⁻3, 6) and (⁻1, ⁻2)
c) (0·6, 3) and (3·6, ⁻9)
d) (2·5, 7) and (4, 2·2)

5 Find the gradient of the line in this graph. What information does it give?

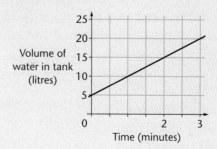

Chapter 19 *The equations of straight-line graphs*

Exercise 19.1B cont'd

6 Find the gradient of each of the sides of triangle ABC.

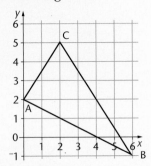

7 The table gives the cost when x metres of ribbon are sold.

Number of metres (x)	0·25	0·5	1·75	3·00
Cost (**C** pence)	21	42	147	252

Find the gradient of the graph of C against x and say what this gradient represents.

8 Draw, on the same diagram, the graphs of
   a) $y = 2x$
   b) $y = 2x + 1$ and find their gradients.

9 Draw a graph for each of these straight lines and find the gradients.
   a) $y = x + 1$ **b)** $y = 2x - 3$
   c) $y = 4x$

10 Draw a graph for each of these straight lines and find their gradients.
   a) $y = {}^-x + 3$ **b)** $y = {}^-3x$
   c) $y = {}^-2x - 5$

Straight-line graphs

If you did the last two questions in the exercises on gradients, you may have noticed a connection between the equation of a line and its gradient.

ACTIVITY 1

Using graph-drawing software draw the following lines on the same axes.
Use different colours for each line if possible.

A $y = 2x$ $y = 2x + 1$ $y = 2x + 2$ $y = 2x + 3$ $y = 2x + 4$ $y = 2x - 1$ $y = 2x - 2$

What do you notice?

Check your ideas with these lines: $y = x$ $y = x + 1$ $y = x + 2$ $y = x + 3$

Do they work for this set?

B $y = {}^-x$ $y = {}^-x + 1$ $y = {}^-x + 2$ $y = {}^-x + 3$

Activity 1 cont'd

Clear the screen of lines already drawn, then draw these two sets.

C $y = x$ $\quad y = 2x$ $\quad y = 3x$ $\quad y = 4x$

D $y = {}^-x$ $\quad y = {}^-2x$ $\quad y = {}^-3x$ $\quad y = {}^-4x$

What do you notice about the lines from **C** and **D**?

Now plot some lines of your own and see if your conclusions are correct.

Now plot these lines in pairs and see if you can see a relationship between the lines.

E $y = x$ and $y = {}^-x$

F $y = 2x$ and $y = {}^-\frac{1}{2}x$

G $y = 5x$ and $y = 0{\cdot}2x$ (notice $0{\cdot}2 = \frac{1}{5}$)

H $y = 4x$ and $y = {}^-0{\cdot}25x$

When the equation is written in the form $y = mx + c$, where m and c are numbers, then m is the gradient of the line and c is the value of y where the graph crosses the y-axis. In other words, the graph passes through $(0, c)$.

Using these facts means that

- you can work out the equation of a line from its graph
- if you know the equation of a line you can easily find its gradient and where it crosses the y-axis.

EXAMPLE 3

Find the equation of this straight line.

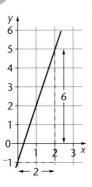

The gradient is $\dfrac{6}{2} = 3$.

The line passes through $(0, {}^-1)$.

So the equation is $y = 3x - 1$.

EXAMPLE 4

The equation of a straight line is $5x + 2y = 10$.
Find its gradient.

Rearranging the equation: $2y = {}^-5x + 10$

$$y = {}^-2{\cdot}5x + 5$$

So the gradient is ${}^-2{\cdot}5$.

EXERCISE 19.2A

1 Write down the equations of the straight lines
   a) with gradient 3 and passing through (0, 2)
   b) with gradient ⁻1 and passing through (0, 4)
   c) with gradient 5 and passing through (0, 0).

2 Find the equations of these lines.

   a)    **b)** 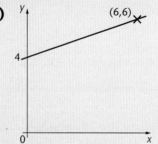   **c)**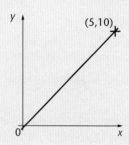

3 Find the equations of these lines.

   a) 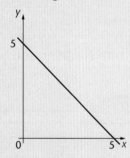   **b)** 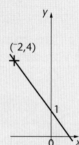   **c)**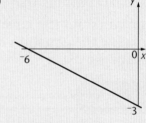

4 Find the gradient of these lines and where they cross the y-axis.

   a) $y = 3x - 2$
   b) $y = 2 + 5x$
   c) $y = 7 - 2x$

5 Find the gradient of these lines and where they cross the y-axis.

   a) $y + 2x = 5$
   b) $4x + 2y = 7$
   c) $6x + 5y = 10$

6 Find an equation for the cost (£C) of travelling m miles for the car hire in question 4, Exercise 14.1A.

7 The table shows the cost of x minutes of calls on a mobile phone (as in question 7, Exercise 19.1A).

Number of minutes (x)	5	12	20	23
Cost (£C)	1·30	3·12	5·20	5·98

Find an equation connecting x and C.

Exercise 19.2A cont'd

8 On the same diagram, sketch the graphs of these three equations.

   a) $y = 2x + 1$ **b)** $y = 2x - 3$
   c) $y = {}^-4x + 1$

9 A lorry is refuelling with diesel.

Time (*t* min)	0	1	2	3
Diesel in tank (*d* litres)	20	30	40	50

   a) Draw a graph of these data.
   b) Find the gradient of the graph and state what it represents.
   c) Find the equation connecting *d* and *t*.

EXERCISE 19.2B

1 Write down the equations of the straight lines

   a) with gradient 4 and passing through $(0, {}^-1)$
   b) with gradient $^-2$ and passing through $(0, 5)$
   c) with gradient 3 and passing through the origin.

2 Find the equations of these lines.

   a)

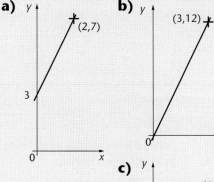

   b)
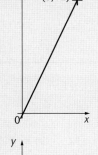

   c)
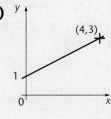

3 Find the equations of these lines.

   a)
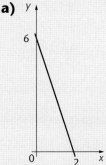

   b)

   c)

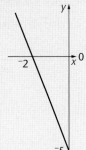

4 Find the gradient of these lines and where they cross the *y*-axis.

   a) $y = 5x - 3$ **b)** $y = 7 + 2x$
   c) $y = 9 - 3x$

Exercise 19.2B cont'd

5 Find the gradient of these lines and where they cross the y-axis.

   a) $y - 5x = 1$ **b)** $3x + 2y = 8$
   c) $2x + 5y = 15$

6 Using the diagram from question 6, Exercise 19.1B, find the equations of the sides of triangle ABC.

7 The table gives the cost when x metres of ribbon are sold (as in question 7, Exercise 19.1B).

Number of metres (x)	0.25	0.5	1.75	3.00
Cost (C pence)	21	42	147	252

Find an equation connecting x and C.

8 On the same diagram, sketch the graphs of these equations.

   a) $y = 3x + 2$ **b)** $y = 3x - 2$
   c) $y = {}^-x + 2$

9 A shop which converts money offers these rates of dollars in exchange for pounds.

Pounds (p)	10	20	30
Dollars (d)	11	27	43

   a) Draw a graph of these data.

   b) Find the gradient of the graph and state what it represents.

   c) What does the intercept on the d-axis represent?

   d) Find the equation connecting d and p.

Parallel or perpendicular lines

You may have noticed from the work in the last few exercises that

Lines with the same gradient are parallel.

For example, these lines are all parallel.

$y = 2x$

$y = 2x + 3$

$y = 2x - 4$

You may also have seen this pattern, but it is less obvious:

If a line has gradient m, then a line perpendicular to it has gradient $\dfrac{^-1}{m}$.

Or: The gradients of two perpendicular lines have a product of $^-1$.

EXAMPLE 5

State an equation for a line which is **a)** parallel to $y = 4x + 1$ **b)** at right angles to $y = 4x + 1$.

a) Any parallel line will have gradient 4. So one possible line is $y = 4x - 3$.

b) Any perpendicular line will have gradient $^-\frac{1}{4}$. So one possible line is $y = ^-\frac{1}{4}x + 1$.

EXERCISE 19.3A

1 Draw the line $y = 2x$. On the same graph, draw a line parallel to it and a line perpendicular to it. Find the equations of the lines you have drawn.

2 Draw the line $x + 3y = 6$. State its gradient. Draw a line perpendicular to this and state its gradient.

3 Find the equation of the line parallel to $y = 6x - 3$ which passes through the point (0, 4).

4 Find the equation of the line perpendicular to $y = 0.5x - 1$ which passes through the point (0, 3).

5 A line joins (1, 2) and (5, $^-$6). Find the gradient of a line perpendicular to this.

EXERCISE 19.3B

1 Draw the line $y = {}^-2x$. On the same graph, draw a line parallel to it and a line perpendicular to it. Find the equations of the lines you have drawn.

2 Draw the line $5x - y = 6$. State its gradient. Draw a line perpendicular to this and state its gradient.

3 Find the equation of the line parallel to $y = 3x - 1$ which passes through the point (0, 2).

4 Find the equation of the line perpendicular to $y = 0.25x + 5$ which passes through the point (0, $^-$1).

5 A line joins ($^-$1, 2) and (1, 14). Find the gradient of a line perpendicular to this.

Key ideas

Gradient of straight lines

- Gradient $= \dfrac{\text{increase in } y}{\text{increase in } x}$.

- Lines with a positive gradient slope forwards /.

- Lines with a negative gradient slope backwards \.

- Flat lines _____ have a gradient of zero.

- For graphs about physical situations, gradient gives the rate of change.

- Lines with the same gradient are parallel.

- If a line has gradient m then a line perpendicular to it has gradient $\dfrac{^-1}{m}$.

Equation of a straight-line graph

- The equation of a line can be written as $y = mx + c$, where m and c are numbers.
  m is the gradient of the line and c is the value of y where the graph crosses the y-axis.
  In other words, the graph passes through (0, c).

Chapter 19 *The equations of straight-line graphs*

20 More on equations and inequalities

You should already know

- how to write a formula using letters
- how to collect together algebraic expressions
- how to expand brackets
- how to form and solve simple linear equations
- how to form and solve simple inequalities.

Solving harder linear equations

Some linear equations you may be asked to solve may include decimals or have brackets. You may be asked to solve an equation with the unknown in the denominator.

EXAMPLE 1

Solve $2(5x - 4) = 3(x + 2)$

$10x - 8 = 3x + 6$	Multiply out the brackets.
$[10x - 8 + 8 = 3x + 6 + 8]$	Add 8 to each side.
$10x = 3x + 14$	
$[10x - 3x = 3x + 14 - 3x]$	Subtract $3x$ from each side.
$7x = 14$	
$x = 14 \div 7 = 2$	Divide by 7.

The lines in square brackets are often missed out.

EXAMPLE 2

Solve $\frac{x}{3} = 2x - 3$.

$x = 3(2x - 3)$ Multiply each side by 3.

$x = 6x - 9$ Multiply out the bracket.

$6x - 9 = x$ Reverse the equation to put the x-term with the larger positive coefficient of the left.

$[6x - 9 + 9 = x + 9]$ Add 9 to each side.

$6x = x + 9$

$[6x - x = x + 9 - x]$ Subtract x from each side.

$5x = 9$

$x = 9 \div 5 = 1\frac{4}{5}$ Divide each side by 5.

EXAMPLE 3

Solve the equation $\frac{400}{x} = 8$.

$400 = 8x$ Multiply each side by x.

$400 \div 8 = x$ Divide each side by 8.

$x = 50$

Exam tip

A common error when multiplying through by a number or letter is to multiply just the first term. Use brackets to make sure. Another common error in examples like these would be to give the answer as $\frac{5}{9}$ rather than $\frac{9}{5}$.

It is helpful to swap the sides if necessary to make the coefficient of x greater on the left-hand side.

EXAMPLE 4

Solve the equation $3 \cdot 6x = 8 \cdot 7$.

$x = 8 \cdot 7 \div 3 \cdot 6$ Divide each side by $3 \cdot 6$.

$x = 2 \cdot 416\,666\,6$ Use a calculator and

$= 2 \cdot 42$ give the answer to three significant figures unless you are told otherwise.

Chapter 20 *More on equations and equalities*

EXERCISE 20.1A

Solve these equations.

1. $5(x - 2) = 4x$
2. $3(2x + 3) = 9$
3. $4(2x - 3) = 3(x + 1)$
4. $2(4x - 5) = 2x + 6$
5. $10(x + 2) = 3(x - 5)$
6. $3(2x - 1) = 2(x + 4)$
7. $\dfrac{x}{2} = 3x - 10$
8. $\dfrac{2x}{3} = x - 2$

9. $\dfrac{3x}{2} = 7 - 2x$
10. $\dfrac{5x}{3} = 4x - 2$
11. $\dfrac{50}{x} = 2$
12. $\dfrac{300}{x} = 15$
13. $\dfrac{75}{2x} = 3$

Now give the answers to the remaining questions correct to three significant figures.

14. $3 \cdot 5x = 9 \cdot 6$
15. $5 \cdot 2x = 25$
16. $4 \cdot 6x = 7 \cdot 5$
17. $\dfrac{x}{1 \cdot 4} = 2 \cdot 6$
18. $2 \cdot 1(x - 3 \cdot 2) = 4 \cdot 4$
19. $2 \cdot 2(2x + 5 \cdot 1) = 4 \cdot 9$
20. $\dfrac{2 \cdot 3}{x} = 4 \cdot 5$

EXERCISE 20.1B

Solve these equations.

1. $2(3x - 5) = 14$
2. $4(3x - 1) = 10x$
3. $3(2x + 1) = 7x + 1$
4. $5(2x - 2) = 2(x + 3)$
5. $3(4x + 3) = 2(x + 6)$
6. $5(x + 2) = 3(4 - x)$
7. $5(x + 2) = 3(2x + 1)$
8. $\dfrac{x}{3} = x - 4$
9. $\dfrac{2x}{5} = x - 3$
10. $\dfrac{3x}{5} = 4 - x$
11. $\dfrac{2x}{3} = 4x - 5$

12. $\dfrac{200}{x} = 4$
13. $\dfrac{25}{2x} = 5$
14. $\dfrac{15}{2x} = 3$

Give the answers to the remaining questions correct to three significant figures.

15. $2 \cdot 4x = 9 \cdot 7$
16. $22x = 7 \cdot 55$
17. $4 \cdot 2x = 9 \cdot 3$
18. $2 \cdot 1(3x - 6 \cdot 4) = 9 \cdot 2$
19. $\dfrac{x}{3 \cdot 4} = 2 \cdot 5$
20. $\dfrac{3 \cdot 5}{x} = 1 \cdot 6$

Chapter 20 *More on equations and equalities*

Solving inequalities

These are more complicated than the inequalities you met in Chapter 13.
For example, you may need to work with brackets.

EXAMPLE 5

Solve $\frac{x}{3} \geq 2x - 3$ and show your answer on a number line.

$x \geq 6x - 9$	Multiply each side by 3.
$x + 9 \geq 6x$	Add 9 to each side.
$9 \geq 5x$	Subtract x from each side.
$1 \cdot 8 \geq x$	Divide each side by 5.
$x \leq 1 \cdot 8$	Rewrite with x as subject. Note that the inequality has changed direction too. With inequalities you can't just swap sides.

EXAMPLE 6

Solve $2(3x - 1) > 4x + 7$

$6x - 2 > 4x + 7$	Work out the brackets.
$6x > 4x + 9$	Add 2 to each side.
$2x > 9$	Subtract $4x$ from each side.
$x > 4\frac{1}{2}$	Divide each side by 2.

Exam tip

Compare the solution for example 5 with example 2. There is often more than one way to solve an equation or inequality.

EXERCISE 20.2A

Solve these inequalities.

1 $2x + 3 < 5$

2 $5x - 4 > 10 - 2x$

3 $3(2x - 1) > 15$

4 $4(x - 4) \geq x - 1$

5 $\frac{x}{2} > 3$

6 $2(x + 3) < 1 - 3x$

7 $3(2x - 1) \geq 11 - x$

8 $x + 4 > 2x$

9 $2x - 5 < 4x + 1$

10 $3(x - 4) > 5(x + 1)$

EXERCISE 20.2B

Solve these inequalities.

1 $4n - 2 > 6$

2 $2n + 6 < n + 3$

3 $4n - 9 \geq 2n + 1$

4 $3(x - 1) \geq 6$

5 $2(3x - 1) > 4x + 6$

6 $x - 2 < 2x + 4$

7 $2x - 1 > x - 4$

8 $3(x + 3) \geq 2x - 1$

9 $\frac{1}{2}x + 4 < 5$

10 $3(2x - 4) < 5(x - 6)$

Forming equations and inequalities

Simple problems can be solved using equations and inequalities.

EXAMPLE 7

The length of a rectangle is a cm, the width is 15 cm shorter. The length is three times the width.

Write down an equation in a and solve it to find the length and width of the rectangle.

If the length = a, the width = $a - 15$ and the length = 3 × width = $3(a - 15)$.

The equation is $a = 3(a - 15)$.

$a = 3a - 45$ — Multiply out the brackets.

$3a - 45 = a$ — Swap sides to write them the other way round.

$[3a - 45 + 45 = a + 45]$ — Add 45 to each side.

$3a = a + 45$

$[3a - a = a + 45 - a]$ — Subtract a from each side.

$2a = 45$

$a = 22.5$

So the length = 22·5 cm and the width = 7·5 cm.

EXAMPLE 8

£400 was shared by n people and each received £16. Set up an equation and find how many people there were.

The equation is $\frac{400}{n} = 16$.

$400 = 16n$

$n = 400 \div 16 = 25$

| Multiply each side by n. |

There were 25 people.

Exam tip

When you are asked to set up an equation and solve it you will not score any marks if you just give the answer without the equation.

EXERCISE 20.3A

1 Two angles in a triangle are x and $2x - 30$. The first angle is twice the size of the second. Set up an equation and solve it to find the size of the two angles.

2 The width of a rectangle is $3\,cm$ and the length is $x + 4\,cm$. The area is $27\,cm^2$. Set up an equation and solve it to find x.

3 In a class of 32 pupils, x are girls. There are three times as many girls as boys. Set up an equation and solve it to find out how many boys and how many girls there are.

4 A greengrocer sells potatoes at x pence per kilogram. He paid $\frac{2x}{3}$ pence per kilogram for them. This is 20p less than x. Set up an equation and solve it to find x.

5 Stephen thinks of a number. If he doubles the number and then subtracts 5, he gets the same answer as if he subtracts 2 from the number and then multiplies by 3. Let the number be n. Set up an equation and solve it to find n.

6 On a bus trip each child pays £p and each adult pays £12 more than each child. There are 28 children and four adults on the bus. The same amount of money is collected from all the children as from all the adults. Set up an equation and solve it to find how much each child and each adult pays.

7 At Joe's Diner one-course meals cost £x. Two-course meals cost £2 more. A group of eight people bought three one-course meals and five two-course meals. They paid £38. Set up an equation and solve it to find the cost of a one-course meal.

8 The square of a number is less than 36. Set up an inequality and find the possible values for the number.

EXERCISE 20.3B

1 Two angles of a pentagon are $x°$ and the other three are each $(2x - 20)°$. The total of all the angles is 540°. Write down an equation and solve it to find the size of the angles.

2 A triangle has a base of x cm and a height of 5 cm. The area is 30 cm^2. Set up an equation in x and solve it to find the length of the base.

3 The cost per person of a flight from Sheffield Airport is the charge by the airline plus £40 tax. Four people flew from Sheffield to Cairo and the total they had to pay was £1640. Let the charge by the airline be £x. Write down an equation in x and solve it to find the charge by the airline.

4 A 32-year-old man has three children who are x, $2x$ and $2x + 4$ years old. The man is four times as old as his eldest child. Set up an equation and solve it to find the ages of the children.

5 Jane thinks of a number. Her number divided by three gives the same answer as taking the number away from sixteen. Let the number be n. Set up an equation and solve it to find what the number was.

6 At Deno's Pizza Place, a basic pizza costs £x and extra toppings are 50p each. Bernard and four of his friends each have pizzas with two extra toppings. They pay £25·50. Set up an equation and find the cost of a basic pizza.

7 Ahmed had £x. He spent £4 on books and still had three-fifths of his money left. Write down an equation in x and solve it to find how much he had to start with.

Key ideas

- If a problem asks you to use algebra to solve it, you must start with an equation.
- Solve hard equations by doing one step at a time. Write down the result of each step.
- Don't try to do several steps at once in your head – this leads to errors.

21 Loci and constructions

You should already know

- how to use a protractor and compasses
- how to construct a triangle, given three sides
- how to construct a triangle given two sides and an angle
- how to construct a triangle given two angles and a side
- how to make scale drawings.

ACTIVITY 1

Scale: 1 cm to 20 m

A farmer wants to plant crops but he must keep at least 1 m from the borders of his field. Trace this diagram into your workbook. Sketch the region where he can plant crops.

The local walkers' group agreed to have a footpath constructed from gate G_1 which is equidistant from the two hedges h_1 and h_2. Construct this path.

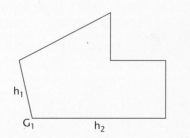

Identifying a locus

The locus of a point is the path or the region that the point covers as it moves according to a particular rule.

The plural of locus is loci.

The locus of a point 3 cm from A is a circle, centre A, radius 3 cm.

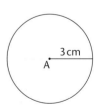

The locus of a point less than (<) 3 cm from A is the region inside a circle centre A, radius 3 cm.

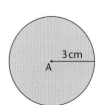

The locus of a point greater than (>) 3 cm from A is the region outside a circle centre A, radius 3 cm.

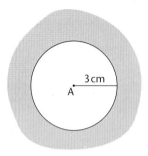

You need to know some other basic loci.

The locus of a point 2 cm from a straight line is a pair of lines parallel to that line, 2 cm away from it on either side.

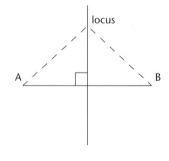

The locus of a point that stays an equal distance from two points is the perpendicular bisector of the line joining the two points.

The locus of a point that stays an equal distance from two intersecting lines is the pair of lines that bisect the angles between the lines. Can you see why this is so?

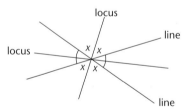

Drawing the perpendiculars to the lines from a point on the locus creates two congruent triangles.

Sketching loci

When you sketch a locus, draw it as accurately as you can but not to size or with accurately constructed bisectors. You must mark all the distances and angles that are equal.

Exam tip

The locus of the points equidistant from two intersecting lines is a pair of lines, but normally you only require one.

EXAMPLE 1

A line is 6 cm long. Sketch the locus of all points that are 2 cm from the line

locus

line $\updownarrow$ 2 cm
$\updownarrow$ 2 cm

The locus is two parallel lines with a semicircle joining them at each end.

Exam tip

Even if you are asked to sketch a locus, use a ruler and draw the angles as near to the required size as you can.

EXAMPLE 2

Two towns A and B are 6 miles apart. Make a sketch and shade the region that is nearer to B than A.

Draw the perpendicular bisector of the line AB and shade the region on B's side of the line. The shading could go past B and up or down the page further.

The two parts of the line AB need to be shown as 3 miles each, and the 90° angle must be indicated.

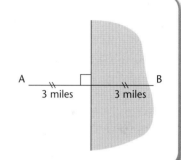

A ———— 3 miles —— 3 miles —— B

Constructing loci

You need to know two constructions: the perpendicular bisector of a line and the bisector of an angle.

The perpendicular bisector of a line is the locus of a point that moves so that it is equidistant from two points.

Draw the line AB.

Open the compasses to a radius that is more than half the length of AB.

Put the compass point at A and draw an arc above and below the line.

Keep the compasses set to the same radius.

Put the compass point at B and draw an arc above and below the line.

Join the two points where the arcs meet.

A ———————— B

Exam tip

To draw a perpendicular from a point to a line, draw an arc, centre the point to cut the line at A and B. Continue as for this construction.

The bisector an an angle is the locus of a point that moves so that it is equidistant from two lines.

Draw an angle and mark the vertex (corner) A.

Put the point of the compasses at A and draw an arc to cut the lines forming the angle at B and C.

Put the point at B and draw an arc in the angle.

Keep the compasses set to the same radius.

Put the point at C and draw an arc in the angle to cut the arc just drawn.

Draw a straight line through A and the point where the arcs cut.

The bisector could be continued to the left of A. If the lines are extended, another bisector could be drawn, perpendicular to the first one.

Use these constructions, and what you already know, to draw various loci.

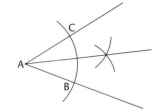

Exam tip

These methods are more accurate than just using measurement.

EXAMPLE 3

Draw a triangle ABC with sides AB = 5 cm, AC = 4 cm and A = 50°.

Use compasses to bisect angle A. Shade in the locus of the points inside the triangle that are nearer to AB than AC.

This diagram is half-size.

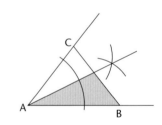

EXERCISE 21.1A

1 Draw a circle, centre A, radius 5 cm. Shade the locus of the points that are less than 5 cm from A.

2 Draw a rectangle 4 cm by 5 cm. Sketch the locus of the points that are 1 cm from the perimeter of the rectangle, outside the rectangle.

3 Draw a rectangle ABCD with AB = 6 cm and BC = 4 cm. Sketch the locus of the points inside the rectangle that are nearer to A than B.

Exercise 21.1A cont'd

4   Draw two parallel lines across the page, 4 cm apart. Draw the locus of the points that are 1 cm from the top line and 3 cm from the bottom line.

5   A fox never travels more than 5 miles from its den. Draw a sketch to show the region where it travels.

6   Draw a line 7 cm long. Construct the perpendicular bisector of the line.

7   Draw an angle of 70°. Construct the bisector of the angle.

8   Construct a triangle ABC with AB = 8 cm, AC = 7 cm and BC = 5 cm. Use compasses and a ruler to bisect angle A. Shade the locus of the points that are nearer to AB than AC and inside the triangle.

9   Draw a square ABCD with side 6 cm. Construct the locus of the points that are equidistant from A and C. What do you notice about the locus?

Exam tip

In most cases you will be asked to construct a locus either to size or to scale. Draw it as accurately as you can. Do not stop the line of a construction at the intersection of the arcs. Draw it through the intersection. When you do a construction, leave in your constructon lines.

10 Draw triangle ABC with AB = 8 cm, A = 90° and B = 40°. Do a construction to find the locus of the points inside the triangle that are nearer to AC than BC.

EXERCISE 21.1B

1   Show, by shading, the locus of the points that are more than 4 cm from a fixed point A.

2   Draw a line 6 cm long. Show, by shading in a sketch, the locus of the points that are less than 2 cm from the line.

3   Draw an angle of 80°. Construct the bisector of the angle.

4   Draw a line AB 6 cm long. Construct the perpendicular bisector of AB.

5   Draw a square with side 4 cm. Label one corner A. Show the locus of the points inside the square that are less than 3 cm from A.

Exercise 21.1B cont'd

6 Draw a rectangle ABCD with sides AB = 7 cm and BC = 5 cm. Use compasses to construct the line equidistant from AB and AC.

7 Construct the triangle ABC with A = 30°, B = 50° and AB = 10 cm. Construct the locus of the points equidistant from A and B.

8 Two towns Bimouth and Tritown are 10 miles apart. Phoebe wants to live nearer to Bimouth than Tritown. Using a scale of 1 cm : 2 miles, make a scale drawing and show, by shading, the region where she can live.

9 Draw a triangle ABC with AB = 7 cm, A = 50° and B = 40°. Show, by shading, the locus of the points within the triangle that are nearer to AC than BC.

10 Sonia has a 20 metre flex on her lawnmower and the socket is in the middle of the back wall of her house. The back of the house is 12 m wide and her garden is a rectangle the same width as the house, stretching 24 m from the house. Using a scale of 1 cm : 4 m, make a drawing of her garden and show, by shading, the region she can reach with the mower.

Problems involving intersection of loci

Combining all you know about loci, you can answer more complicated questions involving more than one locus.

EXAMPLE 4

Construct triangle ABC with AB = 7 cm, AC = 6 cm and BC = 4 cm. By using constructions, find the point that is equidistant from all three vertices. Mark this point D.

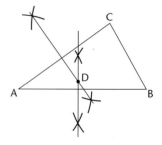

This diagram is half-size.

First you need the line equidistant from two vertices. If you choose AB you need to construct the perpendicular bisector of AB. Then you need to construct the perpendicular bisector of another side. Where they cross is the required point.

You could also bisect the third side and that line would also pass through the same point.

EXAMPLE 5

Two points A and B are 4 cm apart. Show, by shading, the locus of the points that are less than 2·5 cm from A, and nearer to B than A.

You need to draw a circle, radius 2·5 cm and centre A. You also need to draw the bisector of the line AB. The region you require is inside the circle and on the B side of the bisector. Here the region required is shaded.

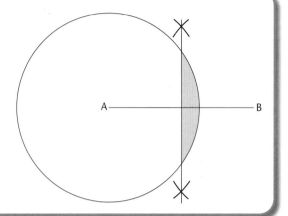

EXAMPLE 6

Erica wants to put a rocking chair in her room. She wants the chair more than 0·5 m from a wall and less than 2 m from corner A. This is a sketch of her room. Using a scale of 1 cm : 1 m, make a scale drawing of the room and show, by shading, the region where the chair can be placed.

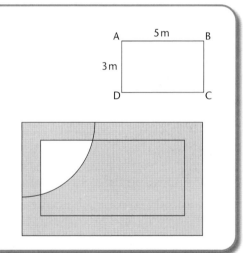

Draw the rectangle and then add lines 0·5 cm from each side. Draw a circle, centre A radius 2 cm. In this diagram the regions not required are shaded, leaving the white region where the chair can be placed.

EXAMPLE 7

Find the centre of the rotation that maps triangle ABC onto triangle A'B'C'.

Chapter 21 *Loci and constructions*

Example 7 cont'd

The centre of rotation must be equidistant from A and A'. It will be on the perpendicular bisector of AA'. Arcs have been omitted to make the diagram clearer.

The centre must also be equidistant from C and C'. The centre of rotation will be the point where the two perpendicular bisectors meet.

The centre must also equidistant from B and B'. Construct the perpendicular bisector of BB' to check.

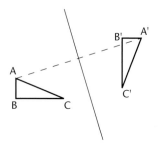

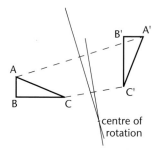

EXERCISE 21.2A

Draw all of these accurately.

1 Two points A and B are 5 cm apart. Show, by shading, the region that is less than 3 cm from A and more than 4 cm from B.

2 A rectangle ABCD has sides AB = 5 cm and BC = 4 cm. Draw the rectangle and show, by shading, the region inside the rectangle that is nearer to AB and CD, and less than 3·5 cm from B.

3 Draw a triangle ABC with AB = 6 cm, A = 60° and B = 55°. Use constructions to find the point D that is equidistant from all three sides.

> **Exam tip**
>
> You can either shade the region required or shade the regions not required. It is often easier to do the latter if the regions are at all complicated. Give a key or label to the diagram to make it clear which you have done.

4 Draw a rectangle ABCD with sides AB = 4 cm and BC = 3 cm. Show the points that are equidistant from AB and BC and 3·5 cm from A.

5 Draw a triangle ABC with sides AB = 9 cm, BC = 6 cm and AC = 5 cm. Show, by shading, the region inside the triangle that is nearer to AB than BC and more than 3 cm from C.

Exercise 21.2A cont'd

6 Two towns, Hilldon and Baton are 20 miles apart. It is proposed to build a new shopping centre within 15 miles of Hilldon but nearer to Baton than Hilldon. Using a scale of 1 cm : 5 miles, make a drawing and show the region where the shopping centre can be built.

7 Richard's bedroom is rectangular with sides 4 m and 6·5 m. He wants to put a desk within 1 metre of a longer wall and within 2.5 m of the centre of the window in the middle of one of the shorter walls. Using a scale of 1 cm : 1 m, make a scale drawing and showing, by shading, the region where the desk can be placed.

8 Kirsty has a triangular patio with sides 6 m, 4 m and 5 m. She wants to put a plant pot on the patio more than 2 m from any corner. Using a scale of 1 cm : 1 m, make a drawing and show, by shading, where she can put the plant pot.

9 This is a sketch of a plot of land that Arun wants to use for camping.

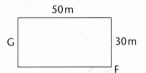

He wants to put a tap in the field within 35 m of the gate which is at the middle of one of the shorter sides. He also wants it to be within 25 m of his farm which is at corner F. Using a scale of 1 cm : 10 m, make a scale drawing of the land. Show, by shading, the position where the tap can be placed.

10 A field is in the shape of a quadrilateral ABCD with AB = 25 m, BC = 30 m, A = 90°, B = 106° and C = 65°. The farmer wants to put a scarecrow within 15 m of corner A and nearer to CD than CB. Using a scale of 1 cm to 5 m, draw the field and show, by shading, the region where the scarecrow can be placed.

EXERCISE 21.2B

1 Show, by shading, the locus of the points that are more than 2 cm from a point A and less than 3 cm from point A.

2 Two points A and B are 4 cm apart. Show, by shading, the locus of all the points that are less than 2·5 cm from A and more than 3 cm from B.

Exercise 21.2B cont'd

3 Draw a triangle ABC with AB = 6 cm, A = 40° and B = 35°. Use constructions to find the point D that is equidistant from A and B and 4 cm from C.

4 Draw a square with side 4 cm. Show, by shading, the region within the square that is more than 2 cm from every vertex.

5 Draw a triangle ABC with AB = 6 cm, AC = 5 cm and A = 55°. Bisect the angle A. Draw the perpendicular bisector of AB. Show, by shading, the region that is inside the triangle, nearer to AB than AC and nearer to B than A.

6 Dave and Clare live 7 miles apart. They set out on bikes to meet. They ride directly towards each other. When they meet, Dave has ridden less than 5 miles and Clare less than 4 miles. Using a scale of 1 cm : 1 mile, make a scale drawing showing where they could have met.

7 Tariq's garden is a rectangle ABCD with AB = 10 m and BC = 4 m. He wants to put a rotary washing line in the garden. It must be more than 4 m from corner C and more than 1 m from side AB. Using a scale of 1 cm : 1 m, make a scale drawing of the garden and show where he can put the rotary washing line.

8 The distances between three towns Arbridge, Beaton and Ceborough are AB = 25 miles, AC = 40 miles and BC = 30 miles. A new garage is to be built as near as possible to all three towns. Use a scale of 1 cm : 5 miles and make constructions to find the point D where the garage should be placed.

9 Sasha has a rectangular garage 2 m by 5 m. It has a door at one end. She wants to put a hook in the ceiling. It must be midway between the two longer sides, less than 3·5 m from the door end and less than 2·5 m from the other end. Make a scale drawing of the ceiling using a scale of 1 cm : 1 m. Show by shading the region where the hook can be fixed.

10 This is a sketch of the playing field in Towbridge.

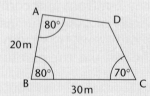

A new swing is to be placed in the field. It must be within 15 m of A and nearer to AB than AD. Use a scale of 1 cm : 5 m to make a drawing and show the region where the swing can be placed.

Key ideas

- A locus is the path or region where a point can move according to a rule.

- The locus of a point x cm from point A is a circle with centre A, radius x cm.

- The locus of a point equidistant from two points A and B is the perpendicular bisector of the line AB.

- The locus of a point equidistant from two parallel lines is a line parallel to the two lines and midway between the lines.

- The locus of a point equidistant from two non-parallel lines is the bisector(s) of the angle(s) between the lines.

Revision exercise

1 Rearrange the following formulae to make the letter in brackets the subject.

a) $x = y - 3b$ (y)

b) $t = \dfrac{u + v}{2}$ (u)

c) $P = 2b - a$ (a)

d) $p = qx + m$ (q)

e) $I = \dfrac{PTR}{100}$ (P)

f) $v^2 = u^2 + 2as$ (s)

2 The sum $s°$ of the interior angles of a polygon with n sides is given by $s = 180(n - 2)$.

a) Make n the subject of this formula.

b) How many sides does a polygon have when the sum of its interior angles is 2880°?

3 Find the gradient of the lines joining these pairs of points.

a) (2, 4) and (4, 9)

b) (2, 4) and (6, 0)

c) (⁻1, 2) and (5, 2)

4 Plot and join the points A(3, 1), B(⁻3, 4) and C(5, 6). Calculate the gradients of the sides of triangle ABC.

5 State the gradients of these lines, and the coordinates of their intersection with the y-axis.

a) $y = 2x - 3$

b) $x = 2y$

c) $3y = x + 2$

d) $2x + 5y = 10$

6 a) Plot a graph for these data for the distance (d km) of a car from a motorway junction at time t minutes.

t	2	4	8	15
d	5·0	7·4	12·2	20·6

b) What was the speed of the car, in km per minute?

c) How far was the car from the junction when t was zero?

d) Write an equation connecting d and t.

7 Find an equation for each of these lines.

a)

b)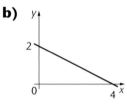

c)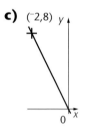

d)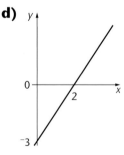

8 Sketch the graphs of these straight lines.

a) $y = 3x - 2$

b) $y = ⁻3x + 1$

c) $x = 2y$

d) $x = 2$

9 Solve these equations.

   a) $3(x - 2) = x$
   b) $5(2x + 3) = 55$
   c) $4(x - 3) = 3(x - 2)$
   d) $2(3x - 4) = 4(x + 1)$
   e) $\frac{x}{2} = 3x - 10$
   f) $\frac{x}{3} = 3 - 2x$
   g) $\frac{500}{x} = 20$
   h) $\frac{300}{x} = 60$

10 Solve these inequalities.

   a) $2x - 1 < 5$
   b) $3x + 4 \leqslant 16$
   c) $5x - 2 > 3 + 4x$
   d) $2(3x - 1) \leqslant 3x + 5$
   e) $2x - 3 < 3x - 1$
   f) $x + 2 > 3x + 1$
   g) $3(2x - 3) > 2(x - 5)$

11 A number x divided by 3 is the same as 3 times the number minus 24. Write down an equation and solve it to find the number.

12 An ice-lolly costs x pence and an ice-cream costs 20 pence more.

   a) Write down the cost of an ice-cream in terms of x.

   Jon buys three ice-lollies and two ice-creams and pays £3·40.

   b) Write down an equation in x and solve it to find the cost of an ice-lolly and of an ice-cream.

13 Marcia is x cm tall and her friend Carole is 25 cm shorter.

   a) Write down Carole's height in terms of x. Carol is $\frac{4}{5}$ as tall as Marcia.

   b) Write down an equation in x and solve it to find Marcia's height.

14 Draw an angle of 65° and construct the bisector of the angle.

15 Draw a line AB, 5 cm long. Construct the perpendicular bisector of AB.

16 Draw a triangle of ABC with AB = 6 cm, A = 40° and B = 60°. Find the point D that is equidistant from A and B and also equidistant from AB and AC. Show your construction lines.

17 Two points A and B are 6 cm apart. Show, by shading, the locus of the points that are less than 5 cm from A and more then 5 cm from B.

18 Draw a rectangle ABCD with sides AB = 4 cm and BC = 3 cm. Show the locus of the points outside the rectangle that are within 2 cm of the sides of the rectangle.

19 Draw a triangle ABC with AB = 8 cm, A = 47° and AC = 5 cm. Show the locus of the points inside the triangle that are nearer to AB than BC.

20 This diagram shows the position of three schools.

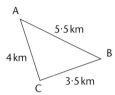

It is decided to build a swimming pool for the three schools. It must not be more than 3·5 km from any of the schools. Using a scale of 2 cm : 1 km, make a scale drawing and show the region where the pool can be located.

21 Carterknowle Church hall is rectangular with sides AB = 12 m and BC = 5 m. The main door is at corner C. A spotlight is to be fixed on the ceiling, more than 6 m from the main door, more than 5 m from the opposite corner and nearer to AB than AD. Using a scale of 1 cm : 1 m, make a scale drawing of the hall and show the region where the light can be fitted.

22 This is a plan of the floor area of a shop.

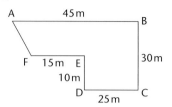

All the corners are 90° except A and F. A heat detector is placed at A and another at D. They both have a range of 20 m and do not work round corners. Using a scale of 1 cm : 5 m, make a scale drawing of the plan and show, by shading, the region that is not covered by heat detectors.

23 This is a sketch of Sanjay's patio.

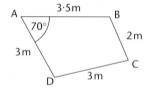

He wants to place a plant pot on the patio, within 1 metre of AB, nearer AB than AD, and no more than 2 metres from A. Using a scale of 2 cm : 1 m, make a scale drawing of the patio and show the region where the pot can be placed.

Stage 8

CONTENTS

Recurring decimals

1

Equivalence of fractions and decimals

You know already that $\frac{1}{2}$ and 0·5 mean the same.

You can say   'half the children in the school are girls'

or   '0·5 of the children in the school are girls'.

You may also realise that $\frac{1}{4}$ and 0·25 mean the same thing.

You have already learnt how to convert fractions to their equivalent decimal.

EXAMPLE 1

Convert $\frac{5}{8}$ to a decimal.

$\frac{5}{8} = 5 \div 8 = 0.625$

EXAMPLE 2

Convert $\frac{1}{6}$ to a decimal.

$\frac{1}{6} = 1 \div 6 = 0.166666\ldots\ldots$

ACTIVITY 1

Write these fractions as decimals $\frac{2}{3}$, $\frac{1}{5}$, $\frac{2}{11}$, $\frac{3}{4}$, $\frac{3}{7}$, $\frac{5}{6}$, $\frac{1}{18}$, $\frac{1}{20}$, $\frac{5}{8}$

What do you notice?

Terminating and recurring decimals

Look again at Examples 1 and 2.

In Example 1 the decimal equivalent of $\frac{5}{8}$ is exactly 0·625. This is an example of a terminating decimal. It is called terminating because it finishes at the digit 5.
In Example 2 the decimal equivalent of $\frac{1}{6}$ goes on forever with the digit 6 repeating itself over and over again. This is an example of a recurring decimal.

The dot notation for recurring decimals

To save a lot of writing, there is a special notation for recurring decimals

$\frac{1}{3} = 0.33333......$ is written as $0.\dot{3}$. You put a dot over the figure that recurs.

Similarly $\frac{1}{6} = 0.1666666......$ is written as $0.1\dot{6}$.

> ## Exam tip
>
> When working out a recurring decimal, your calculator may round off the last figure using the normal rounding rules. This means that $0.166666 ......$ may appear as 0.16666667. Even so, it should be obvious that the decimal recurs. In practical problems, if answers come to long decimals, it is best to round your answers to a suitable degree of accuracy.

EXAMPLE 3

Write $\frac{7}{11}$ as a recurring decimal.

$7 \div 11 = 0.636363......$

This time both the 6 and 3 recur. To show this you put a dot over both the 6 and the 3.

That is, you write $0.\dot{6}\dot{3}$.

EXAMPLE 4

Write $\frac{171}{333}$ as a recurring decimal.

$171 \div 333 = 0.513513513......$ This time there are three figures that recur.

You write this as $0.\dot{5}1\dot{3}$. Put a dot over the first and last figures that recur.

This means that for example 0.4325132513251 is written as $0.4\dot{3}25\dot{1}$.

Sometimes, because so many figures recur, it is difficult to see the recurring figures on a calculator.

For example $\frac{3}{7}$ will be shown as 0.428571428 on many calculators. It is only just noticeable that this means all six digits will recur.

That is $\frac{3}{7} = 0.428571428571428571...... = 0.\dot{4}2857\dot{1}$.

On calculators which show fewer digits it may be even less obvious.

ACTIVITY 2

Can you find a rule for the maximum number of recurring digits? Use your answers to Activity 1.

EXERCISE 1.1A

Convert these fractions to decimals. When the answers are recurring decimals, use the dot notation.

1 $\frac{3}{8}$ **2** $\frac{5}{6}$ **3** $\frac{5}{16}$ **4** $\frac{11}{40}$

5 $\frac{5}{9}$ **6** $\frac{17}{25}$ **7** $\frac{5}{27}$ **8** $\frac{16}{33}$

9 $\frac{7}{110}$ **10** $\frac{7}{111}$ **11** $\frac{79}{250}$ **12** $\frac{79}{2500}$

13 $\frac{5}{7}$ **14** $\frac{79}{222}$ **15** $\frac{19}{11}$ **16** $\frac{73}{64}$

17 $\frac{1}{27} = 0.\dot{0}3\dot{7}$

Without using a calculator, find the decimal equivalent of

a) $\frac{2}{27}$ **b)** $\frac{5}{27}$.

18 Put these fractions into ascending order (smallest first).

$\frac{1}{3}, \frac{3}{10}, \frac{5}{18}, \frac{4}{11}, \frac{2}{7}, \frac{7}{19}, \frac{2}{5}, \frac{9}{24}$.

EXERCISE 1.1B

Convert these fractions to decimals. When the answers are recurring decimals, use the dot notation.

1 $\frac{7}{8}$ **2** $\frac{7}{9}$ **3** $\frac{9}{11}$ **4** $\frac{7}{32}$

5 $\frac{3}{80}$ **6** $\frac{17}{36}$ **7** $\frac{29}{125}$ **8** $\frac{23}{60}$

9 $\frac{37}{64}$ **10** $\frac{57}{132}$ **11** $\frac{7}{54}$ **12** $\frac{576}{625}$

13 $\frac{457}{1111}$ **14** $\frac{457}{1110}$ **15** $\frac{1}{303}$ **16** $\frac{813}{11111}$

17 $\frac{1}{3} = 0.\dot{3}$ and $\frac{1}{11} = 0.\dot{0}\dot{9}$.

Without using a calculator, find the decimal equivalent of

a) $\frac{2}{3}$ **b)** $\frac{2}{11}$ **c)** $\frac{5}{11}$ **d)** $\frac{6}{11}$.

18 Put these fractions in ascending order (smallest first).

$\frac{3}{5}, \frac{3}{4}, \frac{1}{2}, \frac{5}{9}, \frac{4}{7}, \frac{11}{18}, \frac{8}{15}$.

Decimals to fractions

All terminating and recurring decimals have fraction equivalents.

Example 5 illustrates the method of changing terminating decimals to fractions.

EXAMPLE 5

Find the equivalent fraction to 0·624.

From the definitions of the columns in decimals

$0·624 = \frac{6}{10} + \frac{2}{100} + \frac{4}{1000} = \frac{600}{1000} + \frac{20}{1000} + \frac{4}{1000} = \frac{624}{1000} = \frac{78}{125}$ (dividing top and bottom by 8)

The quick method is simply to write 624 over 1000 straight away since the 4 represents 'four thousandths'.

EXAMPLE 6

Convert **a)** 0·48

b) 0·035 into fractions.

a) $0·48 = \frac{48}{100} = \frac{12}{25}$

b) $0·035 = \frac{35}{1000} = \frac{7}{200}$

Converting recurring decimals to fractions is more difficult and the general method will be dealt with later. Only simple cases will be dealt with here.

These ones are worth remembering.

$0·\dot{3} = \frac{1}{3}$ $0·\dot{6} = \frac{2}{3}$ therefore $0·0\dot{3} = \frac{1}{30}$ $0·0\dot{6} = \frac{2}{30} = \frac{1}{15}$

$0·\dot{1} = \frac{1}{9}$ $0·\dot{2} = \frac{2}{9}$ $0·\dot{4} = \frac{4}{9}$ $0·\dot{5} = \frac{5}{9}$ and so on

therefore $0·0\dot{1} = \frac{1}{90}$ $0·0\dot{2} = \frac{2}{90}$ $0·0\dot{4} = \frac{4}{90}$ and so on

EXERCISE 1.2A

Convert the following to fractions in their lowest terms.

1 0·7   **2** 0·29
3 0·85   **4** 0·07
5 0·312   **6** 0·255
7 0·056   **8** 0·008
9 0·$\dot{7}$ **10** 0·0$\dot{7}$
11 $0·\dot{1} = \frac{1}{9}$ Write as fractions
    a) $0·\dot{2}$ **b)** $0·\dot{3}$ **c)** $0·\dot{5}$.

EXERCISE 1.2B

Convert the following to fractions in their lowest terms.

1 0·8   **2** 0·37
3 0·68   **4** 0·02
5 0·545   **6** 0·892
7 0·018   **8** 0·1345
9 0·$\dot{8}$ **10** 0·00$\dot{8}$
11 $0·0\dot{1}\dot{8} = \frac{1}{55}$ Write as fractions
    a) $0·03\dot{6}$ **b)** $0·05\dot{4}$ **c)** $0·30\dot{9}$.

Key ideas

- Recurring decimals are written using the dot notation, for example
  $0·33333333...... = 0·\dot{3}$ $0·342342342...... = 0·\dot{3}4\dot{2}$ $0·018181818...... = 0·0\dot{1}\dot{8}$.
- Terminating decimals are changed to fractions using the fraction that the last digit represents, for example $0·723 = \dfrac{723}{1000}$ because the digit 3 represents thousandths.

2 Accuracy

You should already know

- how to round a given number to the nearest unit or a given number of decimal places or significant figures
- convert one metric unit to another.

Discrete and continuous measures

Discrete measures can be counted. They can only take particular values.

Continuous measures include length, time and mass. They cannot be measured exactly.

Look at this table of some data for a bicycle.

In the table, the discrete measures are:

      number of wheels

      number of gears

      price

The continuous measures are: diameter of wheel

                              frame size

Number of wheels	2
Number of gears	15
Diameter of wheel	66 cm
Frame size	66 cm
Price	£99·99

Accuracy

Although the table does not make this clear, the frame size is given to the nearest centimetre. A less accurate measurement, such as to the nearest 10 cm, would not give enough information about the size of the bicycle. Someone wanting to buy a bicycle would not be able to tell whether it would be the right size for them. A more accurate measurement would be unnecessary in the context.

Exam tip

When giving the answers to practical situations, think what would be an appropriate degree of accuracy to use. Where there are no practical considerations, answers requiring rounding are usually given to three significant figures.

Similarly, giving a person's height to the nearest millimetre would not be sensible, since a person's height varies by more than a millimetre during the day.

When solving problems, the accuracy of your answer is limited by the accuracy of the data available. The answer cannot be accurate to more significant figures than the data. It is often accurate to one less significant figure.

EXAMPLE 1

Bryn is asked to calculate the hypotenuse of a right-angled triangle, for which the other two sides are given as 2·8 cm and 5·1 cm. To what accuracy should he give his answer?

The data are given to two significant figures, so his answer should be accurate to within one or two significant figures. An accuracy of one significant figure would give the answer to the nearest centimetre, which may not be sufficiently accurate. He should round to two significant figures, which is to the nearest millimetre.

EXERCISE 2.1A

In questions 1 and 2, look at the description from catalogues. For each measurement, identify whether the data are discrete or continuous.

1 Prestige 20 cm polyester golf bag, 6-way graphite-friendly top, 2 accessory pockets.

2 Black attaché case. 2 folio compartments, 3 pen holders, size (H) 3·15 cm, (W) 44·5 cm, (D) 11·5 cm.

Read this extract from a newspaper article.

Andy James has now scored 108 goals in just 167 games, making him the Town's most prolific scorer ever. In Saturday's game a penalty brought his first goal after 30 minutes, with Pete Jeffreys having been fouled. Six minutes later, James volleyed into the net again, after a flick on from Neil Matty, five yards outside the penalty box.

3 Give two examples of discrete data in the newspaper article.

4 Give three examples of continuous data in the article.

5 Write a description including two discrete measurements and three continuous measurements.

6 What is the appropriate degree of accuracy for the length of a line that could be drawn on this page?
   a) to the nearest cm
   b) to the nearest 10 cm
   c) to the nearest mm
   d) to the nearest 0·1 mm

7 To what degree of accuracy would a field be measured?

Exercise 2.1A cont'd

8 What is the usual degree of accuracy on road signs
   a) on motorways
   b) on country lane signposts?

9 For teenagers, what is the usual degree of accuracy for giving their age?

10 What is the usual degree of accuracy for measuring flour in cake recipes?

EXERCISE 2.1B

In questions 1 and 2, look at the descriptions from catalogues. For each measurement, identify whether it is discrete or continuous.

1 16 piece dinner set, 4 dinner plates (dia. 24·5 cm), side plates and bowls.

2 Food blender, 1·5 litre working capacity, 3 speed settings, 400 watt.

Read this extract from a newspaper article.

Lightning killed two people in Hyde Park yesterday as storms swept the Southeast, where 1.75 in of rain fell in 48 hours. In Pagham winds of up to 120 m.p.h. damaged more than 50 houses and bungalows and several boats. One catamaran was flung 100 ft into the air and landed in a tree.

3 Give two examples of discrete data in the newspaper article.

4 Give three examples of continuous data in the article.

5 Write a description including three discrete measurements and two continuous measurements.

6 What is the appropriate degree of accuracy for a waist measurement?
   a) to the nearest cm
   b) to the nearest 10 cm
   c) to the nearest mm
   d) to the nearest 0·1 mm

7 To what degree of accuracy is the length of a garden usually given?

8 To what degree of accuracy is **a)** a baby's **b)** an adult's mass usually given?

9 To what degree of accuracy would the time for the winner of a 50 m swimming race normally be given?

10 To what degree of accuracy is body temperature usually given?

Bounds of measurement

ACTIVITY 1

Write down three numbers which round to each of these.

a) 26   **b)** 26·5   **c)** 43   **d)** 43.0   **e)** 50

Suppose a measurement is given as 26 cm 'to the nearest centimetre'. This means the next possible measurements on either side are 25 cm and 27 cm. Where does the boundary between these measurements lie?

Any measurement that is nearer to 26 cm than to 25 cm or 27 cm will be counted as 26 cm. This is the marked interval on the number line.

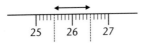

The boundaries of this interval are 25·5 cm and 26·5 cm. These values are exactly halfway between one measurement and the next. Usually when rounding to a given number of decimal places or significant figures, you would round 25·5 up to 26 and 26·5 up to 27.

So this gives:

The interval for 26 cm to the nearest centimetre is m cm where $25\cdot5 \leqslant m < 26\cdot5$.

25·5 cm is called the **lower bound** of the interval.

26·5 cm is called the **upper bound** of the interval (although it is not actually included in the interval).

EXAMPLE 2

Simon won the 200 m race in his year in a time of 24·2 s, to the nearest tenth of a second.

Complete the sentence below:

Simon's time was between … s and … s.

As the measurement is stated to the nearest tenth of a second, the next possible

times are 24·1 s and 24·3 s.

Simon's time was between 24·15 s and 24·25 s.

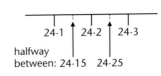

EXERCISE 2.2A

Give the upper and lower bounds of the measurements in questions 1 to 5.

1 Given to the nearest centimetre

   a) 27 cm   **b)** 30 cm
   c) 128 cm

2 Given to the nearest 10 cm

   a) 10 cm   **b)** 30 cm
   c) 150 cm

3 Given to the nearest millimetre

   a) 5·6 cm   **b)** 0·8 cm
   c) 12·0 cm

4 Given to the nearest centimetre

   a) 1·23 m   **b)** 0·45 m
   c) 9·08 m

5 Given to the nearest hundredth of a second

   a) 10·62 s   **b)** 9·81 s
   c) 48·10 s

Complete the sentences in questions 6 to 10.

6 A mass given as 57 kg to the nearest kilogram is between … kg and … kg.

7 A height given as 4·7 m to two significant figures is between … m and … m.

8 A volume given as 468 ml (to the nearest ml) is between … ml and … ml.

9 A winning time given as 34·91 s to the nearest hundredth of a second is between … s and … s.

10 A mass given as 0·634 kg to the nearest gram is between … kg and … kg.

11 Write down the smallest and largest numbers which will round to 100 if it is corrected to

   a) 3 significant figures
   b) 2 significant figures
   c) 1 significant figure.

EXERCISE 2.2B

Give the upper and lower bounds of the measurements in questions 1 to 5.

1 Given to the nearest centimetre

   a) 34 cm   **b)** 92 cm
   c) 210 cm

2 Given to the nearest 10 cm

   a) 20 cm   **b)** 60 cm
   c) 210 cm

3 Given to the nearest millimetre

   a) 2·7 cm   **b)** 0·2 cm
   c) 18·0 cm

Exercise 2.2B cont'd

4   Given to the nearest centimetre

   a) 8·17 m   **b)** 0·36 m
   c) 2·04 m

5   Given to the nearest hundredth of a second

   a) 15·61 s   **b)** 12·10 s
   c) 54·07 s

Complete the sentences in questions 6 to 10.

6   A mass given as 64 kg to the nearest kilogram is between … kg and … kg.

7   A height given as 8·3 m to two significant figures is between … m and … m.

8   A volume given as 234 ml (to the nearest ml) is between … ml and … ml.

9   A winning time given is 27·94 s to the nearest hundredth of a second is between … s and … s.

10 A mass given as 0·256 kg to the nearest gram is between … kg and … kg.

11 Write down four numbers that round to 60, stating how many significant figures you have used.

12 Tom measures his pencil to be 18 cm and his pencil case states a length of 18·5 cm. Can he be sure that his pencil will fit in inside his case? Explain your answer.

13 A chimney sweep uses a pole made up of ten identical, flexible pieces. Each piece is 1 metre long, measured to the nearest cm. What height of chimney can you be sure that he could reach?

Key ideas

- Discrete measures can be counted. They can only take particular values.
- Continuous measures include length, time, mass and so on. They cannot be measured exactly.
- When giving the answers to practical situations, think what is an appropriate degree of accuracy to use. Where there are no practical considerations, answers requiring rounding are usually given to three significant figures.
- A time of 5·47 s to the nearest one-hundredth of a second lies between 5·465 and 5·475 s.

3 Cubic and reciprocal graphs

You should already know

- how to plot and read points using (x, y) coordinates
- how to substitute numbers into equations.

Cubic graphs

EXAMPLE 1

a) Draw the graph of $y = x^3$ for values of x from $^-3$ to 3.
   Label the x-axis from $^-3$ to 3 and the y-axis from $^-30$ to 30.

b) Use your graph to solve the equation $x^3 = 12$. Give your answer to one decimal place.

a)

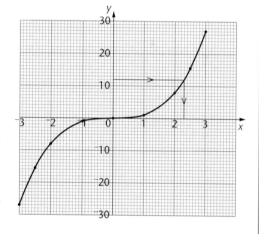

x	$^-3$	$^-2{\cdot}5$	$^-2$	$^-1$	0	1	2	$2{\cdot}5$	3
$y = x^3$	$^-27$	$^-15{\cdot}6$	$^-8$	$^-1$	0	1	8	$15{\cdot}6$	27

The outside points are a long way apart and plotting the values for $2{\cdot}5$ and $^-2{\cdot}5$ helps with the drawing of the curve.

b) To solve $x^3 = 12$, you need to draw across from $y = 12$ to the curve and then down to the x-axis.

Answer $x = 2{\cdot}3$

Notice the shape of the curve in Example 1. It goes from bottom left to top right and has a 'double bend' in the middle. All cubic curves with a positive x^3 term have a similar shape.

If the x^3 term is negative the curve goes from top left to bottom right.

Notice that, the y-scale is not the same as the x-scale. This is because the y-values are much larger than the x-values.

EXAMPLE 2

a) Draw the graph of $y = x^3 - 2x$ for values of x from $^-2$ to 2. Label the x-axis from $^-2$ to 2 and the y-axis from $^-4$ to 4.

b) Use the graph to solve the equation $x^3 - 2x = 0$. Give your answers correct to one decimal place.

a)

x	$^-2$	$^-1$	0	1	2	$^-0.5$	0.5
x^3	$^-8$	$^-1$	0	1	8	$^-0.125$	0.125
^-2x	4	2	0	$^-2$	$^-4$	1	$^-1$
$y = x^3 - 2x$	$^-4$	1	0	$^-1$	4	0.875	$^-0.875$

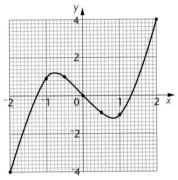

It helps to see more clearly where the curve is highest and lowest if you work out the values of y for $x = ^-0.5$ and $x = 0.5$.
The graph is drawn here with a scale of 1 cm to 1 unit for x and 1 cm to 2 units for y.

b) To solve $x^3 - 2x = 0$, you need to find where $y = x^3 - 2x$ crosses $y = 0$, which is the x-axis.
From the graph, the answers are $x = ^-1.4$ or 0 or $x = 1.4$

The shape of the curve is similar to the one in Example 1. The ^-2x term makes the 'double bend' more pronounced.

Reciprocal graphs

EXAMPLE 3

Draw the graph of $y = \dfrac{4}{x}$.

x	$^-4$	$^-3$	$^-2$	$^-1$	1	2	3	4
$y = \dfrac{4}{x}$	$^-1$	$^-1.3$	$^-2$	$^-4$	4	2	1.3	1

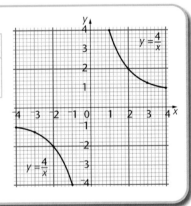

You cannot use 0 as a point in this type of graph, since you cannot divide 4 (or any other number) by 0. Again it is helpful to work out extra points to give a better curve. In this case you might work out the value of y when $x = ^-1.5$ and 1.5, giving y-values of $^-2.7$ and 2.7 to one decimal place.
It is also useful to have the same scale for both x and y in this case.

All equations of this type ($y = \dfrac{a}{x}$) have graphs of the same shape.

There are two separate branches, one in the top right quadrant and one in the bottom left quadrant. Plotting points for $x = 0.5$ and $x = 0.1$ would show that the curve gets closer to the axes without ever meeting them.

EXERCISE 3.1A

1 **a)** Copy and complete the table for $y = x^3 + 5$.

x	⁻3	⁻2	⁻1	0	1	2	3
x³	⁻27			0		8	
+5	+5						
y	⁻22						

b) Draw the graph of $y = x^3 + 5$.
c) Use your graph to solve the equation $x^3 + 5 = 0$.

2 **a)** Copy and complete the table for $y = -x^3$.

x	⁻3	⁻2	⁻1	0	1	2	3
x³	⁻27			0		8	
y	27						

b) Draw the graph of $y = -x^3$.
c) Use your graph to solve the equation $-x^3 = 6$.

3 Draw up a table of values for $y = x^3 - 12x + 2$, for $x = ⁻3$ to 4. Do not draw the graph.

4 Draw up a table of values for $y = x^3 - x^2 + 5$, for $x = ⁻2$ to 4. Do not draw the graph.

5 Draw up a table of values for $y = \dfrac{8}{x}$ for $x = ⁻8, ⁻4, ⁻2, ⁻1, 1, 2, 4, 8$. Do not draw the graph.

6 **a)** Draw the graph of $y = x^3 - 12x + 2$, for $x = ⁻3$ to 4.
b) Solve the equation $x^3 - 12x + 2 = 0$.

7 Draw the graph of $y = \dfrac{8}{x}$ for values of x from ⁻8 to 8. Use a scale of 1 cm to 1 unit on both axes.

8 **a)** Draw up a table of values for $y = \dfrac{5}{x}$ for $x = ⁻5, ⁻4, ⁻2\cdot5, ⁻2, ⁻1, 1, 2, 2\cdot5, 4, 5$.
b) Draw the graph of $y = \dfrac{5}{x}$. Use a scale of 1 cm to 1 unit on both axes.
c) On the same grid, draw the graph of $y = x$.
d) Use your graph to solve $x^2 = 5$, giving the answers to one decimal place.

Remember: always draw up a table of values.

9 **a)** Draw the graph of $y = x^3 - 3x$, for $x = ⁻3$ to 3.
b) Solve the equation $x^3 - 3x = 0$.

10 **a)** Draw the graph of $y = x^3 - 4x$ for values of x from ⁻3 to 3.
b) Use the graph to solve the equation $x^3 - 4x - 2 = 0$.

Chapter 3 *Cubic and reciprocal graphs*

EXERCISE 3.1B

1 a) Copy and complete the table for $y = x^3 - 4$.

x	⁻3	⁻2	⁻1	0	1	2	3
x³	⁻27			0		8	
–4	⁻4						
y	⁻31						

b) Draw the graph of $y = x^3 - 4$.
c) Use your graph to solve the equation $x^3 - 4 = 0$.

2 a) Draw the graph of $y = 4 - x^3$ for $x = {}^-3$ to $x = 3$.
b) Use your graph to solve the equation $4 - x^3 = {}^-15$.

3 a) Copy and complete the table of values for $y = \dfrac{1}{x}$.

x	⁻10	⁻5	⁻2	⁻1	⁻0·5	⁻0·1	0·1	0·5	1	2	5	10
$Y = \dfrac{1}{x}$						⁻10					0·2	

b) Draw the graph of $y = \dfrac{1}{x}$.
Use a scale of 1 cm to 2 units on both axes.
c) Use your graph to solve
(i) $\dfrac{1}{x} = 0·3$, **(ii)** $\dfrac{1}{x} = {}^-5$.

4 Draw up a table of values of $y = x^3 - 3x + 4$, for $x = {}^-3$ to 4. Do not draw the graph.

5 Draw up a table of values for $y = x^3 + 2x^2 - 3$, for $x = {}^-4$ to 2. Do not draw the graph.

6 a) Draw up a table of values for $y = x^3 - x^2 - 6x$, for $x = {}^-3$ to 4. Draw the graph.
b) Use the graph to solve the equation $x^3 - x^2 - 6x = 0$.

7 a) Draw up a table of values for $y = \dfrac{12}{x}$, for $x = {}^-12, {}^-8, {}^-6, {}^-4, {}^-3, {}^-2, {}^-1, 1, 2, 3, 4, 6, 8, 12$.
b) Draw the graph.

8 a) On the same grid, draw the graphs of $y = x^3$ and $y = 5x$, for $x = {}^-3$ to 3.
b) (i) Show that when the two curves cross the equation is $x^3 - 5x = 0$.
(ii) Find the solution to the equation $x^3 - 5x = 0$, giving the answer correct to one decimal place.

Exercise 3.1B cont'd

9 **a)** Draw the graph of
$y = x^3 - 8x + 12$ for values of
x from $^-3$ to 3.

b) Use the graph to solve the
equation $x^3 - 8x = 0$, giving
the answers correct to one
decimal place.

10 In this question accurate plotting
is **not** required.

a) On the same axes sketch the
graphs of $y = x^3$ and $y = \dfrac{10}{x}$.

b) Use your sketch to find out
how many solutions there
are to the equation $x^3 = \dfrac{10}{x}$.

11 Here are four equations.

① $y = x^2(x + 5)$ ② $y = x^3$

③ $y = \dfrac{6}{x}$ ④ $y = x^3 + 2$

The graphs of these equations are
sketched here. They are not in
the correct order. State which
graph goes with which equation.

a)   **b)**

c)    **d)**

Key ideas

- Always draw up a table of values
before you plot a graph.

- Cubic graphs have the basic shapes
shown here.

  x^3 term positive x^3 term negative

  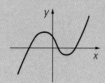   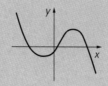

- Reciprocal
graphs are
shaped like this.

Chapter 3 *Cubic and reciprocal graphs*

4 Indices

You should already know

- the terms 'square number' and 'cube number'
- the meaning of a power such as 2^2 and 2^3.

Indices (or powers) are a form of mathematical shorthand:

$3 \times 3 \times 3 \times 3$ is written as 3^4 and

$2 \times 2 \times 2 \times 2 \times 2 \times 2 \times 2 \times 2$ is written as 2^8.

ACTIVITY 1

Example: $2^2 \times 2^5 = (2 \times 2) \times (2 \times 2 \times 2 \times 2 \times 2) = 2^7$.

By writing the powers out fully like this $2^3 = 2 \times 2 \times 2$, find the missing powers indicated with question marks.

a) $2^3 \times 2^2 = 2^?$ **b)** $2^4 \times 2^5 = 2^?$ **c)** $3^6 \div 3^4 = 3^?$ **d)** $4^8 \div 4^3 = 4^?$ **e)** $(3^3)^2 = 3^?$

Multiplying numbers in index form

$$3^4 \times 3^8 = (3 \times 3 \times 3 \times 3) \times (3 \times 3 \times 3 \times 3 \times 3 \times 3 \times 3 \times 3)$$
$$= 3 \times 3 \times 3 \times 3 \times 3 \times 3 \times 3 \times 3 \times 3 \times 3 \times 3 \times 3$$
$$= 3^{12}$$

The indices or powers are added: $3^4 \times 3^8 = 3^{4+8} = 3^{12}$

The rule is $n^a \times n^b = n^{a+b}$

Powers of numbers can also be raised to powers.

If the numbers are in brackets then powers are multiplied.

EXAMPLE 1

$(3^4)^2 = (3^4) \times (3^4) = 3^8$ and $3^{4\times2} = 3^8$

The rule is $(n^a)^b = n^{a\times b}$

Dividing numbers in index form

$2^6 \div 2^4 = (2 \times 2 \times 2 \times 2 \times 2 \times 2)$
$\qquad\qquad \div (2 \times 2 \times 2 \times 2)$

$\qquad = 2 \times 2$

$\qquad = 2^2$

so $2^6 \div 2^4 = 2^{(6-4)}$

$\qquad\qquad = 2^2$

The rule is $n^a \div n^b = n^{a-b}$

EXERCISE 4.1A

1 Write these in a simpler form, using indices.

  a) $3 \times 3 \times 3 \times 3 \times 3$

  b) $7 \times 7 \times 7$

  c) $8 \times 8 \times 8 \times 8 \times 8$

  d) $3 \times 3 \times 5 \times 5 \times 5$

  e) $2 \times 2 \times 2 \times 3 \times 3 \times 4 \times 4$
  $\qquad \times 4 \times 4 \times 4$

2 Write these in a simpler form, using indices.

  a) $5^2 \times 5^3$ **b)** $6^2 \times 6^7$

  c) $10^3 \times 10^4$ **d)** $3^6 \times 3^5$

  e) $8^3 \times 8^2$

3 Work these out, giving your answers in index form.

  a) $\dfrac{3^9}{3^5 \times 3^2}$ **b)** $\dfrac{(2^3)^4}{2^5}$

  c) $\dfrac{5^4 \times 5^5}{5^2 \times 5^3}$

4 Write as a single power of a.

  a) $a^2 \times a^3$ **b)** $a^4 \times a^5$

  c) $a^6 \div a^4$ **d)** $a^7 \div a^3$

5 Simplify these. Your answers to question 4 will help.

  a) $2a^2 \times 3a^3$ **b)** $4a^4 \times 3a^5$

  c) $6a^6 \div 2a^4$ **d)** $10a^7 \div 5a^3$

EXERCISE 4.1B

1 Write these in a simpler form, using indices.

  a) $4 \times 4 \times 4 \times 4 \times 4$ **d)** $5 \times 4 \times 4 \times 4 \times 5$

  b) $8 \times 8 \times 8$ **e)** $7 \times 7 \times 7 \times 8 \times 8 \times 9 \times 9 \times 9$

  c) $2 \times 2 \times 2 \times 2 \times 2$

Exercise 4.1B cont'd

2 Write these in a simpler form, using indices.

a) $4^2 \times 4^3$ b) $9^2 \times 9^7$

c) $10^5 \times 10^2$ d) $3^5 \times 3^2$

e) $8^4 \times 8^2$ f) $6^2 \times 6^6$

g) $7^5 \div 7^3$ h) $6^3 \div 6^2$

3 Work these out, giving your answers in index form.

a) $\dfrac{4^{12}}{4^5 \times 4^4}$ b) $\dfrac{(2^4)^2}{2^4}$

c) $\dfrac{6^5 \times 6^4}{6^2 \times 6}$

4 Write as a single power of a.

a) $a^4 \times a^2$ b) $a^3 \times a^6$

c) $a^8 \div a^2$ d) $a^5 \div a^2$

5 Simplify these. Your answers to question 4 will help.

a) $3a^4 \times 4a^2$ b) $5a^3 \times 3a^6$

c) $6a^8 \div 3a^2$ d) $12a^5 \div 4a^2$

Powers and roots

The set of numbers 1, 4, 9, 16, 25, 36, 49, 64, 81, 100, 121, 144, 169, 196, 225, … are 'squares' of the counting numbers as you can see from this table.

Number	1	4	9	16	25	36	49	64	81	100	121	144	169	196	225
Square	1^2	2^2	3^2	4^2	5^2	6^2	7^2	8^2	9^2	10^2	11^2	12^2	13^2	14^2	15^2

and so on.

You are expected to know the squares up to $15^2 = 225$ so you should learn these.

Because $16 = 4^2$ the 'square root' of 16 is 4. This is written as $\sqrt{16} = 4$.

Similarly $\sqrt{36} = 6$ and $\sqrt{81} = 9$.

But $(^-4)^2 = 16$ as well as $4^2 = 16$. It follows that the square root of 16 could be 4 or $^-4$. This is often written ±4. Similarly the square root of 81 = ±9.

The numbers 1, 8, 27, 64, 125, …, 1000, … are cube numbers because each of them can be written as the cube of a whole number.

Exam tip

In many practical problems where the answers are square roots, the negative answer would not have a meaning and so it should be left out.

Number	1	8	27	64	125	....	1000	....
Cube	1^3	2^3	3^3	4^3	5^3	....	10^3	....

The cube numbers shown are the ones you are expected to remember and so you should learn them.

Because $27 = 3^3$ the cube root of 27 is 3. This is written as $\sqrt[3]{27} = 3$.

You may get easy square roots and cube roots in the non-calculator section of the paper, but make sure you can find the $\boxed{\sqrt{}}$ and $\boxed{\sqrt[3]{}}$ button on your calculator.

On older calculators you may have to put the number in first and then press the correct button. On most modern calculators you press the root button, then the number, then $\boxed{=}$.

So $\boxed{\sqrt{}}$ $\boxed{52}$ $\boxed{=}$ $7 \cdot 211\ldots$

EXERCISE 4.2A

1 Write down the square of each number.

a) 7 **b)** 12 **c)** 8
d) 11 **e)** $\sqrt{10}$

2 Write down the square root of each number.

a) 36 **b)** 81 **c)** 169
d) 196 **e)** 23^2

3 Write down the cube of each number.

a) 4 **b)** 5 **c)** 3
d) 10 **e)** $\sqrt[3]{18}$

4 Write down the cube root of each number.

a) 8 **b)** 1 **c)** 64
d) 1000 **e)** 20^3

5 Find the area of a square of side 4 mm.

6 I think of a number, I find its cube root and then square that. The answer is 9. What is the number I thought of?

7 Solve the equation $x^2 = 81$.

EXERCISE 4.2B

1 Write down the square of each number.

a) 25 **b)** 40 **c)** 35
d) 50 **e)** 73

2 Write down the square root of each number.

a) 400 **b)** 289 **c)** 361
d) 10 000 **e)** 7921

Chapter 4 *Indices*

Exercise 4.2B cont'd

3 Write down the cube of each number.

a) 7 **b)** 9 **c)** 20 **d)** 25
e) 1·5 **f)** 2·7 **g)** 5·4

4 Write down the cube root of each number.

a) 343 **b)** 729
c) 1331 **d)** 1 000 000 **e)** 216
f) 1728 **g)** 512

5 Work these out, giving your answer to two decimal places.

a) $\sqrt{56}$ **b)** $\sqrt{27}$ **c)** $\sqrt{60}$
d) $\sqrt{70}$ **e)** $\sqrt{39}$ **f)** $\sqrt{90}$
g) $\sqrt{280}$ **h)** $\sqrt{678}$ **i)** $\sqrt{380}$
j) $\sqrt{456}$

6 Find the length of a square of area 14 cm^2. Write your answer to 3 significant figures.

7 Find the length of a cube whose volume is 45 cm^3. Write your answer to 3 significant figures.

8 Put these numbers in ascending order.

2^3, 3^2, 4^2, $\sqrt{25}$, $\sqrt[3]{343}$, 5^2.

9 **a)** Which number is $3^2 \times 4^2$?
b) Write 36 as a product of prime factors.

10 Find two numbers less than 200 which are both square numbers and cube numbers.

11 Find $(\sqrt[3]{16})^3$. You should be able to do it without a calculator. If you could not, try it with a calculator. What do you notice?

Key ideas

- To multiply using powers use the rule $n^a \times n^b = n^{a+b}$.
- To divide using powers use the rule $n^a \div n^b = n^{a-b}$.
- You should know the squares from 1^2 to 15^2.
- You should know the values 2^3, 3^3, 4^3, 5^3 and 10^3.
- You should know where the square root and cube root buttons are on your calculator.

Revision exercise

1 Convert these fractions to decimals. When the decimals recur, use the dot notation.

a) $\frac{1}{8}$ **b)** $\frac{3}{11}$ **c)** $\frac{21}{125}$

d) $\frac{17}{33}$ **e)** $\frac{5}{32}$ **f)** $\frac{63}{132}$

2 Convert these decimals to fractions in their lowest terms.

a) 0.02 **b)** $0.\dot{6}$ **c)** $0.0\dot{6}$

d) 0.72 **e)** 0.027 **f)** 0.1825

3 The dimensions of a picture frame were given as 17 cm and 28 cm. Assuming these were given to the nearest centimetre, what is the least these dimensions could be?

4 A length is stated as between 6·805 cm and 6·815 cm.

a) What measurement would be recorded?

b) What is its degree of accuracy?

5 A boy gives his mass at 52·3 kg to 3 significant figures. Give upper and lower bounds for his mass.

6 What would be an appropriate degree of accuracy to measure

a) the length of your desk top

b) the distance from Manchester to London?

7 **a)** Draw the graph of $y = x^3 - 7x$ for values of x from $^-3$ to 3.

b) Use your graph to solve the equation $x^3 - 7x = 0$.

8 Sketch the graphs of these curves.

a) $y = x^3$ **b)** $y = \dfrac{12}{x}$

9 Match these graphs with the correct equation.

a) 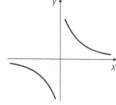 **b)**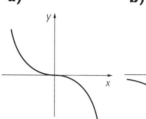

c) 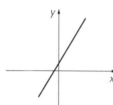 **d)**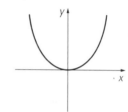

(i) $y = 2x^2$ **(ii)** $y = 2x + 1$

(iii) $y = {}^-2x^3$ **(iv)** $y = \dfrac{2}{x}$

10 Write these numbers in simpler form.

a) $7^2 \times 7^3$ **b)** $6^3 \times 6^6$

c) $10^9 \times 10^3$ **d)** $3^4 \times 3^8$

e) $8^9 \div 8^3$ **f)** $6^9 \div 6^7$

g) $4^3 \div 4^2$ **h)** $9^6 \div 9^2$

i) $\dfrac{3^7 \times 3^3}{3^4}$

11 Simplify

a) $x^2 \times x^4$ **b)** $x^5 \div x^2$

c) $3a^3 \times 4a^2$ **d)** $6y^5 \div 2y^2$

12 Without using a calculator, write down

a) $\sqrt{121}$ **b)** 14^2 **c)** $\sqrt{169}$

d) $\sqrt[3]{64}$

5 Probability

You should already know

- probabilities are expressed as fractions, decimals or percentages
- all probabilities lie on a scale of 0 to 1 (0 to 100%)
- how to find probability from a set of equally likely outcomes
- the probability of an outcome happening is 1 – the probability of the outcome not happening
- what mutually exclusive events are
- if events A, B and C are mutually exclusive and cover all possible outcomes then P(A) + P(B) + P(C) = 1
- how to add and subtract simple fractions.

Tree diagrams

In this method 'branches' are drawn from a starting point to show the possibilities for the first trial. From the end of each of the first branches, further branches are drawn showing each of the possibilities for the second trial, and so on.

The tree diagram for tossing two coins looks like this:

The probabilities are $\frac{1}{4}$ because there are 4 equally likely outcomes.

The advantages of a tree diagram are:

- it can easily be extended for a third and subsequent trials
- it can also be used when the outcomes are not equally likely.

1st coin	2nd coin	Probabilities
H	H	$\frac{1}{4}$
	T	$\frac{1}{4}$
T	H	$\frac{1}{4}$
	T	$\frac{1}{4}$

The main disadvantage of a tree diagram is that it can look very messy if there are two many possibilities. For example it is difficult to organise in the case of throwing two dice. However, if there are only two or three possible outcomes for each trial it is often the best method.

Exam tip

When drawing a tree diagram:

1 allow plenty of space on the page
2 always line up the possibilities for each trial underneath each other
3 for the first trial, draw the branches to points approximately $\frac{1}{4}$ way from the top of your space to $\frac{1}{4}$ way from the bottom of your space.

EXAMPLE 1

Fatima throws an ordinary die and tosses a coin. Show the possible outcomes on a tree diagram and find the probability that

a) Fatima scores a 6 and a head, which can be written P(6 and head)

b) Fatima scores an odd number and a tail.

a) P(6 and head) = $\frac{1}{12}$ since there are 12 equally likely outcomes.

b) P(odd number and tail) = P[(1, T) or (3, T) or (5, T)]
= $\frac{3}{12}$ = $\frac{1}{4}$

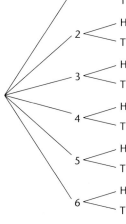

EXAMPLE 2

Rachel is selecting a main course and a sweet from this menu.

MENU

Main Course
Sausage & Chips
Ham Salad
Vegetable Lasagne

Sweet
Apple Pie
Fruit Salad

Draw a tree diagram to show Rachel's possible selections. If she is equally likely to select any of the choices, what is the probability that she selects Vegetable Lasagne and Apple Pie?

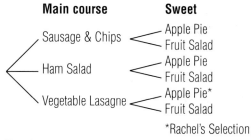

*Rachel's Selection

Therefore there are six possible outcomes.

P(Vegetable Lasagne and Apple Pie) = $\frac{1}{6}$

EXERCISE 5.1A

1 Mr and Mrs Green plan to have two children. Copy and complete the tree diagram for the possible sexes of the children.

Assuming that all outcomes are equally likely find the probability that **a)** both children are girls, **b)** Mr and Mrs Green have one child of each sex.

Exercise 5.1A cont'd

2 In tennis one player must win; a draw is not possible. Alex plays three games of tennis against Meiling. Copy and complete the tree diagram to show the possible winners of the games.

1st game   2nd game   3rd game

A
M

Assuming each player is equally likely to win any game, find the probability that

a) Alex wins all three games

b) Alex wins one and loses two.

3 Marie can choose a sweet from each of two bags. In the first bag are an equal number of toffees and jelly babies. In the second bag are an equal number of fruit pastilles, mints and pear drops.

a) Draw a tree diagram to show the results of Marie's two choices.

b) What is the probability that she chooses a jelly baby and a mint?

4 Lisa travels to school by bus or walks, or her mother takes her by car. To go home she either walks or goes by bus. Copy and complete the tree diagram to show her possible methods of travel.

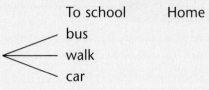
To school   Home
bus
walk
car

If she is equally likely to travel by any of the methods, find the probability that she goes by bus both ways.

5 Nicola is choosing from this menu.

MAIN COURSE & SWEET FOR £6·50	
Main Course	**Sweet**
Chicken Chow Mein	Banana Fritter
Sweet & Sour Pork	Ice Cream
Vegetable Curry	

Draw a tree diagram to show her possible choices.

You could use the initial letters, for example CCM, to save you writing the names in full. Assuming she is equally likely to choose any of the items, find the probability that she chooses Vegetable Curry and Ice Cream.

EXERCISE 5.1B

1 Anne tosses three coins. Draw a tree diagram to show the result of the three tosses. Find the probability that Anne tosses
a) three heads
b) two heads and a tail.

2

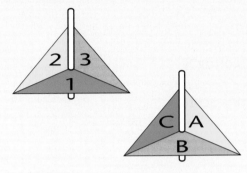

In a game, Bobbie spins both of the spinners. Draw a tree diagram showing all the possible outcomes. What is the probability of getting a B and a 3?

3 Mike and Fiona are planning a fundraising event. It will be held in May or June. They are deciding between a sponsored walk or swim or cycle ride. Since they cannot agree they decide to choose randomly. Copy and complete the tree diagram to show the possible choices. What is the probability that they choose a walk in June?

4 Asif is choosing his year 10 options.

In Pool A he can choose Business Studies, ICT or Design.

In Pool B he can choose History or Geography or Economics.

Copy and complete the tree diagram to show his possible choices.

Assuming that he is equally likely to choose any of the subjects, find the probability that Asif chooses ICT and History.

Pool A   Pool B

BS

ICT

D

5 Mr Jones is choosing his new company car. He can choose a Vauxhall or a Ford or a Nissan. He can choose red or blue. Draw a tree diagram to show his possible choices. If he chooses randomly, what is the probability that he chooses **a)** a red Ford **b)** a blue car?

Probability of event A *or* event B happening

Look at the grid for throwing two dice.

Suppose Louise needs a score of 8 or 11. Out of a total of 36 possible outcomes, there are seven that give 8 or 11.

The probability of scoring 8 or 11 is therefore $\frac{7}{36}$.

But the probability of scoring 8 is $\frac{5}{36}$ and the probability of scoring 11 is $\frac{2}{36}$.

and $\frac{5}{36} + \frac{2}{36} = \frac{7}{36}$

So P(8 or 11) = P(8) + P(11)

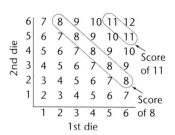

If the two events are 'scoring a double' or 'scoring 8' the situation is different.

There are ten outcomes that give a double or a score of 8 and therefore:

P(double or 8) = $\frac{10}{36}$ P(double) = $\frac{6}{36}$ P(8) = $\frac{5}{36}$

and $\frac{6}{36} + \frac{5}{36}$ does not equal $\frac{10}{36}$.

So P(double or 8) does not equal P(double) + P(8).

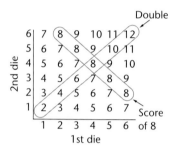

This is because the events 'scoring a double' and 'scoring 8' are not mutually exclusive events. It is possible to do both by throwing a double 4.

The addition rule only applies to mutually exclusive events.

> If events A and B are mutually exclusive then P(A or B) = P(A) + P(B)

Independent events

If two coins are tossed, the way the first one lands cannot possibly affect the way the second one lands.

Similarly, if two dice are thrown, the way the first one lands cannot possibly affect the way the second one lands.

If there are six red balls and four black balls in a bag, and one is selected and replaced before a second one is selected, the probability of getting a red ball is exactly the same on the second choice as on the first: $\frac{6}{10}$.

> When an event is unaffected by what has happened in another event, the events are said to be **independent**.

In the example of six red balls and four black ones, if the first ball is not replaced then the probability of getting a red ball on the second draw is no longer $\frac{6}{10}$ as there are fewer balls in the bag.

> In this case the events are **dependent**.

Probability of event A *and* event B happening

In Example 1 Fatima tossed a coin and threw a die. Since there were 12 equally likely outcomes, and scoring a head and a 6 was one of them, it was concluded that:

P(head and a 6) = $\frac{1}{12}$

Now P(head) = $\frac{1}{2}$ and P(6) = $\frac{1}{6}$

But $\frac{1}{2} \times \frac{1}{6} = \frac{1}{12}$ so P(head and a 6) = P(head) × P(6)

> When two coins are tossed the possible outcomes are (H, H) (H, T) (T, H) and (T, T).

P(2 head) = $\frac{1}{4}$

Now P(head) = $\frac{1}{2}$

But $\frac{1}{2} \times \frac{1}{2} = \frac{1}{4}$ so P(2 heads) = P(head) × P(head)

These results are only true because the events are independent. If they were dependent events, the second probability in the multiplication sum would be different.

> For independent events P(A and B) = P(A) × P(B)

Clearly it is more of a coincidence to throw two heads than one, so it is to be expected that the probability will be less. Multiplying fractions and decimals less than one gives a smaller answer, whereas adding them gives a bigger answer.

The result for events A and B extends to more than two events. For example in Exercise 5.1B, question 1 you should have found that when tossing three coins, the probability of getting all three heads is $\frac{1}{8}$.

P(head) × P(head) × P(head) = $\frac{1}{2} \times \frac{1}{2} \times \frac{1}{2} = \frac{1}{8}$

So included in the multiply rule are words such as 'both' and 'all'.

Exam tip

It is very common for examination candidates to add probabilities when they should have multiplied. If you get an answer to a probability question that is more than one you have almost certainly added instead of multiplied.

EXAMPLE 3

The probability that the school hockey team will win their next match is 0·4. The probability that they draw their next match is 0·3. What is the probability that they will win or draw their next match?

The events are mutually exclusive, since they cannot both win and draw their next match, so:

P(win or draw) = P(win) + P(draw) = 0·3 + 0·4 = 0·7

EXAMPLE 4

Matt spins the fair spinner shown in the picture twice.

What is the probability that Matt scores a 4 on both his spins?

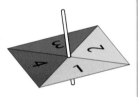

The events are independent, since the second spin cannot be affected by the first.

P(4 and 4) = P(4) × P(4) = $\frac{1}{4}$ × $\frac{1}{4}$ = $\frac{1}{16}$

EXAMPLE 5

There are six red balls and four black balls in a bag. Gina selects a ball, notes its colour and replaces it. She then selects another ball. What is the probability that Gina selects:

a) two red balls

b) one of each colour?

Since Gina replaces her first ball before choosing the second the events are independent.

a) P(2 reds) = P(red) × P(red) = $\frac{6}{10}$ × $\frac{6}{10}$ = $\frac{36}{100}$
= $\frac{9}{25}$ or in decimals 0·6 × 0·6 = 0·36

b) Before doing this question it is important to think about what the outcomes are.

Gina requires   first ball red and second ball black
or   first ball black and second ball red.

Both the add and multiply rules are needed.

P(one of each colour) = ($\frac{6}{10}$ × $\frac{4}{10}$) + ($\frac{4}{10}$ × $\frac{6}{10}$)
= $\frac{24}{100}$ + $\frac{24}{100}$ = $\frac{48}{100}$ = $\frac{12}{25}$ or in decimals (0·6 × 0·4) +
(0·4 × 0·6) = 0·24 + 0·24 = 0·48

Questions like part (b) of Example 5, which requires both rules, are clearly more difficult. Later you will see that these can often be more easily tackled using tree diagrams.

EXERCISE 5.2A

1 There are five green balls, three red balls and two yellow balls in a bag. If a ball is selected at random, find the probability that it is green or red.

2 Craig is choosing his next holiday. The probability that he will choose Ibiza is 0·4, the probability that he will choose

Corfu is 0·35 and the probability that he will choose Tenerife is 0·25. Find the probability that Craig choose Ibiza or Corfu.

3 There are four kings and four queens in a pack of 52 playing cards. Salim chooses a card at random from the pack. What is the probability that it is a king or queen?

Exercise 5.2A cont'd

4   There are five green balls, three red balls and two yellow balls in a bag. Ian chooses a ball at random, notes its colour and puts it back in the bag. He then does this a second time. Find the probability that both Ian's choices are red.

5   The probability that I take sandwiches for dinner is 0·4. The probability that I have a school lunch is 0·6. Assuming the events are independent, what is the probability that I have sandwiches on Monday and a school lunch on Tuesday?

6   What is the probability that I get a multiple of 3 when I throw a single fair die?

    If I throw the die twice, what is the probability that both throws give a multiple of 3?

7   There are four kings in a pack of 52 playing cards. Roger selects a card at random from the pack, returns it to the pack, shuffles the pack and then selects another. Find the probability that both Roger's selections were kings.

8   Alice and Carol are choosing clothes to go out. The probability that Alice chooses jeans is 0·6. The probability that Carol chooses jeans is 0·5. Assuming that their choices are independent, find the probability that they both choose jeans. Explain why this assumption may not be true.

EXERCISE 5.2B

1   The probability that the school hockey team will win their next game is 0·3. The probability that they draw the next game is 0·45. What is the probability that they will not lose their next game? (That is, they win or draw the game.)

2   If the results of the hockey team are independent, use the probability given in question 1 to find the probability they win both their next two games.

3   Janine travels to school by bus, cycle or car. She says that the probability that she travels by bus is 0·25, by cycle is 0·1 and by car is 0·6. Why must she be incorrect?

4   Rachel is selecting a main course and a sweet from this menu.

MENU	
Main Course	**Sweet**
Sausage & Chips (0·35)	Apple Pie (0·4)
Ham Salad (0·4)	Fruit Salad (0·6)
Vegetable Lasagne (0·25)	

Exercise 5.2B cont'd

The numbers next to the items are the probabilities that Rachel chooses those items.

a) Find the probability that Rachel chooses Ham Salad or Vegetable Lasagne for her main course.

b) Assuming her choices are independent, find the probability that Rachel chooses Vegetable Lasagne and Fruit Salad.

5 There are 12 picture cards in a pack of 52 playing cards. Ubaid picks a card at random. He then replaces the card and chooses another.

a) Find the probability, as a fraction in its lowest terms, that Ubaid's first card is a picture card.

b) Find the probability that both Ubaid's cards are picture cards.

6 The weather forecast says 'there is a 40% chance of rain tomorrow'.

a) Write 40% as a decimal.

b) Assuming the probability that it rains on any day is independent of whether it rained or not the previous day, find the probability that it rains on two successive days.

c) State why the assumption made in b) is unlikely to be correct.

7 There is an equal likelihood that someone is born on any day of the week. What is the probability that Gary and Rushna were both born on a Monday?

8 Sally spins this five-sided spinner three times.

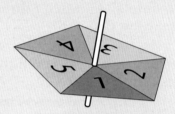

What is the probability that all Sally's spins landed on 1?

Using tree diagrams for unequal probabilities

In the first section, tree diagrams were used as a way of organising work on probability when the outcomes were equally likely. It is possible to use them when outcomes are not equally likely.

Look again at Rachel's choices on the menu, from question 4 in Exercise 5.2B. These can be shown on a tree diagram with the probabilities written on the branches.

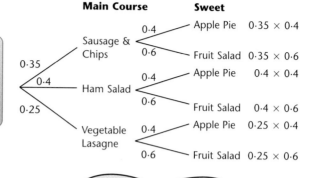

So the probability of choosing Sausage & Chips and Fruit Salad = 0·35 × 0·6 = 0·21

and the probability of choosing Ham Salad and Apple Pie is 0·4 × 0·4 and so on.

Exam tip

If you are going along the 'branches' of a tree diagram, **multiply** the probabilities. At the end, if you want more than one route through the tree, **add** the probabilities.

Now look at Example 5 in a different way.

EXAMPLE 6

There are six red balls and four black balls in a bag. Gina selects a ball, notes its colour and replaces it. She then selects another ball. What is the probability that Gina selects:

a) two red balls

b) one of each colour?

A tree diagram can be drawn to show this information.

Notice that at each stage the probabilities add up to 1 and at the end all four probabilities add up to 1.

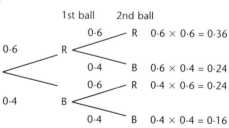

a) Probability of red followed by red = 0·6 × 0·6 = 0·36.

b) For one of each colour, Gina needs either the second route or the third route through the tree diagram.

So P(one of each colour) = (0·6 × 0·4) + (0·4 × 0·6) = 0·24 + 0·24 = 0·48.

EXERCISE 5.3A

1 There are seven red balls and three yellow balls in a bag. Lee chooses a ball at random, notes its colour and replaces it. He then chooses another. Copy and complete the tree diagram to show Lee's choices.

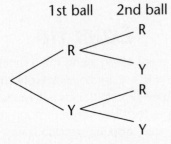

1st ball   2nd ball

What is the probability that Lee chooses:

a) two red balls
b) a red ball and then a yellow ball
c) a yellow ball and then a red ball
d) a red ball and a yellow ball in either order?

2 Li is choosing a starter and main course from this menu. The probabilities of each of her choices are in brackets next to the items.

> ## MENU
> **Starter**
> Soup (0·3)
> Spring Rolls (0·7)
> **Main Course**
> Chicken Fried Rice (0·3)
> Beef Satay (0·2)
> Sweet & Sour Pork (0·5)

a) Draw a tree diagram to show Li's choices.
b) Calculate the probability that Li chooses:

  (i) Spring Rolls and Beef Satay
  (ii) Soup and Sweet & Sour Pork.

3 The probability that Aftab wakes up when his alarm goes off is 0·8. Copy the tree diagram and complete it for the first two days of the week.

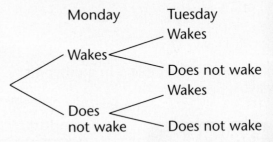

Calculate the probability that Aftab

a) wakes on both days
b) wakes on one of the two days.

4 There are five red balls, two blue balls and three yellow balls in a bag. Susan chooses a ball at random, notes its colour and replaces it. She then chooses another.

a) Draw a tree diagram to show the results of Susan's choices.
b) Calculate the probability that Susan chooses

  (i) two red balls
  (ii) two balls of the same colour.

Exercise 5.3A cont'd

5 Mr and Mrs Jones plan to have three children. Assuming there is an equal chance of a boy and girl, draw a tree diagram to show the possible sexes of the three children.

Calculate the probability that Mr and Mrs Jones have

a) three girls

b) two girls and a boy.

EXERCISE 5.3B

1 On any day the probability that Sarah's bus is late is 0·2. Copy the tree diagram and complete it for two days.

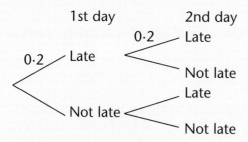

1st day   2nd day

0·2   Late

0·2   Late

Not late

Late

Not late

Not late

Calculate the probability that Sarah's bus is

a) late on both days

b) late one one of the two days.

2 In an experiment a drawing pin falls point up 300 times in 500 throws.

a) Write down, as a fraction in its lowest terms, the probability of the pin landing point up.

b) Draw a tree diagram to show the result of two throws, and the pin landing point up or point down.

c) Find the probability that the pin lands point up on

  (i) both throws

  (ii) one of the two throws.

3 Extend the tree diagram you drew for question 2 to show the results of three throws.

Find the probability that the pin lands point up on

a) all three throws

b) one of the three throws.

4 There are ten red balls, three blue balls and seven yellow balls in a bag. Waseem chooses a ball at random, notes it colour and replaces it. He then chooses another.

a) Draw a tree diagram to show the results of Waseem's choices.

b) Calculate the probability that Waseem chooses:

  (i) two blue balls

  (ii) two balls of the same colour

  (iii) two balls of different colours. (Look for the quick way of doing it.)

Exercise 5.3B cont'd

5 Brian drew this tree diagram for the results of choosing coloured balls from a bag.

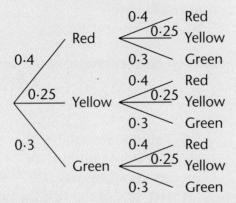

Explain why Brian must have made a mistake.

Key ideas

- Tree diagrams can be used in probability questions to show the possible events. They have the advantage of being able to be used for more than two successive events. They have the disadvantage of being messy if there are a large number of outcomes.

- If events are mutually exclusive then P(A or B) = P(A) + P(B)

- For independent events P(A and B) = P(A) × P(B).

- The multiply rule should be used for words like 'both' and 'all'.

6 Percentage increase and decrease

You should already know

- fraction, decimal and percentage notation
- multiplication and division of decimals by 100
- how to calculate a percentage of a given quantity
- how to increase and decrease a quantity by a given percentage (This will be looked at again in this chapter.)
- how to calculate simple interest
- how to round an amount of money to the nearest penny.

Percentage increase

You already know how to increase a quantity by, for example, 3%.
You find 3% of the quantity and add it on to the original.
The following example shows how this can be done by a quicker method.

EXAMPLE 1

Increase £24 000 by 3%.

You need to calculate 3% of £24 000 and add it on to the original £24 000.

You need 3% of 24 000 + 100% of 24 000.

This is the same as 103% of £24 000.

The calculation now becomes

£24 000 × $\frac{103}{100}$ = £24 000 × 1·03 = £24 720.

Using this method, you carry out the percentage calculation and the addition in one step.

Percentage decrease

In the same way you already know how to reduce a quantity by, for example, 15%. You find 15% of the quantity and take it off the original. The following example shows how this can be done by a quicker method.

EXAMPLE 2

Reduce £17·60 by 15%.

You need to find 15% of £17·60 and subtract the answer from £17·60.

You need 100% of £17·60 − 15% of £17·60.

This is the same as 85% of £17·60 (since 100% − 15% = 85%).

The calculation now becomes £17·60 × $\frac{85}{100}$ = £17·60 × 0·85 = £14·96.

Using this method, you carry out the percentage calculation and the subtraction in one step.

EXERCISE 6.1A

1 What do you multiply a quantity by if it is increased by
   a) 6%   b) 9%
   c) 17·5%   d) 1·25% ?

2 What do you multiply a quantity by if it is decreased by
   a) 6%   b) 9%
   c) 17·5%   d) 1·25% ?

3 Increase £400 by
   a) 5%   b) 20%   c) 80%

4 Decrease £200 by
   a) 4%   b) 30%   c) 70%

5 Saira's electricity bill is £160 before V.A.T. is added on. What is the bill after V.A.T. at 5% is added on?

6 The area of a sports field is 80 000 m². 15% of the field is sold for housing. How much is left?

7 Train fares went up by 7%. What is the new price of a ticket which previously cost £4?

8 In a sale all items are reduced by 20%. What is the sale price of an article which originally cost £24?

9 Samina earns £4 per hour. What will she earn if she receives a wage increase of 3%?

10 Mike earns £150 per week. He pays 6% of this into a pension fund. How much money is he left with?

EXERCISE 6.1B

1 What do you multiply a quantity by if it is increased by
   a) 4%   b) 18%
   c) 12·5%   d) 5·6% ?

2 What do you multiply a quantity by if it is decreased by
   a) 4%   b) 18%
   c) 12·5%   d) 5·6% ?

Exercise 6.1B cont'd

3 Increase £4800 by
   a) 5%   **b)** 23%   **c)** 79%

4 Decrease £760 by
   a) 8%   **b)** 17%   **c)** 63%

5 A factory employs 1350 people. The management decides to make cut backs which will reduce the number of employees by 18%. How many employees will be left?

6 A piece of elastic is stretched by 17%. If it was originally 90 cm long, what is its new length?

7 Colin pays 6% of his pay into a pension fund. If he earns £840 per month. What will his pay be after taking off his pension payments?

8 A computer costs £690 before V.A.T. is added on. What will it cost after V.A.T. is added on at 17·5%?

9 A firm claims that its insulation will cut heating bills by 25%. Mr and Mrs Brown's annual heating bill is at the moment £830. What will the bill be if the firm's claim is justified?

10 The price of petrol went up by 120% in the period from 1990 to 2000. If it was 36p per litre in 1990, what was it in 2000?

Finding the original

If a quantity is increased by 20%, then you have just found that

new amount = original amount × 1·2

It follows that

original amount = new amount ÷ 1·2

EXAMPLE 3

Berwyn received an increase of 20% in his salary. After the increase he was earning £31 260. What was his salary before the rise?

new salary = old salary × 1·2

old salary = new salary ÷ 1·2 = £31 260 ÷ 1·2 = £26 050

If a quantity is decreased by 10%, then you have just found that

new amount = original amount × 0·9

It follows that

original amount = new amount ÷ 0·9

EXAMPLE 4

Irene paid £38·70 for a skirt in a sale. This was after it had been reduced by 10%.

What was the original price of the skirt?

new price = original price × 0·9

original price = new price ÷ 0·9

= £38·70 ÷ 0.9 = £43

189

EXERCISE 6.2A

In this exercise, some of these questions ask for the original amount and some ask for the new amount.

1   A price of £50 is increased by 7·5%. What is the new price?

2   A quantity is decreased by 3%. It is now 38·8. What was it to start with?

3   A coat was advertised at £79. In a sale the price was reduced by 5%. What was the new price?

4   Mr Diffom made a profit of £13 250 in the year 2000. This was an increase of 6% on his profit in 1999. What was his profit in 1999?

5   In a local election in 1997, Labour received 1375 votes. This was increased by 12% in 1998. How many people voted Labour in 1998?

6   Stephen was given a rise of 7%. His salary after the rise was £28 890. What was it before the rise?

7   Between 1978 and 1979 house prices increased by 12·5%. A house was valued at £27 000 in 1979. What was its value in 1978?

8   A holiday cost £564, including V.A.T. at 17·5%. What was the cost without V.A.T.?

9   At Jack's café all prices were increased by 5% (to the nearest penny).

   a)   A cup of tea cost 75p before the increase. What is the new price?

   b)   The new price of a cup of coffee is £1·30. What did it cost before the increase?

EXERCISE 6.2B

In this exercise, some of these questions ask for the original amount and some ask for the new amount.

1   After an increase of 12%, a quantity is 84 tonnes. What was it before the increase?

2   In a sale everything is reduced by 5%. A pair of shoes costs £47·50 in the sale. How much did they cost before the sale?

3   A newspaper increased its circulation by 3% and the new number sold was 58 195. What was it before the increase?

4   Santos sold his car for £8520. This was 40% less than he paid for it five years before. What did he pay for it?

Exercise 6.2B cont'd

5 A charity's income has been reduced by $2\frac{1}{2}$%. Its income is now £8580. What was it before the reduction?

6 It was announced that the number of people unemployed had decreased by 3%. The number who were unemployed before the decrease was 2·56 million. How many are now unemployed? Give the answer to three significant figures.

7 The cost of a car, including V.A.T. at 17·5%, is £12 925. What is the cost without V.A.T.?

8 At Percival's sale the price of everything is reduced by $7\frac{1}{2}$%, rounded to the nearest penny.

   a) A pair of boots cost £94·99 before the sale. What is the price in the sale?

   b) Delia is charged £13·87 for a blouse in the sale. What was its original price?

Key ideas

- To increase a quantity by, for example 5%, a quick way is to multiply by 1·05.

- To reduce a quantity by, for example 12%, a quick way is to multiply by 0·88 (as 100 − 12 = 88).

- If an amount has been increased by, for example 5% and you know the new amount, you find the original by dividing by 1·05.

- If an amount has been reduced by, for example 12% and you know the new amount, you find the original by dividing by 0·88.

7 Trial and improvement

You should already know

- how to substitute numbers into algebraic expressions.

Solving cubic equations by trial and improvement

You found in Chapter 3 that solving a cubic equation by a graphical method is not very accurate. In fact, it is difficult to be accurate even to one decimal place.

A more accurate method is **trial and improvement**.

EXAMPLE 1

A solution of the equation $x^3 - 4x + 1 = 0$ lies between 1 and 2. Use trial and improvement to find the solution correct to one decimal place.

For the first trial

try 1	$1^3 - 4 \times 1 + 1 = {}^-2$	too small
try 1·5	$1 \cdot 5^3 - 4 \times 1 \cdot 5 + 1 = {}^-1 \cdot 625$	too small, try solutions between 1·5 and 2·0.
try 1·8	$1 \cdot 8^3 - 4 \times 1 \cdot 8 + 1 = {}^-0 \cdot 368$	too small
try 1·9	$1 \cdot 9^3 - 4 \times 1 \cdot 9 + 1 = 0 \cdot 259$	too big

The solution lies between 1·8 and 1·9.

To find which is nearer, try 1·85

$1 \cdot 85^3 - 4 \times 1 \cdot 85 + 1 = {}^-0 \cdot 0684$ too small

> **Exam tip**
>
> Make sure you give the x-value (not the value on the right-hand side of the equation) to the required accuracy.

So the solution lies between 1·85 and 1·9. It is nearer to 1·9 than 1·8.

The solution is $x = 1 \cdot 9$ correct to one decimal place.

You should be able to find the solution to an equation within about five or six trials.

EXAMPLE 2

Show that $x^3 - 3x = 6$ has a solution between 2 and 3. Find the solution correct to one decimal place.

$2^3 - 3 \times 2 = 2$ ⎫
$3^3 - 3 \times 3 = 18$ ⎭

Because 6 is between 2 and 18 there is a solution for x between 2 and 3.

Example 2 cont'd

try 2	$2^3 - 3 \times 2 = 2$	too small
try 2·5	$2·5^3 - 3 \times 2·5 = 8·125$	too big, try solutions between 2 and 2·25
try 2·3	$2·3^3 - 3 \times 2·3 = 5·267$	too small, try solutions between 2·3 and 2·5
try 2·4	$2·4^3 - 3 \times 2·4 = 6·624$	too big, try solutions between 2·3 and 2·4
try 2·35	$2·35^3 - 3 \times 2·35 = 5·928$	too small, the solution is between 2·35 and 2·4

The solution is $x = 2·4$ correct to one decimal place.

Find the two values between which the answer lies to the required degree of accuracy and then try midway values.

Exam tip

Always give the answer to the trial you have done as well as 'too big' or 'too small'.

EXERCISE 7.1A

Use trial and improvement to find the solutions.

1 **a)** If $1^3 = 1$ and $2^3 = 8$, explain how shows that there is a solution to the equation $x^3 = 5$ between 1 and 2.

   b) Find the solution correct to one decimal place.

2 **a)** If $2^3 - 8 \times 2 = {}^-8$ and $3^3 - 8 \times 3 = 3$, explain how that shows there is a solution to the equation $x^3 - 8x = 0$ between 2 and 3.

   b) Find the solution correct to one decimal place.

3 Show that a solution of $x^3 - 5x = 8$ lies between 2 and 3. Find it correct to one decimal place.

4 Show that a solution of $x^3 - x = 90$ lies between 4 and 5. Find it correct to one decimal place.

5 Show that a solution of $x^3 - x^2 = 30$ lies between 3 and 4. Find it correct to one decimal place.

6 A solution of $x^3 = 12$ lies between 2 and 3. Find it correct to two decimal places.

7 A solution of $x^3 + 50 = 0$ lies between $^-4$ and $^-3$. Find it correct to one decimal place.

8 A solution of $x^3 + 4x + 25 = 0$ lies between $^-3$ and $^-2$. Find it correct to one decimal place.

9 **a)** Find two consecutive integers between which the solution of $x^3 - 2x^2 = 4$ lies.

   b) Find the solution correct to two decimal places.

10 A solution of $x^3 + 3x^2 + x = 0$ lies between $^-3$ and $^-2$. Find it correct to two decimal places.

EXERCISE 7.1B

Use trial and improvement to find the solutions.

1 **a)** If $2^3 = 8$ and $3^3 = 27$, explain how that shows there is a solution to the equation $x^3 = 15$ between 2 and 3.

   b) Find the solution correct to one decimal place.

2 **a)** If $1^3 - 2 \times 1 = {}^-1$ and $2^3 - 2 \times 1 = 6$, explain how that shows there is a solution to the equation $x^3 - 2x = 0$ between 1 and 2.

   b) Find the solution correct to one decimal place.

3 Show that a solution of $x^3 - 7x = 25$ lies between 3 and 4. Find it correct to one decimal place.

4 Show that a solution of $x^3 + 2x = 2$ lies between 0 and 1. Find it correct to one decimal place.

5 Show that a solution of $x^3 - x^2 = 1$ lies between 1 and 2. Find it correct to one decimal place.

6 A solution of $x^3 = 56$ lies between 3 and 4. Find it correct to two decimal places.

7 A solution of $x^3 + 12 = 0$ lies between $^-3$ and $^-2$. Find it correct to one decimal place.

8 A solution of $x^3 - 2x + 6 = 0$ lies between $^-3$ and $^-2$. Find it correct to one decimal place.

9 **a)** Find two consecutive integers between which the solution of $x^3 - 4x^2 + 9 = 0$ lies.

   b) Find the solution correct to two decimal places.

10 A solution of $x^3 - 5x^2 + 2x = 0$ lies between 0 and 1. Find it correct to two decimal places.

Key ideas

- Find two consecutive integers that the solution lies between.
- Next choose the halfway point.
- Keep making improvements until the required accuracy is achieved.
- Remember that when you are finding a solution to an equation like $x^3 - 5x = 8$, correct to one decimal place, it is the x that is needed to 1 decimal place, not the 8.

8 Linear inequalities

You should already know

● how to plot straight line graphs such as $y = 3$, $y = 3x + 2$, $2x + 3y = 12$.

Showing regions on graphs

It is often possible to show the area on a graph that satisfies an inequality.

EXAMPLE 1

Write down the inequality that describes the region shaded in each graph.

a)

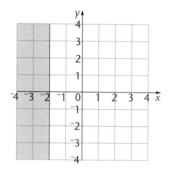

b)

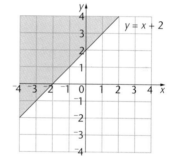

a) $x < {}^{-}2$ The line drawn is $x = {}^{-}2$. This line divides the graph into two regions $x < {}^{-}2$ and $x > {}^{-}2$. The shaded region is $x < {}^{-}2$. Check by testing any point in the region.

b) $y > x + 2$ The line is $y = x + 2$ and divides the graph into two regions $y < x + 2$ and $y > x + 2$. To decide which side is shaded choose any point not on the line and test it, for example $(0, 0)$. Here $x + 2 = 2$, and $y = 0$, so $y < x + 2$ at $(0, 0)$ and $(0, 0)$ is not in the region. So the shaded region is $y > x + 2$.

EXAMPLE 2

On separate grids shade the regions **a)** $y > 2$ **b)** $y < 2x - 3$.

a)

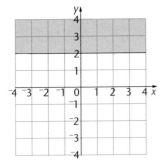

It is clear that $y > 2$ is above the line $y = 2$.

b)

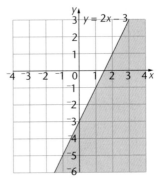

Draw the line $y = 2x - 3$. Then the two regions are $y > 2x - 3$ and $y < 2x - 3$. To test which side is wanted, choose any point not on the line, for example $(0, 0)$. Here $y = 0$ and $2x - 3 = {}^-3$, so $y > 2x - 3$ at $(0, 0)$.

Therefore $(0, 0)$ is not in the region required. Shade the other region.

In Examples 1 and 2 the region required has been shaded. If more than one region is required, then it is best to shade out the regions not required and leave blank the required region.

Exam tip

Either shading in or shading out is acceptable, but indicate the required region by labelling it clearly.

Exam tip

When testing a region, if possible use $(0, 0)$. If the line goes through $(0, 0)$ choose a point with positive coordinates for example $(1, 0)$ to test the region.

EXAMPLE 3

Show by shading the region where $x > 0$, $y > 0$ and $x + 2y < 6$.

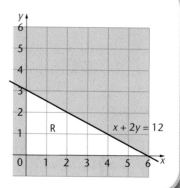

Shade out the regions $x < 0$ and $y < 0$. Draw the line $x + 2y = 6$ and test $(0, 0)$; $x + 2y = 0 < 6$ so $(0, 0)$ is in the region $x + 2y < 6$, which is the required region. So shade out the region not containing $(0, 0)$. R is the region required.

EXERCISE 8.1A

For questions 1 to 4, write down the inequality that describes the region shaded.

1

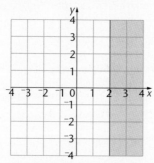

2

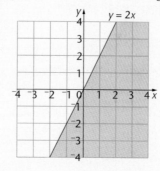

3

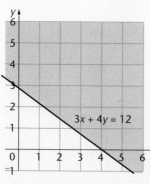

4

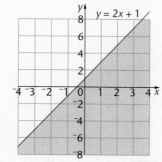

5 Draw a set of axes and label them from ⁻4 to 4 for x and y. Shade the region $y > ⁻3$.

Chapter 8   *Linear inequalities*

Exercise 8.1A cont'd

6 Draw a set of axes and label them from ⁻3 to 6 for x and from ⁻3 to 5 for y. Shade the region $2x + 5y < 10$.

7 Draw a set of axes and label them from 0 to 5 for x and y. Show by shading the region where $y > 0$, $x > 0$ and $3x + 5y < 15$.

8 Draw a set of axes and label them from ⁻3 to 3 for x and from ⁻6 to 10 for y. Show by shading the region where $x > 0$, $y < 8$ and $y > 2x$.

EXERCISE 8.1B

For questions 1 to 4, write down the inequality that describes the region shaded.

1

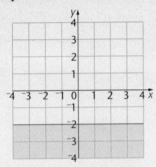

2

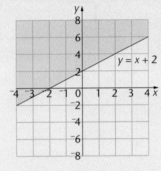

$y = x + 2$

3

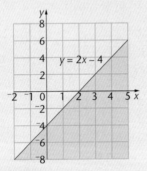

$y = 2x - 4$

4

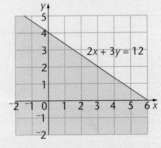

$2x + 3y = 12$

5 Draw a set of axes and label them from ⁻4 to 4 for x and y. Shade the region $x > ⁻1$.

6 Draw a set of axes and label them from ⁻2 to 6 for x and from ⁻2 to 5 for y. Shade the region $4x + 5y < 20$.

7 Draw a set of axes and label them from 0 to 12 for x and from 0 to 8 for y. Show by shading the region where $y > 0$, $x > 0$ and $3x + 5y < 30$.

Exercise 8.1B cont'd

8 Draw a set of axes and label them from ⁻3 to 3 for x and from ⁻6 to 10 for y.

Show by shading the region where $x > 0$, $3x + 8y > 24$ and $5x + 4y < 20$.

Key ideas

- When representing inequalities like $2x + 3y > 12$ on a graph, first plot the straight line $2x + 3y = 12$ and then decide which side of the line to shade.

- When representing inequalities on a graph, if there is more than one region, it is best to shade out the regions not required. This leaves the region required clear.

Revision exercise

1 Mr and Mrs Brown intend to have three children. Draw a tree diagram for the possible sexes of the three children.

Assuming that for each child they are equally likely to have a boy or a girl, find the probability that

a) all three children are girls

b) Mr and Mrs Brown have two boys and a girl

2 Colin throws two dice. He is not interested in all the individual results, just whether he gets a six or not.

Complete the tree diagram for the results of Colin's two throws.

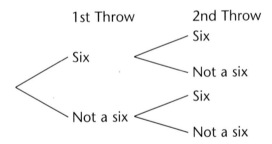

Find the probability that Colin gets

a) 2 sixes,   **b)** at least 1 six.

3 The whole of year 9 takes tests in English, Maths and Science. The probability that a randomly chosen pupil passes English is 0·8, Maths is 0·7 and Science is 0·9.

Copy and complete the tree diagram for the three subjects.

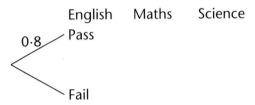

Calculate the probability that a randomly chosen year 9 pupil

a) passes all three subjects

b) passes two out of the three subjects.

4 Uzma receives an increase in salary of 4%. If her old salary was £17 000, what will her new salary be.

5 In a sale all prices are reduced by 15%. Find the new price of a pair of trainers that originally cost £65.

6 A headline in a newspaper says 'Petrol prices up 20% in a year'. If the price is 85p per litre now, what was the price 1 year ago? Give your answer to the nearest penny.

7 Damien sold his bicycle for £286 at a loss of 45% on what he paid for it. How much did he pay?

8 There is a solution to the equation $x^3 - 7x = 0$ between 2 and 3. Use trial and improvement to find the solution correct to 1 decimal place.

9 Show that there is a solution to the equation $x^3 - 2x = 5$ between 2 and 3. Use trial and improvement to find the solution correct to 1 decimal place.

10 There is a solution to the equation $x^3 + 40 = 0$ between $^-4$ and $^-3$. Use trial and improvement to find the solution correct to 1 decimal place.

11 Write down the inequality satisfied by the shaded region in each diagram.

a)

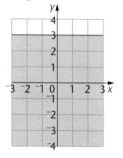

b)

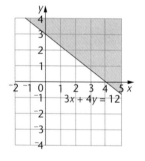

12 Draw sets of axes and label them from $^-4$ to 4 for x and y. Shade these regions.

a) $x < 1$

b) $2y < 3x + 2$

13 Draw a set of axes and label them from $^-1$ to 8 for x and y. Show, by shading, the region where $x > 0$, $y > 0$, $x < 7$, $y < x - 1$.

14 Draw a set of axes and label x from $^-1$ to 8 and y from $^-1$ to 6. Show, by shading, the region where $x > 0$, $y > 0$, $y < x + 2$, $3x + 7y < 21$.

9 Repeated percentage and proportionate change

You should already know

- how to calculate with percentage decimals and fractions, including percentage increases and decreases.

Successive percentage increases

You found in Chapter 6 that a quick way of increasing by, for example 18%, is to multiply by 1·18. Similarly to increase by 7%, a quick way is to multiply by 1·07. This method is particularly useful when doing successive increases.

EXAMPLE 1

Due to inflation, prices increase by 5% per year. An item costs £12 now. What will it cost in 2 years' time?

In 1 year the price will be £12 × 1·05 = £12·60.

In 2 years the price will be £12·60 × 1·05 = £13·23.

Alternatively, this repeated calculation could be worked out as

£12 × 1·05 × 1·05 = £13·23

EXAMPLE 2

Selena invested £4000 and received 5% interest a year which was added on each year. How much had she in total after **a)** 1 year **b)** 6 years?

A 5% increase means that the new amount is 100 + 5 = 105% of the old amount each year.

105% is 1·05, so multiply by 1·05 each year.

a) After one year the total amount is £4000 × 1·05
= £4200

b) After 6 years the total amount is
$4000 × 1·05 × 1·05 × 1·05 × 1·05 × 1·05 × 1·05$
$= 4000 × (1·05)^6$
$= £5360·38$ (to the nearest penny)

On the calculator, the calculation for Example 2 **b)** is done using the power button. This is usually labelled $\boxed{y^x}$ $\boxed{x^y}$ or, on many modern calculators, $\boxed{\wedge}$.

The calculation is then simply $4000 \times 1\cdot05 \boxed{\wedge} 6 = £5360\cdot38$

Example 2 is an example of calculating **compound interest**. Compound interest is added on to what was in the bank at the beginning of the year. So each year the interest increases. In contrast, if the investment only received **simple interest**, the £200 interest received in the first year would be the same for every year.

Successive percentage decreases

Successive percentage decreases are calculated in a similar way.

EXAMPLE 3

Each year a car loses value by 12% of its value at the beginning of the year. If its starting value was £9000 find its value after 3 years.

$100\% - 12\% = 88\%$

So after 1 year the value $= £9000 \times 0\cdot88$

$\qquad\qquad\qquad\qquad = £7920$

after 2 years the value $= £7920 \times 0\cdot88$

$\qquad\qquad\qquad\qquad = £6969.60$

after 3 years the value $= £6969\cdot60 \times 0\cdot88$

$\qquad\qquad\qquad\qquad = £6133\cdot25$ (to the nearest 1p)

Alternatively, this repeated calculation could be worked out as

$£9000 \times 0\cdot88 \times 0\cdot88 \times 0\cdot88 = £9000 \times (0\cdot88)^3 = £6133\cdot25$

EXERCISE 9.1A

1   Craig puts £240 into a savings account. Each year the savings earn interest at 6% of the amount in the account at the start of the year. What will his savings be worth after 3 years? Give your answer to the nearest penny.

2   Each year a car loses value by 11% of its value at the start of the year. If it was worth £8000 when it was new, what will it be worth after 2 years?

Exercise 9.1A cont'd

3 Calculate the amount that £3000 invested with compound interest would be worth in each of the following cases. Give your answers to the nearest penny.

   a) 5% for 4 years
   b) 6% for 20 years
   c) 3·5% for 10 years

4 A population of bacteria is estimated to increase by 12% every 24 hours. The population was 2000 at midnight on Friday. What was the population (to the nearest whole number) by midnight the following Wednesday?

5 The insurance premium for Della's car was £360. The firm reduced it by 12% for each year she had no claim. What was the cost after six years with no claims? Give the answer to the nearest pound.

6 Mr Costa was offered an 8% rise every year whilst he worked at the same firm. This year he earned £28 500. How much will he earn after four rises? Give the answer to the nearest pound.

7 Ambrose invested £3500 in a six-year bond that added 5% to the amount each year for the first three years and 7·5% each year for the next three years. What is the amount in the bond, to the nearest penny **a)** after three years **b)** after six years?

8 Is it better to invest £1000 for five years at 8% or for four years at 9%?

9 Tina insures a car with the Suffolk Mutual for fully comprehensive cover for a premium of £463. The table shows the NCD (No Claims Discount) that she gets if she does not make a claim. For example, if she does not make a claim for 2 years, there will be a 30% reduction in her premium.

Years without claim	1	2	3	4 or more
Reduction	15%	30%	45%	60%

   a) What is the cost of the insurance if she does not make a claim for four years?
   b) The Norfolk and East charge the same basic premium of £453 but reduce the premium by 15% each year she does not make a claim. This continues for four years. Which is the cheapest and by how much?

EXERCISE 9.1B

1 Calculate the amount each of these items is worth if they reduce in value by the given percentage for the given number of years.

	Original value	% reduction	Number of years
a)	£250	4%	5
b)	£3500	11%	7
c)	£1400	15%	4
d)	£10 500	12%	10

2 Interest of 4% was added to an investment of £1500 each year for four years. How much was it then worth? Give the answer to the nearest pound.

3 Martyn had shares worth £8000. They increased in value by 7·5% each year. What was their value after 10 years? Give the answer to the nearest pound.

4 Tony says his narrow boat is increasing in value by 6% a year. It was worth £25 000 in 1999. How much would it be worth, to the nearest hundred pounds, in 2005 (six years later) if he is correct?

5 Sheila joined a keep-fit club that claimed you would reduce your running time by 1% each week. She could run 500 metres in 12 minutes to start with. According to the club, how long would it take her after five weeks? Give the answer to the nearest second.

6 Mordovia has high inflation. In 1999 it was 15% a month for the first six months and 12·5% for the next six months.

A car cost 78 000 scuds (their unit of currency) in January 1999. How much did it cost:

a) after six months
b) in January 2000?

Give the answers to the nearest whole number.

Exercise 9.1B cont'd

7 Find the difference in interest earned by investing £500 for three years at 12% simple interest or for three years at 10% compound interest.

8 I invest £500 at 7% compound interest. How many years must I leave it, before it doubles in value?

9 Tony invests £250 at an annual interest (compound) rate of 4%. How many years will it take for the amount to exceed **a)** £400 **b)** double its original value?

Proportionate increases and decreases

Proportionate increases and decreases are worked out in exactly the same way, but fractions are used instead of percentages.

EXAMPLE 4

Andrew said he would increase his giving to charity by $\frac{1}{25}$ each year. He gave £120 at the start. How much did he give at the end of the fifth year?

Each year he gave $\frac{26}{25}$ × what he gave in the previous year. $(1 + \frac{1}{25} = \frac{26}{25})$

At the end of the fifth year he gave £120 × $(\frac{26}{25})^5$

Key in:

| 1 | 2 | 0 | × | (| 2 | 6 | ÷ | 2 | 5 |) | y^x | 5 | = |

= £145·998

= £146·00 to the nearest penny.

EXAMPLE 5

The distance that Patrick can walk in a day is reducing by $\frac{1}{15}$ each year. This year he can walk 12 miles in a day. How far will he be able to walk in five years' time?

The distance reduces by $\frac{1}{15}$ in 1 year, so multiply by $\frac{14}{15}$ for each year.

In five years he will be able to walk 12 × $(\frac{14}{15})^5$ = 8·499 = 8·50 miles.

EXERCISE 9.2A

1 What do you multiply a quantity by if it is increased by
a) $\frac{1}{5}$ **b)** $\frac{2}{9}$ **c)** $\frac{1}{8}$ **d)** $\frac{2}{7}$?

2 What do you multiply a quantity by if it is decreased by
a) $\frac{1}{5}$ **b)** $\frac{2}{9}$ **c)** $\frac{1}{8}$ **d)** $\frac{2}{7}$?

3 Calculate the amount each of these items are worth if they increase by the given fraction for the given number of years. Give your answers to the nearest penny.

	Original value	Fraction increase	Number of years
a)	£280	$\frac{1}{5}$	5
b)	£3500	$\frac{1}{8}$	7
c)	£1400	$\frac{2}{9}$	4
d)	£10 500	$\frac{1}{7}$	10

4 At Premda department store they said they would reduce the price of goods still not sold by $\frac{1}{3}$ for each day of the sale.

A coat was offered originally at £65. What was its price after three days, to the nearest penny?

5 An investment firm says it will add $\frac{1}{5}$ to your money each year. If you invested £3000, how much would it amount to after 10 years? Give the answer to the nearest pound.

EXERCISE 9.2B

1 What do you multiply a quantity by if it is increased by
a) $\frac{1}{6}$ **b)** $\frac{1}{11}$ **c)** $\frac{3}{5}$ **d)** $\frac{3}{7}$?

2 What do you multiply a quantity by if it is decreased by
a) $\frac{1}{6}$ **b)** $\frac{1}{11}$ **c)** $\frac{3}{5}$ **d)** $\frac{3}{7}$?

Exercise 9.2B cont'd

3 Calculate the amount each of these items are worth if they decrease by the given fraction for the given number of years. Give your answers to the nearest penny.

	Original value	Fraction decrease	Number of years
a)	£420	$\frac{1}{6}$	5
b)	£1500	$\frac{2}{5}$	7
c)	£1400	$\frac{1}{9}$	4
d)	£10 500	$\frac{1}{12}$	10

4 Cathy said she would withdraw $\frac{1}{5}$ of the money she had in the bank every time she made a withdrawal. She had £187·50 in the bank to start with. How much did she have after three withdrawals?

5 At Patnik shoe shop they offered to decrease the price of a pair of shoes by $\frac{1}{4}$ each day until they were sold. They were priced at £47 to start with. Jean bought them after they had been reduced four times. How much did she pay? Give the answer to the nearest penny.

6 It is claimed that the number of rabbits in Freeshire is increasing by $\frac{1}{12}$ each year. It is estimated that there are 1700 rabbits now. How many will there be after four years if the statement is true? Give the answer to three significant figures.

Key ideas

- When a quantity is increased by, for example 5%, for six years, multiply by $1·05^6$.
- When a quantity is reduced by, for example 3%, for four years, multiply by $0·97^4$.
- When a quantity is increased by a fraction, for example $\frac{1}{10}$ for five years multiply by $\left(\frac{11}{10}\right)^5$.
- When a quantity is reduced by a fraction, for example $\frac{1}{6}$ for four years multiply by $\left(\frac{5}{6}\right)^4$.

10 Simultaneous equations

You should already know

- how to write a formula using letters
- how to rearrange equations by doing the same operation to both sides
- how to add and subtract simple algebraic expressions
- how to draw graphs of linear equations such as $y = 3x - 2$ and $3x + 2y = 12$.

An equation in two unknowns does not have a unique solution. For example, the graph of the equation $x + y = 4$ is a straight line. Every point on the line will have coordinates that satisfy the equation.

When you are given two equations in two unknowns, such as x and y, they usually have common solutions where the two lines meet in a point. These are called **simultaneous equations**.

Solving by the method of elimination

EXAMPLE 1

Solve the simultaneous equations $x + y = 4$ and $2x - y = 5$.

$$x + y = 4 \quad ① $$
$$2x - y = 5 \quad ②$$

Write the two equations, one under the other, and label them.

Look to see if either of the unknowns (x or is y) has the same coefficient in both equations. In this case there is $1y$ in equation ① and $1y$ in equation ②. As their signs are different, the two y-terms will be eliminated (cancel each other out) if the two equations are added.

$$x + 2x + y + (-y) = 4 + 5 \quad \text{Adding ① + ②.}$$
$$3x = 9$$
$$x = 3$$

Example 1 cont'd

To find the value of y, substitute $x = 3$ in equation ①.

| $3 + y = 4$ | Replacing x by 3. |
| $y = 1$ | |

So the solution is $x = 3$ and $y = 1$.

Check in equation ②: the left-hand side is $2x - y = 6 - 1 = 5$ which is correct.

EXAMPLE 2

Solve the simultaneous equations $2x + 5y = 9$ and $2x - y = 3$.

| $2x + 5y = 9$ ① | Set out in line. |
| $2x - y = 3$ ② | |

This time $(+)2x$ appears in each equation, so subtract to eliminate the x-terms.

$2x - 2x + 5y - (-y) = 9 - 3$	① – ② Take care with the signs. $5y - (^-y) = 5y + y$.
$6y = 6$	
$y = 1$	
$2x + 5 = 9$	Substitute $y = 1$ in ①: $5y$ is replaced by $5 \times 1 = 5$.
$2x = 4$	
$x = 2$	

The solution is $x = 2$, $y = 1$.

Check in equation ②: the left-hand side is $2x - y = 4 - 1 = 3$ which is correct.

EXAMPLE 3

Solve the simultaneous equations $x + 3y = 10$, $3x + 2y = 16$.

| $x + 3y = 10$ ① | Set out in line. |
| $3x + 2y = 16$ ② | |

This time the coefficients of x and y are different in both equations.

Multiply ① by 3 to make the coefficient of x the same as in equation ②.

| $3x + 9y = 30$ ③ | ① × 3 |
| $3x + 2y = 16$ ② | |

> **Exam tip**
>
> When eliminating, if the signs of the letter to be eliminated are the same, subtract. If they are different, add. When subtracting, take great care with the signs. This is where most errors are made. If your check is wrong, see if you have made an error with any signs.

Example 3 cont'd

Now (+)$3x$ appears in both equations, so subtract.

$3x - 3x + 9y - 2y = 30 - 16$ ③ – ②

$7y = 14$

$y = 2$

$x + 6 = 10$ Substitute in ①.

$x = 4$

The solution is $x = 4$, $y = 2$.

Check in equation ②: the left-hand side is
$3x + 2y = 12 + 4 = 16$ which is correct.

Exam tip

When subtracting equations, you can do equation ① – equation ② or equation ② – equation ①. It is better to make the letter positive. Always write down clearly what you are doing.

There is no need to write as much detail as in Example 3. The next example shows what is required. The commentary can be omitted.

EXAMPLE 4

Solve simultaneously $4x - y = 10$ and $3x + 2y = 13$.

$4x - y = 10$ ① Set out in line.

$3x + 2y = 13$ ②

① × 2: $8x - 2y = 20$ ③ To get $2y$ in each equation.

② + ③: $8x + 3x + 2y + (^-2y) = 13 + 20$ To eliminate y.

$11x = 33$

$x = 3$

Substitute in ①: $12 - y = 10$

$^-y = ^-2$

$y = 2$

The solution is $x = 3$, $y = 2$.

Check in ②: LHS = $3x + 2y = 9 + 4 = 13$ which is correct.

EXERCISE 10.1A

Solve these simultaneous equations.

1 $x + y = 5$
$2x - y = 7$

2 $3x + y = 9$
$2x + y = 7$

3 $2x + 3y = 11$
$2x + y = 5$

4 $2x + y = 7$
$4x - y = 5$

5 $2x + 3y = 13$
$3x - 3y = 12$

6 $2x + 3y = 14$
$5x + 3y = 26$

7 $3x + y = 7$
$2x + 3y = 7$

8 $2x - 3y = 0$
$3x + y = 11$

9 $2x + 3y = 13$
$x + 2y = 8$

10 $3x + 2y = 13$
$x + 3y = 16$

11 $2x + 3y = 7$
$3x - y = 5$

12 $x + y = 4$
$4x - 2y = 7$

13 $2x + 2y = 7$
$4x - 3y = 7$

14 $4x - 2y = 14$
$3x + y = 8$

15 $2x - 2y = 5$
$4x - 3y = 11$

EXERCISE 10.1B

Solve these simultaneous equations.

1 $x + y = 3$
$2x + y = 4$

2 $2x + y = 6$
$2x - y = 2$

3 $2x - y = 7$
$3x + y = 13$

4 $2x + y = 12$
$2x - 2y = 6$

5 $3x - y = 11$
$3x - 5y = 7$

6 $2x + y = 6$
$3x + 2y = 10$

7 $x + 3y = 9$
$2x - y = 4$

8 $x + 2y = 19$
$3x - y = 8$

9 $x + 2y = 6$
$3x - 3y = 9$

10 $2x + y = 14$
$3x + 2y = 22$

11 $2x + y = 3$
$3x - 2y = 8$

12 $2x + 4y = 11$
$x + 3y = 8$

13 $2x - y = 4$
$4x + 3y = 13$

14 $2x - 4y = 2$
$x + 3y = {}^-9$

15 $x + y = 0$
$2x + 4y = 3$

Further simultaneous equations

Sometimes the letters in the equations are not in the same order, so the first thing to do is to rearrange them.

EXAMPLE 5

Solve simultaneously the equations $y = 3x - 4$, $x + 2y = {}^-1$.

$^-3x + y = {}^-4$ ①	Rearrange the equation.
$x + 2y = {}^-1$ ②	

This can be solved in two ways, either ① × 2 and subtract or ② × 3 and add. It is normally easier to add.

② × ③ $3x + 6y = {}^-3$ ③	
$^-3x + y = {}^-4$ ①	① is copied down.

③ + ① $3x + ({}^-3x) + 6y + y = {}^-3 + ({}^-4)$

$$7y = {}^-7$$
$$y = {}^-1$$

Substitute in ① : $^-3x - 1 = {}^-4$	Replace y by $^-1$.

$$[^-3x - 1 + 1 = {}^-4 + 1]$$
$$^-3x = {}^-3$$
$$x = 1$$

The solution is $x = 1$, $y = {}^-1$.

Check in ② :   LHS $= x + 2y = 1 - 2 = {}^-1$ which is correct.

Sometimes each of the equations needs to be multiplied by a different number.

EXAMPLE 6

Solve the equations $3y = 4 - 4x$, $6x + 2y = 11$.

$4x + 3y = 4$ ①	Rearrange the first equation.
$6x + 2y = 11$ ②	

To eliminate x multiply ① by 3 and ② by 2 and subtract, or to eliminate y multiply ① by 2 and ② by 3 and subtract.

① × 3 $12x + 9y = 12$ ③	Eliminate x.
② × 2 $12x + 4y = 22$ ④	
③ − ④ $5y = {}^-10$	
$y = {}^-2$	

Example 6 cont'd

Substitute in ①: $4x - 6 = 4$ | $3y$ is replaced by $^-6$.

$$[4x - 6 + 6 = 4 + 6]$$
$$4x = 10$$
$$x = 2\tfrac{1}{2}$$

The solution is $x = 2\tfrac{1}{2}$ and $y = ^-2$.

Check in ②: LHS $= 6x + 2y = 15 - 4 = 11$ which is correct.

> **Exam tip**
>
> If the equations are not already in that form, rearrange them so that they are in the form $ax + by = c$.

EXERCISE 10.2A

Solve these simultaneous equations.

1 $y = 2x - 1$
   $x + 2y = 8$

2 $y = 3 - 2x$
   $3x - 3y = 0$

3 $3y = 11 - x$
   $3x - y = 3$

4 $3x + 2y = 7$
   $2x - 3y = ^-4$

5 $3x - 2y = 3$
   $2x - y = 4$

6 $2x + 3y = 7$
   $7x - 4y = 10$

7 $3x + 4y = 5$
   $2x + 3y = 4$

8 $4x - 3y = 1$
   $5x + 2y = ^-16$

9 $3x + 2y = 5$
   $2x + 3y = 10$

10 $4x - 2y = 3$
   $5y = 23 - 3x$

> **Exam tip**
>
> If there is a choice whether to add or subtract it is usually easier to add.

EXERCISE 10.2B

Solve these simultaneous equations.

1 $3y = 5 - x$
   $2x + y = 5$

2 $5y = x + 1$
   $2x + 2y = 10$

3 $y = 3x - 3$
   $2x + 3y = 13$

4 $4x - y = 2$
   $5x + 3y = 11$

5 $3x - 2y = 11$
   $2x + 3y = 16$

6 $2x - 3y = 5$
   $3x + 4y = 16$

7 $2x + 3y = 4$
   $3x - 2y = ^-7$

8 $4x + 3y = 1$
   $3x + 2y = 0$

9 $y = x + 2$
   $2x - 4y = ^-9$

10 $2y = 4x - 5$
   $3x - 5y = 9$

Graphical methods of solving equations

One way to solve simultaneous linear, quadratic and cubic equations is to use a graph. The point(s) where the lines or curves meet will give the solution.

EXAMPLE 7

Solve the simultaneous equations $y = 2x - 4$ and $3y = 12 - 2x$ graphically. Use values of x from 0 to 6.

Three points for equation ① are $(0, {}^-4)$, $(3, 2)$, $(6, 8)$.

Three points for equation ② are $(0, 4)$, $(3, 2)$, $(6, 0)$.

The two lines cross at $(3, 2)$ so the solution is $x = 3$, $y = 2$.

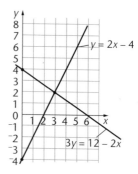

EXERCISE 10.3A

Solve the simultaneous equations in questions 1 to 4 graphically.

1 $y = 2x$ and $y = 8 - 2x$. Use values of x from $^-1$ to 4.

2 $y = 3x + 5$ and $y = x + 3$. Use values of x from $^-3$ to 2.

3 $y = 5 - x$ and $y = 2x - 7$. Use values of x from $^-1$ to 5.

4 $2y = 2x + 1$, $2y + x = 7$. Use values of x from 0 to 7.

EXERCISE 10.3B

Solve the simultaneous equations in questions 1 to 4 graphically.

1 $y = 3x$ and $y = 4x - 2$. Use values of x from $^-1$ to 4.

2 $y = 2x + 3$ and $y = 4x + 1$. Use values of x from $^-2$ to 3.

3 $y = x + 4$ and $4x + 3y = 12$. Use values of x from $^-3$ to 3.

4 $y = 2x + 8$ and $y = -2x$. Use values of x from $^-5$ to 1.

Problems that lead to simultaneous equations

EXAMPLE 8

In a café two cups of tea and three cups of coffee cost £5·30. Three cups of tea and a cup of coffee cost £4·10.

Let a cup of tea cost t pence and a cup of coffee cost c pence.

a) Write down two equations in t and c.

b) Solve them to find the cost of a cup of tea and a cup of coffee.

a) $2t + 3c = 530$ ①   Working in pence.

    $3t + c = 410$ ②

b) ② × 3 $9t + 3c = 1230$ ③

                     $2t + 3c = 530$ ①

  ③ − ① $7t = 700$

                          $t = 100$

Substitute in ① : $200 + 3c = 530$

                       $3c = 330$

                        $c = 110$

So tea costs £1 a cup, coffee costs £1·10 a cup.

Check in the problem: 2 teas + 3 coffees cost £2 + £3·30 = £5·30 and 3 teas + 1 coffee cost £3 + £1·10 = £4·10.

EXERCISE 10.4A

1 Two numbers x and y have a sum of 47 and a difference of 9.

    a) Write down two equations in x and y.

    b) Solve them to find the numbers.

2 Cassettes cost £c each and compact discs cost £d each. John bought two cassettes and three discs and paid £27·50. Shahida bought three cassettes and one disc and paid £18·50.

    a) Write down two equations in c and d.

    b) Solve them to find the cost of a cassette and a disc.

3 Paint is sold in small and large tins. Peter needs 13 litres and he buys one small and two large tins. Gamel needs 11 litres and he buys two small and one large tin. Both have exactly the correct amount.

    Let the small tin hold s litres and the large tin hold b litres.

    a) Write down two equations in s and b.

    b) Solve them to find the amount each tin holds.

Exercise 10.4A cont'd

4 A coach journey costs each adult £a and each child £c. Tickets for one adult and two children cost £31. Tickets for two adults and three children cost £54. Use algebra to find the cost of each ticket.

5 John's age and his father's age added together make 56. His father is 28 years older than John. Write these statements as equations and solve them to find their ages.

EXERCISE 10.4B

1 Two numbers x and y have a sum of 86 and a difference of 16.

   a) Write down two equations in x and y.

   b) Solve them to find the two numbers.

2 At Turner's corner shop beans cost b pence a tin and spaghetti costs s pence a tin. Three tins of beans and two tins of spaghetti cost £1·37. Two tins of beans and a tin of spaghetti cost 81p.

   a) Write down two equations in b and s.

   b) Solve them to find the cost of each tin.

3 Orange juice is sold in cans and bottles. Cans hold c ml and bottles hold b ml. Three cans and four bottles contain 475 cl altogether. Four cans and three bottles hold 400 cl altogether. Use algebra to find how much each holds.

4 The line $x + by = c$ passes through the points (⁻1, 3) and (2, 9). Write down two equations and solve them to find b and c. Hence write down the equation of the line.

5 One boy bought 3 red lollies and 2 green lollies for a total of 48p. Another boy bought 2 red lollies and 4 green lollies for a total of 64p. Work out the cost of each lolly.

Key ideas

- To solve simultaneous equations, make the coefficient (number) of one of the letters the same in both equations. If they are the same sign subtract the equations. If they are different signs add the equations.

- To solve linear simultaneous equations graphically, draw the lines on a graph and find where they cross.

11 Cumulative frequency graphs and box plots

You should already know

● how to calculate mode, median, mean and range.

Analysing data

This section suggests one way of analysing data. There are others, including calculating the mean or the mode.

ACTIVITY 1

Cumulative frequency tables and diagrams

A plant grower wants to find out if one sort of compost is better than another. He sows equal numbers of seeds, from the same packet, in each compost and measures the height, to the nearest centimetre, of 60 plants which grow in each.

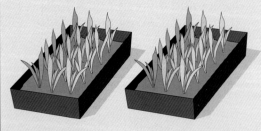

This gives a total of 120 results (60 for each compost), which is a lot to analyse.

In cases like this it is better to group the results in intervals. A sensible interval for the heights in this case would be 10 cm.

Compost A

22	13	33	31	51	24	37	83	39	28
31	64	23	35	9	34	42	26	68	38
63	34	44	77	37	15	38	54	34	22
47	25	48	38	53	52	35	45	32	31
37	43	37	49	24	17	48	29	57	33
30	36	42	36	43	38	39	48	39	59

Compost B

33	43	17	50	37	59	21	58	45	78
36	34	45	77	52	42	79	38	63	48
47	71	63	49	8	53	47	66	49	69
55	33	54	28	40	68	55	67	36	76
27	86	29	67	57	47	64	55	48	65
58	41	35	57	44	39	59	23	64	36

Activity 1 cont'd

This is like sorting the results into 'bins'.

	13	22	33		
		24	31 37		
		28	39		
$0 \leqslant h < 10$	$10 \leqslant h < 20$	$20 \leqslant h < 30$	$30 \leqslant h < 40$	$40 \leqslant h < 50$	and so on

Here are the figures for compost A, grouped into a frequency table.

Height h (cm)	Frequency	Height h (cm)	Cumulative frequency
$0 \leqslant h < 10$	1	$h < 10$	1
$10 \leqslant h < 20$	3	$h < 20$	4
$20 \leqslant h < 30$	9	$h < 30$	13
$30 \leqslant h < 40$	25	$h < 40$	38 ←38 = 1 + 3 + 9 + 25
$40 \leqslant h < 50$	11	$h < 50$	49
$50 \leqslant h < 60$	6	$h < 60$	55
$60 \leqslant h < 70$	3	$h < 70$	58
$70 \leqslant h < 80$	1	$h < 80$	59
$80 \leqslant h < 90$	1	$h < 90$	60

Exam tip

Remember that $\leqslant$ means 'less than or equal to' and $<$ means 'less than' so $30 \leqslant h < 40$ means all the heights between 30 and 40, including 30 but excluding 40.

Exam tip

In a cumulative frequency diagram, you can join the points with straight (ruled) line segments instead of a curve.

The cumulative frequency in the last column gives the running total. In this case it is the number of plants less than a certain height, for example there are 38 plants less than 40 cm high. Make sure you can see how the cumulative frequency values are obtained.

The values for cumulative frequency can be plotted to give a cumulative frequency diagram.

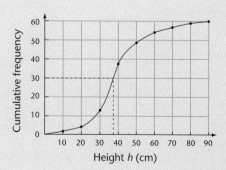

Chapter 11 *Cumulative frequency graphs and box plots*

Activity 1 cont'd

Note that the cumulative frequency values are plotted at the upper value of each interval, in this case at 10, 20, 30 and so on.

You can use a cumulative frequency diagram to estimate the median value.

There are 60 results so the median will be the halfway value, which is the 30th.

Note: If you were using a list of numbers, then for an even number of numbers the median is halfway between the two middle values.

Find 30 on the vertical scale and look across the graph until you reach the curve. Read off the corresponding value on the horizontal scale (see the dotted line on the graph).

The median height is about 37 cm; check you agree. It is also possible to calculate the quartiles. As the name suggests these are quarters: the cumulative frequency is divided into four equal parts. The median is the middle quartile. The lower quartile will be at $\frac{1}{4}$ of 60, which is the 15th value, giving a height of 31 cm. The upper quartile is at $\frac{3}{4}$ of 60, which is the 45th value, giving a height of 45 cm. The difference between these two values is called the interquartile range.

Interquartile range = 45 cm − 31 cm = 14 cm

The interquartile range shows how widely the data are spread out. Half the data are within the interquartile range, and if that range is small then the data are bunched together.

You can also use the cumulative frequency graph to estimate how many plants were taller than a given height, such as 55 cm. From the graph, a height of 55 cm corresponds to cumulative frequency 52, so the number of plants that were taller than 55 cm is 60 − 52 = 8.

1 Now construct a grouped frequency table and find the cumulative frequency for the plant heights for compost B.

2 Copy the cumulative frequency diagram for compost A. Using the same axes, draw the cumulative frequency diagram for compost B and calculate the median value and the interquartile range.

3 Compare the results for the two composts, writing down what you notice.

ACTIVITY 2

Repeat Activity 1 for a survey or an experiment of your own choice. Write up your findings.

There are several things you need to remember when you are writing up your work. Look back at the table and reread the Advice given in the Introduction.

You need to:
- show evidence of the planning that you did
- show how you found the information, who you asked and how you chose them

- include ideas for extending the task, for example suggesting other questions that you could ask
- present the information clearly
- explain or state what you wanted to find out
- state what you notice, how your analysis supports this and try to explain why the results occur.

Box plots

Look again at the results for the two composts in Activity 1.

	Lowest value	Lower quartile	Median	Upper quartile	Highest value
A	9	31	37	45	83
B	8	38	49	61	86

These figures can be shown in a diagram called a box plot.

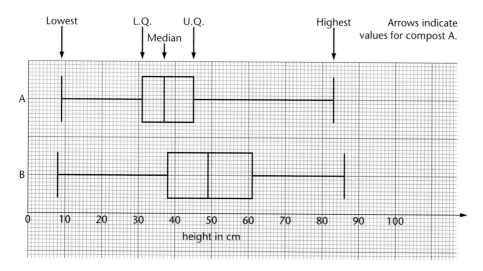

The rectangular 'box' goes from the lower quartile to the upper quartile with a line drawn through the median. The lines, sometimes called 'whiskers', extend from the smallest value to the lower quartile and from the upper quartile to the highest value.

These plots give a very quick visual comparison of the two sets of figures. It can be clearly seen that the median for B is higher. The fact that the 'box' for B is wider indicates that B has a wider spread of values.

When information is grouped and the raw scores are not available, it is often difficult to say what the highest and lowest values are. In this case estimates have to be made.

Chapter 11 *Cumulative frequency graphs and box plots*

EXERCISE 11.1A

1 The cumulative frequency curve below shows the masses of 160 boys and 160 girls in a sixth form college.

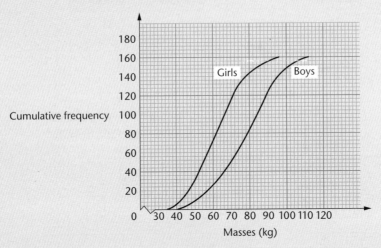

a) Use the graphs to find the medians, quartiles and interquartile ranges for both the boys and the girls.

b) Draw box plots for both the boys and the girls.

2 The table shows the yield, in litres of milk, produced by 120 cows at a certain farm on a certain day.

Yield in litres (x)	$x \leqslant 5$	$5 < x \leqslant 10$	$10 < x \leqslant 15$	$15 < x \leqslant 20$	$20 < x \leqslant 25$	$25 < x \leqslant 30$	$30 < x \leqslant 35$
Number of cows	0	10	23	35	26	17	9

a) Make a cumulative frequency table for the data and use it to draw a cumulative frequency curve. Use a scale of 2 cm to 5 litres on the horizontal axis and 2 cm to 20 cows on the vertical axis.

b) Use the curve to find the median, quartiles and interquartile range for the data.

c) Draw a box plot to show the figures in part **b)**. Assume a minimum yield of 5 litres and a maximum yield of 35 litres.

Exercise 11.1A cont'd

3 The table below shows the heights of 120 people.

Height in cm (h)	$h \leqslant 130$	$130 < h \leqslant 140$	$140 < h \leqslant 150$	$150 < h \leqslant 160$
Number of people	0	5	12	26

Height in cm (h)	$160 < h \leqslant 170$	$170 < h \leqslant 180$	$180 < h \leqslant 190$	$190 < h \leqslant 200$
Number of people	35	23	15	4

   a) Make a cumulative frequency table for the data and use it to draw a cumulative frequency curve. Use a scale of 2 cm to 10 cm on the horizontal axis and 2 cm to 20 people on the vertical axis.
   b) Use the curve to find the median, quartiles and interquartile range for the data.
   c) Draw a box plot to show the figures in part **b)**. Assume a minimum height of 130 cm and a maximum height of 200 cm.

EXERCISE 11.1B

1

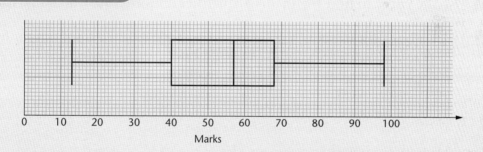

The diagram shows a box plot for the marks obtained in an examination. Use the box plot to fund these statistics for the distribution of marks.

   a) the median   **b)** the range   **c)** the interquartile range

2 The table shows the times taken for the 200 runners in a half-marathon.

Time in mins (t)	$t \leqslant 60$	$60 < t \leqslant 80$	$80 < t \leqslant 100$	$100 < t \leqslant 120$
Number of runners	0	10	37	72

Time in mins (t)	$120 < t \leqslant 140$	$140 < t \leqslant 160$	$160 < t \leqslant 180$	$180 < t \leqslant 200$
Number of runners	55	18	7	1

Chapter 11 *Cumulative frequency graphs and box plots*

Exercise 11.1B cont'd

a) Make a cumulative frequency table for the data and use it to draw a cumulative frequency curve. Use a scale of 2 cm to 20 mins on the horizontal axis and 1 cm to 20 runners on the vertical axis.

b) Use the curve to find the median, quartiles and interquartile range for the data.

c) Draw a box plot to show the figures in part **b)**. Assume a minimum time of 60 mins and a maximum time of 200 mins.

3 The length of lives of 90 light bulbs, in hours, were tested and the results recorded in the following table.

Time in hours (t)	$t \leqslant 600$	$600 < t \leqslant 625$	$625 < t \leqslant 650$	$650 < t \leqslant 675$	$675 < t \leqslant 700$	$700 < t \leqslant 725$	$725 < t \leqslant 750$
Number of bulbs	0	3	18	29	25	13	2

a) Make a cumulative frequency table for the data and use it to draw a cumulative frequency curve. Use a scale of 2 cm to 20 hours on the horizontal axis and 1 cm to 10 bulbs on the vertical axis.

b) Use the curve to find the median, quartiles and interquartile range for the data.

c) Draw a box plot to show the figures in part **b)**. Assume a minimum life of 600 hours and a maximum life of 750 hours.

Key ideas

- Grouped data are used when there are a lot of results to analyse.
- Cumulative frequency diagrams are useful for estimating the interquartile range and median of a set of data.
- Distributions can be compared using box plots.

12 Transformations

You should already know

- the terms 'object' and 'image' as they apply to transformations
- how to recognise and draw the reflection of a simple shape in a mirror line
- how to recognise and draw an enlargement of a shape using a centre and scale factor of enlargement
- how to rotate a simple shape about its centre or the origin through 90°, 180° or 270°
- how to recognise and draw simple translations
- the lines $y = x$ and $y = {}^-x$ (or $y + x = 0$).

Drawing reflections

To draw a reflection you need an object and a mirror line.

EXAMPLE 1

Reflect the L-shape in the given mirror line.

Method 1
For each vertex or corner of the L-shape, use a ruler to measure the perpendicular distance from the mirror line. Then measure the same distance on the other side of the mirror line to find the corresponding image point.

> Remember to keep the ruler at right angles to the mirror line.

Method 2
Using tracing paper, trace the object point and the mirror line. Turn the tracing paper over and line up the tracing of the mirror line with the original mirror line, but with the object on the other side. Using a pin or compass point, prick through the corners of the object on to the paper below. Remove the tracing paper and join up the pinpricks to draw the image.

> Method 2 is often the easier one when the mirror line is sloping, as it is difficult to keep the ruler at right angles to the mirror line.

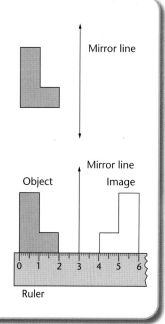

If the mirror line is easy to work with, for example the *x*-axis on a graph, it may be possible to plot the reflection by counting squares. It is still advisable to use tracing paper to check the reflection.

In mathematics all mirror lines are regarded as 'double-sided'. This means that any shape that crosses the mirror line will have part of its reflection on each side of the line.

becomes

Recognising reflections

It should be easy to recognise when a transformation is a reflection. If there is any doubt, check that the tracing paper needs to be **turned over** before it will fit on the image. Finding the mirror line can be more difficult.

EXAMPLE 2

Describe the transformation that maps shape ABC on to shape PQR.

It should be fairly obvious that the transformation is a reflection but this could be checked using tracing paper.

To find the mirror line, put a ruler between two corresponding points (B and Q) and mark a point halfway between them, at (3, 3).

Repeat this for two other corresponding points (C and R). The midpoint is (4, 4).

Join the two midpoints to find the mirror line. The mirror line is $y = x$.

The transformation is a reflection in the line $y = x$.

Again, the result can be checked using tracing paper.

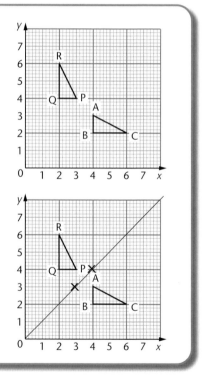

Exam tip

Tracing paper is always stated as optional extra material in examinations. When doing transformation questions, always ask for it.

Chapter 12 *Transformations*

Rotations

A rotation involves turning the object about a point, called the centre of rotations.

Drawing rotations

EXAMPLE 3

Rotate triangle ABC through 90° clockwise about C.

Measure an angle of 90° clockwise from the line AC.

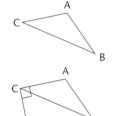

Trace the shape ABC. Put a pencil or pin at C to hold the tracing to the diagram at that point. Rotate the tracing paper until AC coincides with the new line you have drawn. Use another pin or the point of your compasses to prick through the other corners (A and B).

Join up the new points to form the image.

If the centre of rotation is not on the object then the method is slightly more difficult.

EXAMPLE 4

Rotate the triangle ABC through 90° clockwise about the point O.

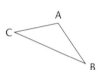

Join O to a point on the object (C). Measure an angle of 90° clockwise from OC and draw a line.

Trace the triangle ABC and the line OC. Rotate the tracing about O until the line OC coincides with the new line you have drawn. Use a pin or the point of your compasses to prick through the corners (A, B and C). Join up the pin holes to form the image.

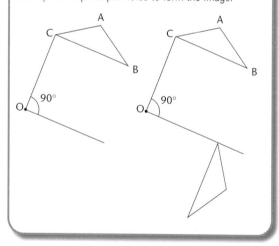

For other angles of rotation (for example 120° clockwise) the first angle is measured as 120° instead of 90°, but otherwise the method is identical.

If the centre of rotation is easy to work with, for example the origin, then you may be able to draw the rotation by counting squares but it is always best to check using tracing paper.

Recognising rotations

It is usually easy to recognise when a transformation is a rotation, as it should be possible to place a tracing of the object over the image without turning the tracing paper over.

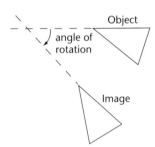

To find the angle of rotation, find a pair of sides that correspond in the object and the image. Measure the angle between them. You may need to extend both of these sides to do this.

If the centre of rotation is not on the object, its position may not be obvious. The easiest method to use is trial and error, either by counting squares or using tracing paper. In a later chapter, you will learn a method which will find the centre directly, without trial (or error!).

EXAMPLE 5

Describe fully the transformation that maps flag A onto flag B.

It is clear that the transformation is a rotation and that the angle is 90° clockwise. You may need to make a few trials, using tracing paper and a compass point centre on different points, to find that the centre of rotation is (7, 4).

If you did not spot it, try it now with tracing paper.

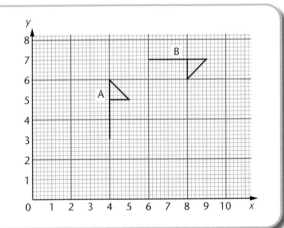

Exam tip

Always remember to state whether the rotation is clockwise or anticlockwise.

Exam tip

When describing transformations, always state the type of transformation first and then give all the necessary extra information. For reflections this is the mirror line; for rotations it is angle, direction and centre.
You will get no marks unless you actually name the transformation.

EXERCISE 12.1A

Label the diagrams you draw in this exercise carefully and keep them, as you will need them in a later exercise.

1 Draw a triangle with vertices at (1, 0), (1, ⁻2) and (2, ⁻2). Label it A. Draw the reflection of triangle A in the line $y = 1$. Label it B.

2 On the same grid as for question 1, reflect triangle B in the line $y = x$. Label the new triangle C.

3 On a new grid draw a triangle with vertices at (2, 5), (3, 5) and (1, 3). Label it D. Draw the reflection of triangle in the line $x = \frac{1}{2}$. Label it E.

4 On the same grid as for question 3, reflect triangle E in the line $y = ⁻x$. Label the new triangle F.

5 Using graph paper, copy this diagram. Rotate the flag G through 90° clockwise about the point (1, 2). Label the new flag H.

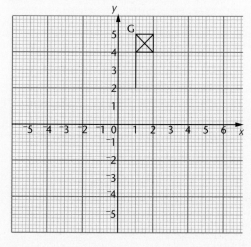

6 On the same grid as for question 5, rotate the flag H through 180° about the point (2, ⁻1). Label the new flag I.

7 Draw a triangle with vertices at (0, 1), (0, 4) and (2, 3). Label it J. Rotate triangle J through 90° anticlockwise about the point (2, 3). Label the new triangle K.

8 On the same grid as for question 7, rotate triangle K through 90° clockwise about the point (2, ⁻1). Label the new triangle L.

9 Study this diagram.

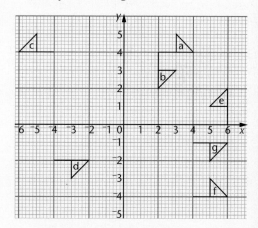

Describe fully the single transformation that maps

a) flag a onto flag b
b) flag a onto flag c
c) flag b onto flag d
d) flag b onto flag e
e) flag e onto flag f
f) flag f onto flag g.

EXERCISE 12.1B

For questions 1 to 6, either use the worksheet or copy the diagrams carefully, making them larger if you wish.

1 Reflect the trapezium in the given mirror line.

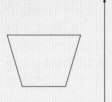

2 Reflect the triangle in the given mirror line.

3 Reflect the triangle in the given mirror line.

4 Rotate the triangle through 180° about the point C.

5 Rotate the triangle through 90° clockwise about the point O.

O×

6 Rotate the triangle through 120° clockwise about the point O.

O×

7 Study the diagram.

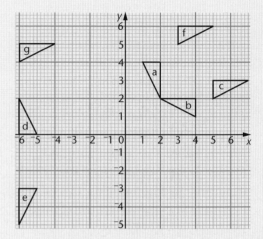

Describe fully the single transformation that maps

a) triangle a onto triangle b
b) triangle a onto triangle c
c) triangle a onto triangle d
d) triangle d onto triangle e
e) triangle e onto triangle f
f) triangle d onto triangle g.

Translations

In a **translation**, every point of an object moves the same distance in the same direction. The object and the image look identical with no turning or reflection. It looks just as if the object has moved to a different position.

Drawing translations

To draw a translation, all you need to know is how far across the page and how far up the page to move the object.

EXAMPLE 6

Translate the shape on the diagram 5 cm to the right and 3 cm down.

The dotted lines show that every point in the object has 'moved' 5 cm to the right and 3 cm down to the corresponding point in the image.

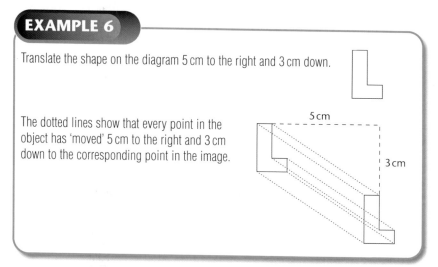

Column vectors

When working with translations, it is usual to work on a grid so it is not necessary to measure the movements.

On a grid, the movements can be described as a movement in the x-direction and a movement in the y-direction. They are written in the form of a column vector, for example $\begin{pmatrix} 5 \\ -3 \end{pmatrix}$.

In a column vector:	The directions are the same as for coordinates.
the top number represents the x-movement	If the top number is positive, move to the right.
	If the top number is negative, move to the left.
the bottom number represents the y-movement.	If the bottom number is positive, move up.
	If the bottom number is negative, move down.

EXAMPLE 7

Translate the shape on the grid through the vector $\begin{pmatrix} -3 \\ 4 \end{pmatrix}$.

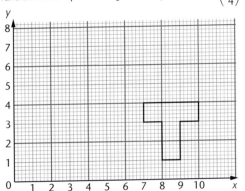

The movement represented

by the vector $\begin{pmatrix} -3 \\ 4 \end{pmatrix}$ is

3 units to the left and 4 units up, so every point in the object 'moves' this amount to form the corresponding point in the image.

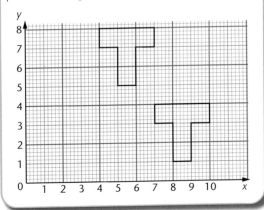

Recognising translations

It should be easy to recognise when a transformation is a translation, as the object and image look identical with no turning or reflecting. Having stated that the transformation is a translation, you need to find the column vector.

Identify a point on the object and its corresponding point on the image. Count how many units left or right and how many units up or down that point has moved. Write these movements as a column vector.

EXAMPLE 8

Describe fully the transformation that maps triangle ABC onto triangle PQR.

Point A translate on to point P. This is a movement of 6 to the right and 3 down. The transformation is

a translation through the vector $\begin{pmatrix} 6 \\ -3 \end{pmatrix}$.

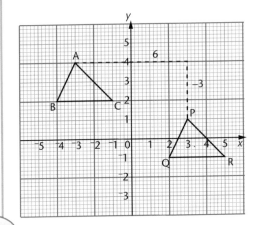

Exam tip

Try not to mix up the words 'transformation' and 'translation'. Transformation is the general name for all the changes made to shapes. Translation is the particular transformation that has been described here.

Enlargements

An **enlargement** produces an image that is exactly similar in shape to the object, but is larger or smaller.

Drawing enlargements

EXAMPLE 9

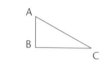

Enlarge the triangle ABC with scale factor $2\frac{1}{2}$ and centre of enlargement O, to form triangle PQR.

Draw lines from O to A, O to B and O to C and extend them.

Measure the lengths OA, OB and OC. These are 2·0 cm, 1·5 cm and 2·9 cm respectively.

Multiply these lengths by 2·5 to give OP = 5·0 cm, OQ = 3·75 cm and OR = 7·25 cm.

Measure these distances along the extended lines OA, OB and OC, and mark P, Q and R.

Join P, Q and R to form the triangle.

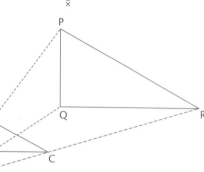

Exam tip

When you have drawn your enlargement check that the ratio of the sides of the image to the corresponding sides in the object is equal to the scale factor (in the case of Example 9, $2\frac{1}{2}$). If it is not, you have probably measured some or all of your distances from the points of the object and not from O.

EXAMPLE 10

Enlarge the shape DEF with scale factor $\frac{1}{2}$ and centre of enlargement O.

The steps are exactly the same as for Example 9 except that, instead of being multiplied by 2·5, the distances are multiplied by 0·5.

Check that OU = $\frac{1}{2}$OD, OV = $\frac{1}{2}$OE and OW = $\frac{1}{2}$OF.

Chapter 12 *Transformations*

Example 10 cont'd

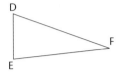

Notice that the length of each side of triangle UVW is half the length of the corresponding side in triangle DEF. In Mathematics this is still called an enlargement even though the image is smaller than the object. It just means that the scale factor is less than 1.

Recognising enlargements

EXAMPLE 11

Describe fully the transformation that maps triangle DEF onto triangle STU.

The shapes are similar, so clearly the transformation is an enlargement.

Since the lengths of the sides of triangle STU are 3 times the lengths of the corresponding sides of triangle DEF, the scale factor is 3. All that remains to be found is the centre of enlargement.

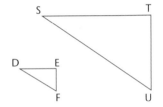

Join SD and extend it. Join UF and extend it to cross the extended line SD. The point where the lines cross, O, is the centre of enlargement.

The transformation is an enlargement, scale factor 3, centre of enlargement O.

If you were working on a grid, you would describe the centre of enlargement by stating the coordinates of the point.

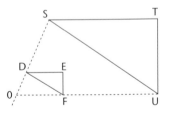

EXERCISE 12.2A

Label the diagrams you draw in this exercise carefully and keep them, as you will need them in a later exercise.

1 Draw a triangle with vertices at (1, 2), (1, 4) and (2, 4). Label it A. Draw the translation of triangle A through the vector $\begin{pmatrix} 5 \\ 2 \end{pmatrix}$. Label it B.

Exercise 12.2A cont'd

2 On the same grid as for question 1, translate triangle B through the vector $\begin{pmatrix} 2 \\ -4 \end{pmatrix}$. Label the new triangle C.

3 On a new grid, draw a triangle with vertices at (0, 2), (1, 4) and (3, 2). Label it D.

Draw the translation of triangle D through the vector $\begin{pmatrix} -4 \\ 2 \end{pmatrix}$. Label it E.

4 On the same grid as for question 3, translate triangle E through the vector $\begin{pmatrix} 8 \\ 0 \end{pmatrix}$. Label the new triangle F.

Draw a set of axes. Label the x-axis from 0 to 13 and the y-axis from 0 to 15. Use it to answer questions 5 and 6.

5 Draw a triangle with vertices at (1, 2), (2, 4) and (1, 3). Label it G. Draw the enlargement of triangle G with scale factor 2 and centre the origin. Label it H.

6 On the same grid as question 5, draw the enlargement of triangle H with scale factor 3 and centre of enlargement (0, 5). Label it I.

7 Copy the diagram. Enlarge the flag J with scale factor $1\frac{1}{2}$ and centre of enlargement (1, 2). Label the new flag K.

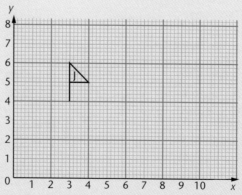

8 On the same grid you drew for question 7 enlarge the flag K with scale factor 2 and centre of enlargement (2, 8). Label the new flag L.

9 Study the diagram below.

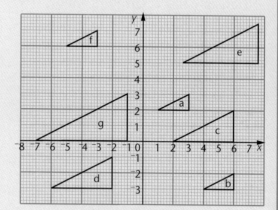

Describe fully the single transformation that maps

a) triangle a onto triangle b
b) triangle a onto triangle c
c) triangle c onto triangle d
d) triangle a onto triangle e
e) triangle a onto triangle f
f) triangle g onto triangle a.

EXERCISE 12.2B

For questions 1 to 6, either use the worksheet or copy the diagrams carefully, making them larger if you wish.

1 Translate flag A through the vector $\begin{pmatrix} -2 \\ -5 \end{pmatrix}$. Label the new flag B.

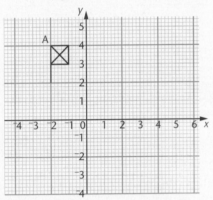

2 On the same grid you drew for question 1, translate flag B through the vector $\begin{pmatrix} 7 \\ 4 \end{pmatrix}$. Label the new flag C.

3 On the same grid you drew for question 1, translate flag C through the vector $\begin{pmatrix} -5 \\ 1 \end{pmatrix}$. Label the new flag D. What do you notice? Try to explain the result.

4 Enlarge the shape with centre O and scale factor 3.

5 Enlarge the shape with centre O and scale factor $\frac{1}{3}$.

6 Enlarge the shape with centre O and scale factor $1\frac{1}{2}$.

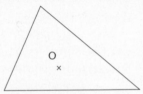

7 Study the diagram below.

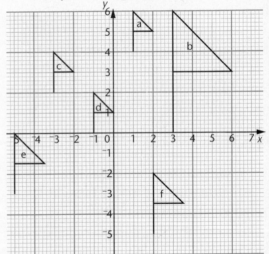

Describe fully the transformation that maps

  a) flag a onto flag b
  b) flag a onto flag c
  c) flag c onto flag d
  d) flag d onto flag e
  e) flag e onto flag f
  f) flag b onto flag d.

Combining transformations

Sometimes when one transformation is followed by another, the result is equivalent to a single transformation. For example, in the following diagram, triangle A has been translated through the vector $\begin{pmatrix} 2 \\ 5 \end{pmatrix}$ on to the triangle B.

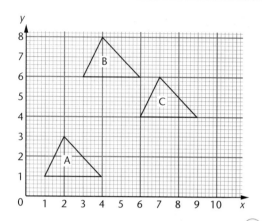

Triangle B has then been translated through the vector $\begin{pmatrix} 3 \\ -2 \end{pmatrix}$ on to triangle C.

Notice that triangle A could have been translated directly onto triangle C through the vector $\begin{pmatrix} 5 \\ 3 \end{pmatrix}$.

So the first transformation followed by the second transformation is equivalent to the single transformation:

translation through the vector $\begin{pmatrix} 5 \\ 3 \end{pmatrix}$.

Exam tip

Make sure you do the transformations in the right order, as it usually makes a difference.

If a question asks for a single transformation, do not give a combination of two transformations as this does not answer the question and will usually score no marks.

EXAMPLE 12

Find the single transformation that is equivalent to a reflection in the line $x = 1$, followed by a reflection in the line $y = ^-2$.

In the diagram, reflecting the object flag A in the line $x = 1$ gives flag B.

Reflecting flag B in the line $y = ^-2$ gives flag C.

The transformation that maps A directly onto C is a rotation through 180°.

The centre of rotation is $(1, ^-2)$, which is where the mirror lines cross.

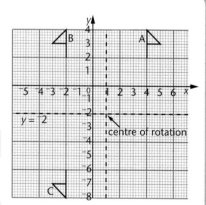

Use tracing paper to check this.

The transformation is a rotation through 180° about the centre of rotation $(1, ^-2)$.

A rotation of 180° is the only rotation for which you do not need to state the direction, as 180° clockwise is the same as 180° anticlockwise.

237

EXERCISE 12.3A

In this exercise you will need some of the diagrams you drew in Exercises 12.1A and 12.2A.

1. Look back at the diagram you drew for questions 1 and 2 of Exercise 12.2A. Describe fully the single transformation that is equivalent to a translation through the vector $\binom{5}{2}$ (A onto B) followed by a translation through the vector $\binom{2}{-4}$ (B onto C).

2. Look back at the diagram you drew for questions 3 and 4 of Exercise 12.2A. Describe fully the single transformation that is equivalent to a translation through the vector $\binom{-4}{2}$ (D onto E) followed by a translation through the vector $\binom{8}{0}$ (E onto F).

3. Look at your answers to the last two questions. Try to make a general statement about the result of translating through the vector $\binom{a}{b}$ followed by translation through the vector $\binom{c}{d}$.

4. Look back at the diagram you drew for questions 5 and 6 of Exercise 12.2A. Describe fully the single transformation that is equivalent to an enlargement, scale factor 2, centre the origin (G on to H) followed by an enlargement scale factor 3, centre (0, 5) (H onto I).

5. Look back at the diagram you drew for questions 7 and 8 of Exercise 12.2A. Describe fully the single transformation that is equivalent to an enlargement, scale factor $1\frac{1}{2}$, centre the point (1, 2) (J onto K) followed by an enlargement, scale factor 2, centre (2, 8) (K onto L).

6. Look again at the answers to the last two questions. Try to make a general statement about the result of enlarging with scale factor p followed by enlarging with scale factor q.

7. Look back at the diagram you drew for questions 1 and 2 of Exercise 12.1A. Describe fully the single transformation that is equivalent to a reflection in the line $y = 1$ (A onto B) followed by a reflection in the line $y = x$ (B onto C).

8. Look back at the diagram you drew for questions 3 and 4 of Exercise 12.1A. Describe fully the single transformation that is equivalent to a reflection in the line $x = \frac{1}{2}$ (D onto E) followed by a reflection in the line $y = -x$ (E onto F).

9. Look again at the answers to the last two questions. Try to make a general statement about the result of reflection in a mirror line followed by reflection in an intersecting mirror line.

Exercise 12.3A cont'd

10 Look back at the diagram you drew for questions 5 and 6 of Exercise 12.1A. Describe fully the single transformation that is equivalent to a rotation through 90° clockwise about the point (1, 2) (G onto H) followed by a rotation through 180° about the point (2, ⁻1) (H onto I).

11 Look back at the diagram you drew for questions 7 and 8 of Exercise 12.1A. Describe fully the single transformation that is equivalent to a rotation through 90° anticlockwise about the point (2, 3) (J onto K) followed by a rotation through 90° clockwise about the point (2, ⁻1) (K onto L).

EXERCISE 12.3B

In this exercise, carry out the transformations on a simple object shape of your choice.

1 Describe fully the single transformation that is equivalent to a reflection in the x-axis followed by reflection in the y-axis.

2 Describe fully the single transformation that is equivalent to a reflection in the line $x = 1$ followed by a reflection in the line $x = 5$.

3 Describe fully the single transformation that is equivalent to a reflection in the line $y = 2$ followed by a reflection in the line $y = 6$.

4 Look again at your answers to the last two questions. Try to make a general statement about the result of reflecting in a mirror line followed by a reflection in a parallel mirror line.

5 Describe fully the single transformation that is equivalent to an enlargement, scale factor 2 and centre the origin, followed by a translation through the vector $\begin{pmatrix} 3 \\ 2 \end{pmatrix}$.

6 Describe fully the single transformation that is equivalent to a rotation through 90° clockwise about the origin, followed by a translation through the vector $\begin{pmatrix} 4 \\ 0 \end{pmatrix}$.

7 Describe fully the single transformation that is equivalent to a reflection in the x-axis followed by a rotation through 90° anticlockwise about the origin.

8 Describe fully the single transformation that is equivalent to a reflection in the y-axis followed by a rotation through 90° anticlockwise about the origin.

Exercise 12.3B cont'd

9 Describe fully the single transformation that is equivalent to a reflection in the line $y = x$ followed by a reflection in the line $y = {}^-x$.

10 Describe fully the single transformation that is equivalent to a rotation through 90° clockwise about the point (2, 1) followed by a rotation through 90° anticlockwise about the point (3, 4).

Key ideas

- Use tracing paper to carry out or check rotations and reflections.
- When describing transformations, always give the name of the transformation and then the extra information required.

Name of transformation	Extra information
Reflection	Mirror line
Rotation	Angle, direction, centre of rotation
Translation	Column vector
Enlargement	Scale factor, centre of enlargement

- When asked to describe a single transformation, do not give a combination of transformations.

Revision exercise

1 Each year the value of an antique increases by 20% of its value at the beginning of the the year. If it was worth £450 on 1st January 1996, what was it worth on 1st January 1997? What was it worth on 1st January 1999?

2 A bacteria culture is growing at 5% a day. There are 1450 bacteria on Tuesday. How many are there three days later?

3 Shahid invests £5000 in the bank at 4% compound interest.

   a) How much will the investment be worth after 5 years?

   b) How many years will it take for the investment to be worth £7000?

4 A paper reported that the number of people taking their main holiday in Britain has reduced by 10% every year for the last five years. There were 560 people from a small town who took their main holiday in Britain five years ago. If the report is true, how many of them do so now? Give your answer to the nearest person.

5 A town's road safety campaign aims to reduce accidents by $\frac{1}{8}$ every year for the next three years. There were 860 accidents last year. If the campaign is successful, what should the number be reduced to after the three years?

6 Solve these simultaneous equations.

   a) $x + y = 15$
      $2x + y = 22$

   b) $2x + 3y = 13$
      $3x - y = 3$

   c) $2x - 3y = 3$
      $4x + 5y = 17$

   d) $3x - 6y = 3$
      $2x + 3y = 16$

   e) $x + 2y = 3$
      $3x + 3y = 3$

   f) $y = x + 5$
      $2x + 3y = 5$

   g) $2x + 3y = 8$
      $5x - 2y = 1$

   h) $x + y = 3$
      $5x + 3y = 10$

   i) $6x + 5y = {}^-2$
      $4x - 3y = 5$

7 Solve these simultaneous equations graphically.

   a) $y = x + 3$ and $y = 6 - 2x$. Use values of x from $^-1$ to 3.

   b) $y = 2x - 1$ and $3x + 2y = 12$. Use values of x from 0 to 4.

8 In 1970, a small factory employed 200 people. The frequency table shows their annual earnings.

Earnings (£E)	Frequency
$400 < E \leqslant 600$	50
$600 < E \leqslant 800$	55
$800 < E \leqslant 1000$	63
$1000 < E \leqslant 1200$	27
$1200 < E \leqslant 1400$	5

   a) Draw a cumulative frequency curve of the data.

   b) Use your graph to find:

      (i) the median earnings

      (ii) the interquartile range

      (iii) the number of employees who earned more then £900.

9 This table shows the numbers of marks obtained by candidates in an examination.

Mark	Number of candidates obtaining less than this mark
10	7
20	16
30	36
40	64
50	102
60	130
70	151
80	162
90	168
100	170

a) Draw a cumulative frequency curve of the data.

b) Use your graph to find

   (i) the median mark

   (ii) the interquartile range

   (iii) the number of candidates who obtained at least 55 marks

   (iv) the mark achieved by at least 60% of the candidates.

10 The table shows the age distribution (in millions) for males in England and Wales for two years.

Age	1881	1966
under 15	4·7	5·6
15 and under 30	3·4	4·9
30 and under 45	2·3	4·4
45 and under 60	1·4	4·4
60 and under 75	0·7	0·7
75 and under 90	0·1	0·7

a) Draw cumulative frequency graphs for the two years.

b) Use your graphs to find the medians and quartiles for the two years.

c) Draw box plots for each of the two years using the same axis. Assume a minimum age of 0 and a maximum of 90 for each year.

d) Use your box plots to compare the distributions.

11 Draw a triangle with vertices at (1, 4), (1, 6) and (2, 6). Label it A. Reflect triangle A in the line $y = x$. Label it B.

12 On the same grid you drew for question 11, rotate triangle B through 90° anticlockwise about the point (5, 5). Label the new triangle C.

13 Look again at the diagrams you drew for the last two questions. Describe fully the single transformation that is equivalent to reflection in the line $y = x$ followed by a rotation through 90° anticlockwise about the point (5, 5).

14 On a new grid, draw a triangle with vertices at (4, 1) (6, 1) and (4, 2). Label it D. Translate triangle D through the vector $\binom{2}{3}$. Label it E.

15 On the same grid you drew for question 14, enlarge triangle E with scale factor 2 and centre of enlargement (5, 7). Label the new triangle F.

16 Look again at the diagrams you drew for the last two questions. Describe fully the single transformation that is equivalent to translation through the vector $\begin{pmatrix} 2 \\ 3 \end{pmatrix}$ followed by enlargement with scale factor 2 and centre of enlargement (5, 7).

17 Study this diagram.

Describe fully the single transformation that maps

a) flag a onto flag b
b) flag b onto flag c
c) flag a onto flag d
d) flag d onto flag b
e) flag e onto flag a
f) flag a onto flag f.

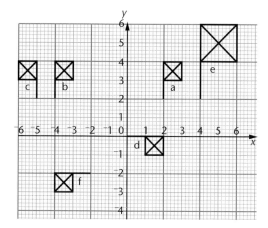

13 Standard form

You should already know

● how to multiply and divide using the rules of powers.

Standard form

Standard form is a very important use of powers and indices. It is a way of writing numbers as a number from 1 to 10 multiplied by a power of 10.

EXAMPLE 1

$4\,000\,000 = 4 \times 10^6$

$0{\cdot}03 = 3 \times 10^{-2}$

EXAMPLE 2

The speed of light is $300\,000\,000$ m/s

$= 3 \times 100\,000\,000$ This line can be omitted.

$= 3 \times 10^8$ m/s

A virus is $0{\cdot}000\,000\,000\,56$ cm in diameter

$= \dfrac{5{\cdot}6}{10\,000\,000\,000}$ This line can be omitted.

$= 5{\cdot}6 \times 10^{-10}$ cm

Exam tip

Standard form is useful for expressing very large or very small numbers.

Exam tip

In standard form, a number is written as a number from 1 to 10 multiplied by a power of 10.

EXERCISE 13.1A

1 Write these numbers in standard form.

a) 5000   **b)** 50
c) 70 000   **d)** 46
e) 0.02   **f)** 546 000
g) 0.000 45   **h)** 16 million

2 These numbers are in standard form. Write them out in full.

a) 5×10^2 **b)** 4×10^5
c) 6×10^{-3} **d)** 4.5×10^3
e) 8.4×10^{-3} **f)** 2.87×10^{-5}
g) 9.7×10^3 **h)** 5.55×10^{-5}

EXERCISE 13.1B

1 Write these numbers in standard form.

a) 6000   **b)** 80
c) 30 000   **d)** 67
e) 0.08   **f)** 897 000
g) 0.000 54   **h)** 18 million

2 These numbers are in standard form. Write them out in full.

a) 7×10^2 **b)** 8×10^5
c) 3×10^{-3} **d)** 2.5×10^3
e) 6.7×10^{-3} **f)** 3.82×10^{-5}
g) 5.7×10^3 **h)** 4.65×10^{-5}

Exam tip

Find out how your calculator deals with standard form. Most do not require '× 10' but have an [EXP] key. On these, to enter [4] × 10³ press [4] [EXP] [3].

Working with numbers in standard form

Always take care when working with numbers written in standard form. With multiplication and division you can deal with the numbers in the normal way.

EXAMPLE 3

Work out $(3 \times 10^2) \times (4 \times 10^3)$.
$(3 \times 10^2) \times (4 \times 10^3) = 3 \times 4 \times 10^2 \times 10^3$
$= 12 \times 10^{2+3}$
$= 12 \times 10^5$
$= 1.2 \times 10^6$

EXAMPLE 4

Work out $(6 \times 10^8) \div (2 \times 10^3)$. Give your answer in standard form.

$(6 \times 10^8) \div (2 \times 10^3) = (6 \div 2) \times (10^8 \div 10^3)$

$$= 3 \times (10^{8-3})$$
$$= 3 \times 10^5$$

On the calculator this can be done as $\boxed{6}\,\boxed{\text{EXP}}\,\boxed{8}\,\boxed{\div}\,\boxed{2}\,\boxed{\text{EXP}}\,\boxed{3}\,\boxed{=}$

This gives the answer as 300 000 which can then be changed into standard form as 3×10^5

Addition and subtraction are not so straightforward.

EXAMPLE 5

Work out $(3 \times 10^2) + (4 \times 10^3)$.

It is safer to write out the numbers in the brackets first, add then change the answer back into standard form.

$(3 \times 10^2) + (4 \times 10^3) = 300 + 4000$

$$= 4300 = 4.3 \times 10^3$$

EXERCISE 13.2A

1 Work out these calculations without using your calculator. Give your answers in standard form.

a) $(4 \times 10^4) \times (2 \times 10^3)$
b) $(3 \times 10^3) \times (2 \times 10^5)$
c) $(9 \times 10^7) \div (3 \times 10^4)$
d) $(7 \times 10^8) \div (2 \times 10^2)$
e) $(6 \times 10^5) \times (2 \times 10^3)$
f) $(5 \times 10^3) + (7 \times 10^4)$
g) $(7 \times 10^6) - (3 \times 10^3)$
h) $(3 \times 10^3) + (3 \times 10^2)$
i) $(6 \times 10^3) - (5 \times 10^2)$

2 The table shows information about the Earth.

Distance from the Sun	149 503 000 km
Circumference of solar orbit	9.4×10^8 km
Speed of the Earth in solar orbit	0.106×10^6 km/h
Speed of the solar system	20.1 km/s

Exercise 13.2A cont'd

   a) Write the speed of the Earth in standard form.

   b) How far does the Earth travel at this speed in one day? Give your answer in standard form correct to two significant figures.

   c) How far does the solar system travel in one day? Give your answer in standard form correct to three significant figures.

   d) If an object travelled from the earth to the sun and back, how far would it travel? Give your answer in standard form correct to two significant figures.

EXERCISE 13.2B

1 Work out these calculations. Give your answers in standard form.

   a) $(4 \cdot 2 \times 10^4) \times (2 \cdot 3 \times 10^3)$

   b) $(3 \cdot 2 \times 10^2) \times (2 \cdot 7 \times 10^5)$

   c) $(9 \cdot 8 \times 10^7) \div (1 \cdot 4 \times 10^4)$

   d) $(8 \cdot 28 \times 10^8) \div (2 \cdot 3 \times 10^2)$

   e) $(5 \cdot 8 \times 10^5) \times (3 \cdot 5 \times 10^3)$

   f) $(4 \times 10^3) + (5 \times 10^4)$

   g) $(8 \times 10^6) - (4 \times 10^3)$

   h) $(2 \times 10^3) + (4 \times 10^2)$

   i) $(4 \times 10^3) - (3 \times 10^2)$

2 The hydrogen atom has a diameter of 10^{-8} cm. It has a mass of $1 \cdot 7 \times 10^{-24}$ g.

   a) How many atoms in a line will give a length of 1 mm?

   b) How many atoms would weigh 1 kg? Give your answer in standard form correct to two significant figures.

Key ideas

- Standard form is used as a way of dealing with very large and very small numbers.
- Numbers are written as $a \times 10^n$ where a is between 1 and 10.
- Large numbers like 93 million (93 000 000) are written as $9 \cdot 3 \times 10^7$.
- Small numbers like 0·000 007 82 are written as $7 \cdot 82 \times 10^{-6}$.
- Standard form numbers are set on the calculator using the EXP button.

Chapter 13 *Standard form*

Sequences

You should already know

● the sets of square and cube numbers.

Linear sequences

Look at this sequence.

2, 5, 8, 11, 14 ......

The terms of the sequence increase by three every time. When the increase is constant the sequence is called a linear sequence.

In the same way the sequence   11, 9, 7, 5, 3, 1, ⁻1, ... is also linear since the terms decrease by the same amount (two) every time.

Another way of thinking of this is that you are adding ⁻2 each time. This idea will help with finding the nth term.

The nth term

It is often possible to find a formula to give the terms in a sequence.

You usually use n to stand for the number of a term.

EXAMPLE 1

If the formula is nth term = $2n + 1$, then

the first term   = $2 \times 1 + 1 = 3$

the second term = $2 \times 2 + 1 = 5$

the third term   = $2 \times 3 + 1 = 7$

EXERCISE 14.1A

Each of these is the formula for the nth term. Find the first four terms of the sequence.

1 $n + 1$ **6** $3n + 1$

2 $2n$ **7** $5n - 3$

3 $2n - 1$ **8** $10n$

4 $n + 5$ **9** $7n - 7$

5 $3n$ **10** $2 - n$

EXERCISE 14.1B

Each of these is the formula for the nth term. Find the first four terms of the sequence.

1 n
2 $n + 3$
3 $4n$
4 $n - 1$
5 $2n + 1$

6 $3n - 1$
7 $6n + 5$
8 $2n - 3$
9 $5 - n$
10 $10 - 2n$

Notice how this works: if the formula contains a $2n$, the terms increase by 2 each time; if it contains $5n$, the terms increase by 5 each time. If it contains ^-3n it increases by $^-3$ (or goes down three) each time. So to find a formula for a given sequence, find how much more (or less) each term is than the one before it.

EXAMPLE 2

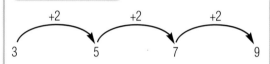

The differences between the terms is 2, so the formula will include $2n$.

When $n = 1$, $2n = 2$, but the first term is 3, which is 1 more.

The formula will be nth term $= 2n + 1$.

Exam tip

This will always work if the differences are the same each time.

EXERCISE 14.2A

Find the nth terms for each of these sequences.

1	1	2	3	4
2	4	6	8	10
3	4	8	12	16
4	0	2	4	6
5	7	11	15	19
6	1	7	13	19
7	11	21	31	41
8	5	8	11	14
9	101	201	301	401
10	25	23	21	19

EXAMPLE 3

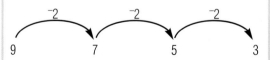

The differences here are still 2 but they must be negative 2, as the terms are getting smaller.

This time the formula will include ^-2n, to make the terms get smaller.

When $n = 1$, $^-2n = ^-2$ but the term is 9, which is 11 more.

The formula for the nth term is $^-2n + 11$ or $11 - 2n$.

EXERCISE 14.2B

Find the *n*th terms for each of these sequences.

1	0	1	2	3
2	2	5	8	11
3	7	9	11	13
4	4	9	14	19
5	15	20	25	30
6	⁻1	3	7	11
7	5	7	9	11
8	101	102	103	104
9	4	3	2	1
10	7	4	1	⁻2

Finding the *n*th term of a quadratic sequence

As you saw in the last section, the *n*th term of a sequence, where the rule is linear, can be found by looking at the first differences, which are constant.

If the rule is not linear, for example a quadratic containing n^2, the first differences will not be constant. Find the second differences.

Exam tip

Check that the *n*th term is correct by trying the first few terms, putting $n = 1, 2, 3$.

EXAMPLE 4

Work out the *n*th term for this sequence.

4   7   12   19   28

Look at the differences.

Sequence:		4		7		12		19		28
First differences:			3		5		7		9	
Second differences:				2		2		2		

The second differences are constant.

The rule for the *n*th term in sequences like this one will involve n^2 and the coefficient of n^2 will be half the second difference.

In the sequence above, dividing 2 by 2 gives 1, so the *n*th term must include $1n^2$ or just n^2.

Now compare the original sequence with the sequence n^2.

Sequence:	4	7	12	19	28
n^2:	1	4	9	16	25
Subtract n^2:	3	3	3	3	3

The *n*th term is $n^2 + 3$.

EXAMPLE 5

Work out the nth term for this sequence.

2 11 26 47 74

Look at the differences.

Sequence:		2		11		26		47		74
First differences:			9		15		21		27	
Second differences:				6		6		6		

Dividing 6 by 2 gives 3, so the nth term will include $3n^2$.

Subtract $3n^2$ from each term.

Sequence:	2	11	26	47	74
$3n^2$	3	12	27	48	75
Subtract	¯1	¯1	¯1	¯1	¯1

So the nth term is $3n^2 - 1$.

Most of the sequences you will have to deal with will be like those in Examples 4 and 5, but you may be asked to find the nth term of sequences that include n^2, n and a number.

EXAMPLE 6

Work out the nth term for this sequence.

2 7 14 23 34

Sequence:		2		7		14		23		34
For differences:			5		7		9		11	
Second differences:				2		2		2		

Dividing 2 by 2 gives 1 so the nth term will include n^2.

Subtract n^2 from the sequence.

Sequence:	2	7	14	23	34
n^2:	1	4	9	16	25
Subtract	1	3	5	7	9

This sequence is like those you dealt with in the last section.

The difference is 2 so the nth term will include $2n$.

When $n = 1$, $2n$ is 2, but the term is 1 so the nth term is $2n - 1$ for this sequence.

The nth term for the main sequence is therefore $n^2 + 2n - 1$.

ACTIVITY 1

Which of these sequences are linear, which are quadratic and which are neither? For the linear and quadratic sequences, write down the next two terms.

3	5	7	9
43	40	38	35
78	75	72	69
1	5	9	13
4	9	16	25
1	6	15	28
2	9	16	23

ACTIVITY 2

Using the numbers from Activity 1, find some quadratic sequences and write down the next two terms.

Write three different quadratic sequences and exchange them with your neighbour. See if you can find the next two terms of the other's sequences.

ACTIVITY 3

For these diagrams copy the sequences and add the next two terms. Try to find a formula for the nth term.

This last sequence is called the sequence of triangle numbers.

EXERCISE 14.3A

Find the *n*th term of each of these sequences.

1	2	5	10	17	26
2	1	7	17	31	49
3	5	8	13	20	29
4	6	15	30	51	78
5	⁻1	2	7	14	23
6	7	16	31	52	79
7	1	13	33	45	97
8	4	9	16	25	36
9	2	8	16	26	38
10	2	6	12	20	30

EXERCISE 14.3B

Find the *n*th term of each of these sequences.

1	3	6	11	18	27
2	4	13	28	49	76
3	6	9	14	21	30
4	6	12	22	36	54
5	1	10	25	46	73
6	8	14	24	38	56
7	1	16	41	76	121
8	1	5	11	19	29
9	0	5	12	21	32
10	⁻2	⁻2	0	4	10

Key ideas

- To find the *n*th term of a sequence, find the differences between the terms. If these differences are all the same the sequence is linear.

- If this difference is '*a*' the *n*th term will be $an \pm b$. Put in a value of *n* to find the value of *b*.

- If the sequence is not linear find the second differences. If these are all the same the sequence is quadratic. The coefficient of n^2 will be half the second difference.

15 Trigonometry

You should already know

● how to measure angles and do scale drawings.

You will need a protractor and a ruler for this section.

The hypotenuse is the longest side of a right-angled triangle. It is the side opposite the right angle.

The other sides are named according to the angle under consideration.

For angle a:

For angle b:

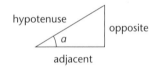

In Activity 1 you will need to draw triangles and identify the sides, like this.

ACTIVITY 1

On copies of these triangles, label the sides of these triangles with the Labels O, A or H opposite the angle, adjacent to the angle and hypotenuse.

For example

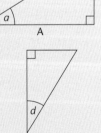

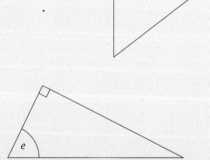

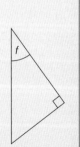

ACTIVITY 2

1 Draw six different triangles. Use these values for *a* but make the adjacent side 5 cm long each time.

a) 10° **b)** 20° **c)** 30° **d)** 40° **e)** 50° **f)** 60°

a is the angle between the adjacent and the hypotenuse.

For each triangle, measure the length of the opposite side and divide this by the length of the adjacent side (5 cm). Record your results in a table like this one. Round each ratio to one decimal place.

Angle *a* (°)	Adjacent (cm)	Opposite (cm)	Opposite Adjacent
10	5		
20	5		
30	5		
40	5		
50	5		
60	5		

Now draw two more triangles. Keep the angle fixed at 30° but change the length of the adjacent side to 10 cm and then 15 cm. Record your results in a table like this.

Angle *a* (°)	Adjacent (cm)	Opposite (cm)	Opposite Adjacent
30	5		
30	10		
30	15		

What do you notice?

What do you think the length of the opposite side would be, if you drew another triangle with *a* = 30° and the adjacent side 20 cm long? Estimate your answer and then check by drawing and measuring.

2 What do you think the length of the adjacent side would be, if you drew another triangle with *a* = 30° and the opposite side 8 cm long? Estimate your answer and check by drawing and measuring.

The radio $\frac{\text{opposite}}{\text{adjacent}}$ is called the tangent (ratio).

The value of the tangent has been calculated for all angles and is one of the functions on a scientific calculator.

3 Now look back at all the triangles you have drawn and for each one measure the length of the hypotenuse.

Copy this table and complete it.

Write the ratios correct to one decimal place.

Activity 2 cont'd

Angle (°)	Adjacent (cm)	Opposite (cm)	Hypotenuse (cm)	Opposite / Hypotenuse	Adjacent / Hypotenuse
10	5				
20	5				
30	5				
40	5				
50	5				
60	5				
30	5				
30	10				
30	15				

What do you notice?

The ratio $\dfrac{\text{opposite}}{\text{hypotenuse}}$ is called the sine (ratio).

The ratio $\dfrac{\text{adjacent}}{\text{hypotenuse}}$ is called the cosine (ratio).

You can use the tangent ratio to calculate the missing side or angle in a right-angled triangle. This is shown in Examples 1 and 2.

Activity 2 cont'd

EXAMPLE 1

Calculate the value of x.

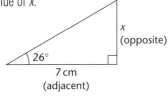

In the triangle, $\quad \tan 26° = \dfrac{\text{opposite}}{\text{adjacent}}$

$$= \dfrac{x}{7}$$

So: $\quad \dfrac{x}{7} = \tan 26°$

$\qquad x = 7 \times \tan 26°$

$\qquad\quad = 7 \times 0{\cdot}4877$

$\qquad\quad = 3{\cdot}414$

$\qquad x = 3{\cdot}41$ cm (to 3 s.f.)

> **Exam tip**
>
> Always label the sides of the triangle as adjacent, opposite and hypotenuse (or A, O and H) when you are using the ratios to calculate sides or angles.

> **Exam tip**
>
> Only label the sides you are given. This helps you to identify which formula to use. Here, since O and A are labelled, use the tan formula.

EXAMPLE 2

Find the size of the angle marked a.

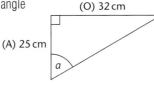

In the triangle, $\tan a = \dfrac{\text{opposite}}{\text{adjacent}}$

$$= \dfrac{32}{25}$$

$\tan a = 1{\cdot}28$

$\qquad a = \tan^{-1} 1{\cdot}28$

$\qquad a = 52{\cdot}0°$ (to 1 d.p.)

> **Exam tip**
>
> Use the $\boxed{\sin^{-1}}$, $\boxed{\cos^{-1}}$ or $\boxed{\tan^{-1}}$ button on your calculator to find the angle.

Chapter 15 *Trigonometry*

Activity 2 cont'd

4 Find the length of the side marked *x* in each of these triangles.

a)

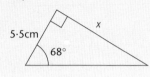

b)

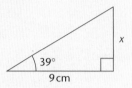

c)

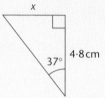

d)

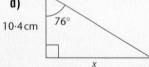

e)

f)

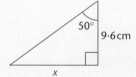

5 Find the size of the angle marked a in each of these triangles.

a)

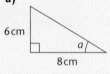

b)

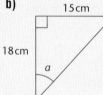

c)

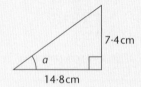

d)

e)

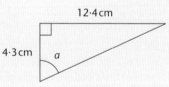

You can also use the sine or cosine radios to calculate the missing side or angle in a right-angled triangle.

Activity 2 cont'd

EXAMPLE 3

Calculate the value of *x*.

(H) 5cm
x (O)
34°

In the triangle, $\sin 34° = \dfrac{\text{opposite}}{\text{hypotenuse}}$

So: since $34° = \dfrac{x}{5}$

$x = 5 \times \sin 34°$

$x = 2·80\,\text{cm}$ (to 2 d.p.)

Exam tip

Take care when you are finding the hypotenuse. Remember to multiply by *x* and divide by cos 61°.

EXAMPLE 4

Calculate the value of *x*.

61°   19cm (A)
x
(H)

In the triangle $\cos 61° = \dfrac{\text{adjacent}}{\text{hypotenuse}}$

$\cos 61° = \dfrac{19}{x}$

$x = \dfrac{19}{\cos 61°}$

$x = 39·19\,\text{cm}$ (to 2 d.p.)

6 Find the length of the side marked *x* in each to these triangles.

a)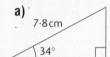
7·8cm
x
34°

b)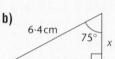
6·4cm
75°
x

c)
x
42° 6·2cm

d)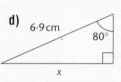
6·9cm
80°
x

e)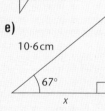
10·6cm
67°
x

Find the size of the angle marked *a* in each of these triangles.

f)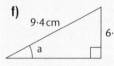
9·4cm
6·3cm
a

g)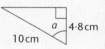
a   4·8cm
10cm

h)
5·8cm
a   13cm

i)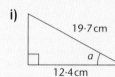
19·7cm
a
12·4cm

j)
6·0cm   *a*   12·0cm

Exam tip

Follow these three steps.

Step 1 Draw and label a diagram.
Step 2 Label the two appropriate sides as O, A or H.
Step 3 Write down the formula to be used and calculate the answer.

Chapter 15 Trigonometry

Activity 2 cont'd

Using trigonometry to solve problems

EXAMPLE 5

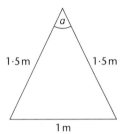

The diagram shows the front view of a tent which is in the shape of an isosceles triangle. The sloping height is 1·5 m and the base is 1 m.

a) Calculate angle *a*.

b) Calculate the perpendicular height of the triangle.

First draw in the perpendicular height (line of symmetry) for the triangle.

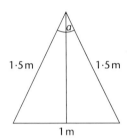

Now use either side of the shape as your right-angled triangle.

a) $\sin\left(\dfrac{1}{2}a\right) = \dfrac{0\cdot5}{1\cdot5} = 0\cdot3$

$\dfrac{1}{2}a = 17\cdot46$

$a = 2 \times 17\cdot46 = 34\cdot9°$ to 3 s.f.

b) $h = \sqrt{(1\cdot5^2 - 0\cdot5^2)} = 1\cdot41$ to 3 s.f.

EXAMPLE 6

A kite flies at the end of a string 20 m long. The string is straight and it makes an angle of 47° with the horizontal. How high is the kite from the ground?

Step 1

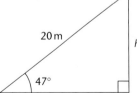

Step 2

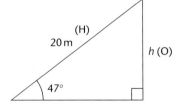

Step 3 In the triangle $\sin 47° = \dfrac{O}{H} = \dfrac{h}{20}$

So $h = 20 \times \sin 47°$

$h = 14\cdot6$ m (1 d.p.)

Activity 2 cont'd

7 Use trigonometric ratios to solve these problems.

a) A ladder of length 4·8 m rests against a vertical wall so that the base of the ladder is 1·8 m from the wall. Calculate the angle between the ladder and the ground.

b) A ladder of length 5 m rests against a vertical wall. The angle between the ladder and the wall is 62°. How far up the wall does the ladder reach?

c) From a distance of 25 m, the angle of elevation from the ground to the top of a tower is 37°. How high is the tower?

25 m

d) A ship is due South of a lighthouse. It sails on a bearing of 065° until it is due East of the lighthouse.

If the ship is now 40 km away from the lighthouse, how far has it sailed?

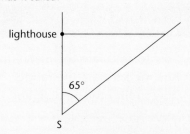

lighthouse •

65°

S

e) An isosceles triangle has sides of length 8 cm, 8 cm and 5 cm. Find the angle between the equal sides.

f) Find the acute angle between the diagonals of a rectangle with sides of 5 cm and 8 cm.

g) A path slopes up a hill at 12° from the horizontal. The path is 2·8 km long. How high is the hill?

h) A ship sails for 70 km on a bearing of 130°. How far South and East of its starting point is it?

Key ideas

In a **right-angled triangle, for angle** x:

$$\tan x = \frac{O}{A}$$

$$\sin x = \frac{O}{H}$$

$$\cos x = \frac{A}{H}$$

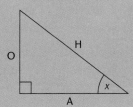

Chapter 15 *Trigonometry*

16 Comparing

> ### You should already know
>
> - how to calculate the mean, median and mode for grouped and ungrouped data
> - how to calculate the range
> - how to find the median and interquartile range from a cumulative frequency graph.

Comparing data

Comparing sizes of sets of data

If there are two (or more) sets of data it is often necessary to make comparisons between them. For instance, if the information in the table gives the marks obtained by John and Aisha in their last five Maths tests, the question may arise as to who is better at Maths.

| John | 7 | 8 | 10 | 4 | 6 |
| Aisha | 8 | 9 | 7 | 8 | 6 |

One way to compare the two sets of figures is to calculate the mean of their scores.

John's mean = 35 ÷ 5 = 7

Aisha's mean = 38 ÷ 5 = 7·6

This would suggest that Aisha is better at Maths than John.

Whilst the mean is often a reliable way of comparing sets of data it is unwise to draw too many conclusions from such a small amount of data. It may be that the topics tested were just more suited to Aisha and, in any case, the difference is not large.

The three measurements of 'average', the mean, median and mode, can all be used to compare the sets of data.

Usually the mean, which takes into account all the data, is the most reliable but there are circumstances where this is not so. One or two very large or very small figures can distort a mean and give a false impression.

EXAMPLE 1

Here are John and Aisha's score in the last ten Maths tests.

John	7	8	10	4	6	3	8	5	9	8
Aisha	8	9	7	8	6	9	8	7	6	9

Who is better at Maths?

John's mean = 68 ÷ 10 = 6·8

Aisha's mean = 77 ÷ 10 = 7·7

These figures suggest that Aisha is better at Maths and, since we now have more evidence, the conclusion is likely to be more reliable than before.

EXAMPLE 2

The tables give the sale prices of houses in two areas. Which area has the higher house prices?

Area A	
Price in pounds (£)	Numbers of houses
40 000–59 999	5
60 000–79 999	17
80 000–99 999	64
100 000–119 999	11
120 000–139 999	3

Area B	
Price in pounds (£)	Numbers of houses
40 000–59 999	0
60 000–79 999	16
80 000–99 999	27
100 000–119 999	47
120 000–139 999	10

The modal class of area A is £80 000–£99 999.

The modal class of area B is £100 000–£119 999.

This suggests that the houses are more expensive in area B.

Exam tip

When comparing relative sizes of data always try to interpret the information in the question. For example in John and Aisha's case, say that Aisha is better at Maths rather than Aisha's mean is higher than John's. In the case of house prices, state that Area B's houses are more expensive, not that their modal class is higher.

Comparing spread of sets of data

When comparing sets of data, it is generally not sufficient to know that values in one set are, on average, 'bigger' than those in the other. It is also helpful to know whether one set of data is more spread out than the other.

The two measurements of spread that have been covered so far are the **range** and the **interquartile range**.

Look again at John and Aisha's scores in the last ten Maths tests.

John	7	8	10	4	6	3	8	5	9	8
Aisha	8	9	7	8	6	9	8	7	6	9

John's range is 10 – 3 = 7

Aisha's range is 9 – 6 = 3

These figures show that John's spread of scores is greater than Aisha's.

Another way of stating the conclusion is to say that Aisha is more **consistent** than John.

The cumulative frequency graphs shown here are for the house prices in Example 2.

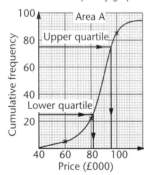
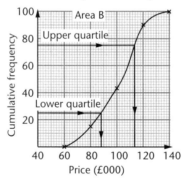

Use the interquartile ranges to compare the spread of the house prices in the two areas.

The interquartile range for area A = £95 000 – £82 000 = £13 000.

The interquartile range for area B = £114 000 – £88 000 = £26 000.

So the spread of house prices is greater in area B than in area A.

The median, range and interquartile range of distributions can be compared visually by means of a box plot.

For the houses in Example 3 the median in area A is £89 000 and the median in area B is £104 000.

The box plots for the two areas look like this.

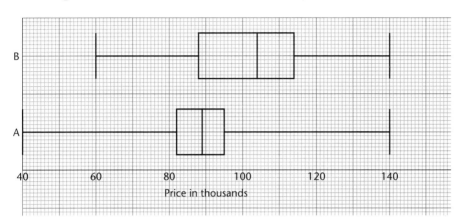

Price in thousands

These box plots assume minimum prices of £40 000 and £60 000 and a maximum price of £139 999 for both areas, but you cannot be certain of that from the tables. In fact there is a strong likelihood that, for example, the maximum price in area A is below £139 999.

It is sometimes possible to compare spreads of distributions if there is a marked difference in the shape of the frequency diagrams.

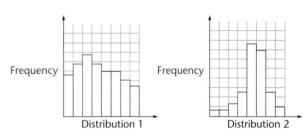

Looking at these frequency diagrams, you can see that the data in distribution 1 are much more spread out than the data in distribution 2.

Exam tip

When comparing spread of data, always try to interpret the information in the question. For example, in John and Aisha's case state that Aisha is more consistent rather than that her range is smaller. In the house price question, state that area B's prices are more spread out rather than that the interquartile range is greater. When asked to compare sets of data, always try to make both comparisons, that is relative size and spread.

EXERCISE 16.1A

1 In golf the lowest score is the best. Colin's mean score in this season's golf rounds is 71. His lowest score is 63 and his highest is 88. Vijay's mean score is 73. His lowest score is 66 and his highest score is 82. Make two comparisons of the two players' scores.

2 The table shows the results of an investigation into costs of dental treatment in two towns.

	Median cost	Interquartile range
Town A	£19·25	£4·20
Town B	£16·50	£5·30

Make two comparisons of the cost of dental treatment in the two towns.

3 Here is a set of nine numbers.

8 6 7 3 12 6 11 5 8

Write down another set of nine numbers with the same median but a larger range.

4 The table shows the amounts of rainfall, in millimetres, in twelve months in Moralia and Sivarium.

	J	F	M	A	M	J	J	A	S	O	N	D
Moralia	25	23	21	18	18	16	15	14	18	17	22	27
Sivarium	5	6	8	12	18	78	70	21	7	4	3	2

Find the mean and range for each of the places and state your conclusions.

5 Here are Tara's and Justin's marks in their last five English homeworks.

Tara	14	15	17	13	15
Justin	10	18	11	19	20

Calculate the mean and range of each of the two pupils' scores and state your conclusions.

Why might these conclusions be somewhat unreliable?

Exercise 16.1A cont'd

6 The numbers of letters delivered to the houses in two roads are shown in this table.

Number of letters	Number of houses	
	Jubilee Road	Riverside Road
0	2	0
1	27	5
2	18	16
3	11	29
4	5	18
5	3	5
6	1	4
7	0	3
8	0	2
9	0	1

Find the mode and range of the numbers of letters delivered in the two roads and state your conclusions.

7 The table shows the amounts of pocket money (to the nearest pound) received by pupils in Class 9a.

Amount of pocket money in pounds (£)	Number of pupils
2	1
3	5
4	10
5	7
6	4

   a) Calculate an estimate for the mean and range of the amounts of pocket money received.

   b) In class 9b the mean amount of pocket money is £3·80 and the range is £8.
Compare the amounts of pocket money in the two classes.

8 The cumulative frequency diagrams show the times of response to 100 alarm calls for two fire brigades.

   a) Use the graphs to find the median and interquartile range of the response times for each fire brigade.

   b) Comment on your results in part a).

   c) Draw box plots to compare the results for each fire brigade.

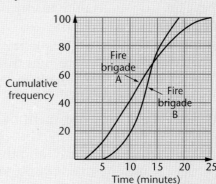

Chapter 16 *Comparing*

Exercise 16.1A cont'd

9 Panesh is buying light bulbs. Britelite have mean life of 300 hours with a range of 200 hours. Lightglo have a mean life of 280 hours and a range of 20 hours. Which would you advise Panesh to buy? Explain why.

EXERCISE 16.1B

1 The median age of the Ribchester hockey team is 24 years 9 months and the range is 8 years 2 months. The median age of Sillington hockey team is 22 years 5 months and the range is 5 years 4 months. Make two statements to compare the ages of the two teams.

2 The lengths of time in minutes spent on homework by Gareth and Salima on five days in a week are listed here.

	M	Tu	W	Th	F
Gareth	50	60	45	80	70
Salima	20	80	100	30	55

Find the mean and range of the two pupils' times. State your conclusions.

3 The table shows the mean and interquartile range of the price of a 'standard basket of shopping' in two regions of the country.

	Mean	Interquartile range
Region A	£43·52	£3·54
Region B	£46·54	£1·68

Compare the prices in the two regions.

4 The table shows the amounts spent on Christmas presents by the 120 pupils in year 10.

Amount of money in pounds (£)	Number of pupils
0·00–4·99	3
5·00–9·99	14
10·00–14·99	36
15·00–19·99	50
20·00–24·99	13
25·00–29·99	4

a) Draw a cumulative frequency diagram and use it to find the median and interquartile range for the money spent.

b) The median amount spent by year 11 pupils was £19, the lower quartile was £17 and the upper quartile was £21·50. The minimum was £5 and the maximum £31. Draw a box plot for each of the years.

c) Compare the distributions of money spent by year 10 and year 11 pupils.

Exercise 16.1B cont'd

5 The frequency diagrams show the number of children per family, in two classes.

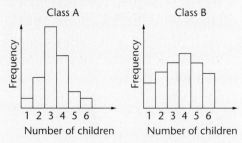

Class A   Class B

Number of children   Number of children

Use the modes and the shapes of the diagrams to compare the distributions.

6 These are the weekly earnings, in pounds, of the employees at a small firm.

96 120 120 125 137 145
157 190 200 220 590

State, with reasons, which measurement of spread you would use to compare this firm with another, similar, small firm.

7 The lengths of 100 leaves from an ash tree in a park in a city centre are shown in the table. The lengths are measured to the nearest centimetre.

Length of leaf (cm)	Frequency
9	12
10	15
11	33
12	19
13	13
14	8

a) Calculate an estimate for the mean length of leaf and estimate the range.

b) Leaves from an ash tree from a country area have a mean length of 12·7 cm and a range of 4·2 cm. Compare the distributions of the leaves from the two different areas.

8 The table shows the means and interquartile ranges of two batsmen's scores in their last 20 innings.

	Mean	Interquartile range
Mike	43·4	6·4
Alec	47·8	15·2

Which batsman would you select? Explain why.

Key ideas

- The mean, median and mode can be used to compare distributions.
- The range and interquartile range can be used to compare the spread of distributions.
- The interquartile range disregards extreme values.
- Distributions can also be compared using box plots.

Revision exercise

1 Write these numbers in standard form.

a) 7600   **b)** 89·9   **c)** 60 000
d) 466   **e)** 0·056   **f)** 564 600
g) 0·0055   **h)** 67 400
i) 0·000 042 **j)** 24 million

2 These numbers are in standard form. Write them out in full.

a) 6×10^3 **b)** 5×10^2
c) 7×10^{-3} **d)** 4.5×10^2
e) 8.4×10^{-3} **f)** 2.87×10^{-3}
g) 4.7×10^3 **h)** 5.5×10^{-2}
i) 7.23×10^6 **j)** 5.48×10^{-5}

3 Without using your calculator, work out these calculations. Give your answers in standard form.

a) $(3 \times 10^5) \times (2 \times 10^3)$
b) $(4 \times 10^8) \times (1.5 \times 10^{-3})$
c) $(8 \times 10^8) \div (2 \times 10^5)$
d) $(6 \times 10^3) \div (2 \times 10^{-4})$
e) $(4 \times 10^3) \times (3 \times 10^6)$
f) $(4 \times 10^7) \div (8 \times 10^3)$
g) $(6 \times 10^4) + (3 \times 10^3)$
h) $(8 \times 10^5) - (3 \times 10^4)$
i) $(6 \times 10^{-4}) + (3 \times 10^{-3})$

4 Use your calculator to work out these calculations. Give your answers, in standard form, correct to 3 significant figures.

a) $(3.2 \times 10^5) \times (2.8 \times 10^2)$
b) $(4.6 \times 10^8) \times (1.7 \times 10^{-4})$
c) $(8.23 \times 10^8) \div (2.6 \times 10^5)$
d) $(6.3 \times 10^3) \div (7.9 \times 10^{-4})$
e) $(8.9 \times 10^3) \times (6.7 \times 10^6)$
f) $(4.53 \times 10^8) \div (8.69 \times 10^4)$
g) $(6.3 \times 10^4) + (3.5 \times 10^3)$

h) $(8.23 \times 10^5) - (3.78 \times 10^4)$
i) $(6.98 \times 10^{-5}) + (3.2 \times 10^{-4})$

5 Each of these is the nth term of a sequence. For each of them find the first four terms.

a) $n + 4$ **b)** $2n + 3$
c) $3n - 2$ **d)** $8n$
e) $15 - 2n$ **f)** $n^2 - 3n$

6 Find the nth term for each of these sequences.

a) 3   5   7   9
b) 5   10   15   20
c) 11   12   13   14
d) 5   8   11   14
e) $^-2$ $^-4$ $^-6$ $^-8$
f) 17   14   11   8

7 Find the nth term for each of these sequences.

a) 4   7   12   19   28
b) 3   9   19   33   51
c) 4   8   14   22   32

8 Calculate the lengths or angles marked with letters. (All lengths are in cm.)

a)

b)

c)

d)

e)

f)
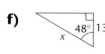

9 A boy is flying a kite with a string of length 45 m. If the string is straight and it makes an angle of 75° with the ground, how high is the kite? Ignore the height of the boy.

10 The sides of a triangle are 5 cm, 5 cm and 7 cm. Calculate the angles of the triangle.

11 A ramp for disabled people must slope at not more than 10°. If the height of the ramp has to be 0·8 m, how long must the ramp be?

12 A man sails for 5 km on a bearing of 285° from a harbour.

   a) How far North and West of the harbour is he?

   He then sails 3 km due North.

   b) Find the bearing on which he needs to sail to return to the harbour, and how far he needs to sail.

13 Over the last month, David's mean journey time to work has been 43 minutes, with an interquartile range of 7 minutes. Angie's mean time is 32 minutes, with an interquartile range of 12 minutes. Make two comparisons of David and Angie's journey times.

14 Eleven members of 10g and eleven members of 10f are given a Maths problem to solve. The times they took to solve the problem are shown in the table.

10f	17	15	11	9	6	27	18	21	6	19	8
10g	4	13	15	11	32	7	9	12	6	10	14

Find the median and range for each class and comment on the results. Why might the interquartile range be a better measurement to use?

15 A survey was carried out on 50 adults in each of England and France to study the amount of wine consumed in a year. The table shows the mean and interquartile range of the number of bottles consumed in each of the counties. Compare the two counties.

	Mean	**Interquartile range**
England	21	9
France	46	8

16 The table shows the prices of a sample of 100 houses in the Northwest of England.

Price (£000)	**Number of houses**
$20 < x \leqslant 40$	4
$40 < x \leqslant 60$	15
$60 < x \leqslant 80$	27
$80 < x \leqslant 100$	41
$100 < x \leqslant 120$	10
$120 < x \leqslant 140$	3

Use mid-interval values of £30 000, £50 000, £70 000, £90 000, £110 000 and £130 000 to estimate the mean house price in the sample. A similar sample in the Southeast gave a mean of £107 000 and a range of £150 000. Compare the two areas.

17 Simplifying surds

You should already know

- the meaning of the square root sign
- the formulae for area and circumference of a circle.

Simplifying surds

A number like $\sqrt{3}$ or $6 + 2\sqrt{5}$ is called a surd.

Surds can often be simplified by using the result $\sqrt{a \times b} = \sqrt{a} \times \sqrt{b}$
This result can be demonstrated using $\sqrt{36}$.
$\sqrt{36} = 6 = 2 \times 3 = \sqrt{4} \times \sqrt{9}$ so $\sqrt{36} = \sqrt{4 \times 9} = \sqrt{4} \times \sqrt{9}$

EXAMPLE 1

Simplify $\sqrt{50}$.
$\sqrt{50} = \sqrt{25 \times 2} = \sqrt{25} \times \sqrt{2} = 5\sqrt{2}$

EXAMPLE 2

Simplify $\sqrt{72}$.
9 is a factor of 72 so $\sqrt{72} = \sqrt{9} \times \sqrt{8} = 3\sqrt{8}$,
but 4 is a factor of 8 so $3 \times \sqrt{8} = 3 \times \sqrt{4} \times \sqrt{2}$
$= 3 \times 2 \times \sqrt{2} = 6\sqrt{2}$
Or if you spot straight away that 36 is a factor of 72
$\sqrt{72} = \sqrt{36 \times 2} = \sqrt{36} \times \sqrt{2} = 6\sqrt{2}$

EXAMPLE 3

Simplify $\sqrt{12} \times \sqrt{27}$
Method 1 $\sqrt{12} = \sqrt{4 \times 3} = \sqrt{4} \times \sqrt{3} = 2 \times \sqrt{3}$
$\sqrt{27} = \sqrt{9 \times 3} = \sqrt{9} \times \sqrt{3} = 3 \times \sqrt{3}$
So $\sqrt{12} \times \sqrt{27} = 2 \times \sqrt{3} \times 3 \times \sqrt{3}$
$= 2 \times 3 \times \sqrt{3} \times \sqrt{3} = 6 \times 3 = 18$
Method 2 $\sqrt{12} \times \sqrt{27} = \sqrt{12 \times 27} = \sqrt{324} = 18$
Although method 2 is probably easier if you have a
calculator, method 1 is probably easier if the question
comes in the non-calculator section of the paper.

Exam tip

Look for as large a factor of the
number as possible which has an
exact square root. In Examples 1 and
2 it is 25 and 36 respectively.

Note that, by definition of what we mean by a square root, $\sqrt{a} \times \sqrt{a} = a$.
Example 3 also illustrates the fact that the product of two surds can be a whole number.

EXERCISE 17.1A

1 Simplify the following.

a) $\sqrt{12}$ b) $\sqrt{1000}$ c) $\sqrt{45}$

d) $\sqrt{300}$ e) $\sqrt{75}$ f) $\sqrt{48}$

g) $\sqrt{125}$ h) $\sqrt{28}$ i) $\sqrt{90}$

j) $\sqrt{80}$

2 Simplify the following.

a) $\sqrt{8} \times \sqrt{2}$ b) $\sqrt{20} \times \sqrt{18}$

c) $\sqrt{20} \div \sqrt{5}$ d) $\sqrt{80} \times \sqrt{50}$

e) $\sqrt{75} \times \sqrt{15}$

3 Solve the following equations. Write your answers as surds in their simplest forms.

a) $x^2 = 2$ b) $3x^2 = 24$

c) $5x^2 - 120 = 0$

EXERCISE 17.1B

1 Simplify the following.

a) $\sqrt{40}$ b) $\sqrt{54}$ c) $\sqrt{98}$

d) $\sqrt{800}$ e) $\sqrt{363}$ f) $\sqrt{60}$

g) $\sqrt{162}$ h) $\sqrt{700}$ i) $\sqrt{128}$

j) $\sqrt{250}$

2 a) $\sqrt{27} \times \sqrt{3}$ b) $\sqrt{250} \times \sqrt{40}$

c) $\sqrt{108} \div \sqrt{12}$ d) $\sqrt{90} \times \sqrt{20}$

e) $\dfrac{\sqrt{60} \times \sqrt{20}}{\sqrt{12}}$

3 Solve the following equations. Write your answers as surds in their simplest forms.

a) $x^2 = 12$ b) $2x^2 = 36$

c) $3x^2 - 60 = 0$

Numbers involving π

Particularly in the non-calculator section of the paper, it is quite common for the answer to a circle question to be left in terms of π.

One of the reasons for this is that you are not dictating accuracy to the person who will use this answer. They can decide on the accuracy themselves.

EXAMPLE 4

Find the circumference and area of a circle with a radius of 5 cm. Leave your answer as a multiple of π.

$C = 2\pi r = 2 \times \pi \times 5 = 2 \times 5 \times \pi = 10\pi$ cm

$A = \pi r^2 = \pi \times 5^2 = 25\pi$ cm^2

EXAMPLE 5

Calculate the shaded area. Leave your answer as a multiple of π.

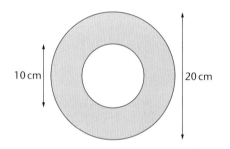

Radii = 10 cm and 5 cm.

Area of large circle = $\pi r^2 = \pi \times 10^2 = 100\pi$ cm^2

Area of small circle = $\pi r^2 = \pi \times 5^2 = 25\pi$ cm^2

Shaded area = $100\pi - 25\pi = 75\pi$ cm^2.

EXERCISE 17.2A

1 Calculate the circumference of each of these circles. Leave your answer as a multiple of π.

  a) diameter = 6 cm
  b) radius = 10 cm
  c) radius = 20 cm
  d) diameter = 26 cm.

2 Calculate the areas of the circles in question 1. Leave your answer as a multiple of π.

3

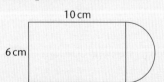

a) Calculate the area of this shape.
b) Calculate the perimeter of the shape. Leave your answers in terms of π.

4 Calculate the shaded area. Leave your answer in terms of π.

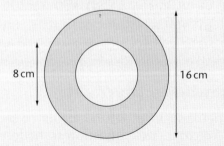

EXERCISE 17.2B

1 Calculate the circumference of each of these circles. Leave your answer as a multiple of π.

   a) diameter = 12 cm
   b) radius = 14 cm
   c) radius = 30 cm
   d) diameter = 5 cm.

2 Calculate the areas of the circles in question 1. Leave your answers as a multiple of π.

3

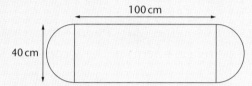

   a) Calculate the area of this shape.
   b) Calculate the perimeter of the shape. Leave your answers in terms of π.

4 The diagram shows a semicircle cut from a larger semicircle.

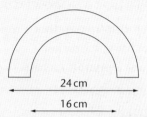

   a) Calculate the area of this shape.
   b) Calculate the perimeter of the shape. Leave your answers in terms of π.

Key ideas

- Surds are non-exact roots such as $\sqrt{2}$, $5 + \sqrt{3}$, $\sqrt[3]{7}$.
- Surds can be simplified using $\sqrt{a \times b} = \sqrt{a} \times \sqrt{b}$. Always look for as big a factor as possible which has a square root.
- By leaving answers as surds or, in circle questions, in terms of π, you are giving an exact answer.

18 Quadratics

You should already know

- how to collect together simple algebraic terms
- expand single brackets
- take out common factors.

Multiplying out two brackets

Expressions such as $a(3a - 2b)$ can be multiplied out to give $a(3a - 2b)$
$= (a \times 3a) - (a \times 2b) = 3a^2 - 2ab$.

This can be extended to working out expressions such as $(2a + b)(3a + b)$.

Each term of the first bracket must be multiplied by each term of the second bracket.

$(2a + b)(3a + b)$

$= 2a(3a + b) + b(3a + b)$ Expanding the first bracket.

$= 6a^2 + 2ab + 3ab + b^2$

$= 6a^2 + 5ab + b^2$ Notice that the middle two terms are **like terms** and so can be collected.

EXAMPLE 1

Multiply out these brackets

a) $(a+3)(a+2)$ **b)** $(a+2)(a-1)$ **c)** $(a-4)(a-3)$

a) $(a+3)(a+2) = a(a+2) + 3(a+2)$
$\qquad = a^2 + 2a + 3a + 6$
$\qquad = a^2 + 5a + 6$

b) $(a+2)(a-1) = a(a-1) + 2(a-1)$
$\qquad = a^2 - a + 2a - 2$
$\qquad = a^2 + a - 2$

c) $(a-4)(a-3) = a(a-3) - 4(a-3)$
$\qquad = a^2 - 3a - 4a + 12$
$\qquad = a^2 - 7a + 12$

> **Exam tip**
>
> Most errors are made in multiplying out the second bracket when the sign in front is negative.

> **Exam tip**
>
> Apart from multiplying out the brackets, you may sometimes be asked to simplify, expand or remove the brackets, which all mean the same thing.

There are two other types of expansions of two brackets that you need to know.

EXAMPLE 2

Expand these brackets.

a) $(x+3)^2$ **b)** $(x-3)^2$ **c)** $(x+3)(x-3)$

a) $(x+3)^2 = (x+3)(x+3)$

$\qquad = x(x+3) + 3(x+3)$

$\qquad = x^2 + 3x + 3x + 9$

$\qquad = x^2 + 6x + 9$

b) $(x-3)^2 = (x-3)(x-3)$

$\qquad = x(x-3) - 3(x-3)$

$\qquad = x^2 - 3x - 3x + 9$

$\qquad = x^2 - 6x + 9$

c) $(x+3)(x-3) = x(x-3) + 3(x-3)$

$\qquad = x^2 - 3x + 3x - 9$

$\qquad = x^2 - 9$

Note that we only get two terms here because the middle terms cancel each other out.
This type is known as the difference of two squares because:
$(A-B)(A+B) = A^2 - B^2$.

> **Exam tip**
> Take care with the negative signs.

> **Exam tip**
> The important thing in Example 2 part a) is to make sure that you write the brackets separately and that you end up with three terms.

> **Exam tip**
> Some people can multiply out two brackets without writing down anything. However, you are more likely to make an error by missing steps and so it is worth showing every step in an examination.

EXAMPLE 3 – EXTENSION

Multiply out the brackets.

a) $(2a+3)(a-1)$ **b)** $(5a-2b)(3a-b)$ **c)** $(2a-b)(a+2b)$

a) $(2a+3)(a-1) = 2a(a-1) + 3(a-1) = 2a^2 - 2a + 3a - 3$

$\qquad = 2a^2 + a - 3$ | Be careful with the signs.

b) $(5a-2b)(3a-2b) = 5a(3a-b) - 2b(3a-b)$

$\qquad = 15a^2 - 5ab - 6ab + 2b^2$

$\qquad = 15a^2 - 11ab + 2b^2$ | Note that it is ^-2b times the bracket.

c) $(2a-b)(a+2b) = 2a(a+2b) - b(a+2b)$

$\qquad = 2a^2 + 4ab - ab - 2b^2$

$\qquad = 2a^2 + 3ab - 2b^2$ | Note that it is ^-b times the bracket.

EXAMPLE 4 – EXTENSION

Expand the brackets.

a) $(2a - 3b)^2$ **b)** $(2a - b)(2a + b)$

a) $(2a - 3b)^2 = (2a - 3b)(2a - 3b)$

$$= 2a(2a - 3b) - 3b(2a - 3b) = 4a^2 - 6ab - 6ab + 9b^2$$

$$= 4a^2 - 12ab + 9b^2$$

Note that $^-6ab - 6ab = ^-12ab$.

b) $(2a - b)(2a + b) = 2a(2a + b) - b(2a + b) = 4a^2 + 2ab - 2ab - b^2 = 4a^2 - b^2$

This is another example of the "difference of two squares" as in Example 2.

EXERCISE 18.1A

Multiply out the brackets.

1 $(x + 2)(x + 3)$

2 $(a + 4)(a + 3)$

3 $(a + 2)(a + 1)$

4 $(x + 5)(x - 2)$

5 $(x + 7)(x - 3)$

6 $(x - 5)(x - 6)$

7 $(x - 3)(x + 6)$

8 $(x - 5)(x - 4)$

9 $(x + 3)^2$

10 $(a - 5)^2$

11 $(b + 1)^2$

12 $(x - 2)^2$

13 $(a + 2)^2$

14 $(x + 2)(x - 2)$

15 $(x + 6)(x - 6)$

16 $(x - 4)(x + 4)$

Extension material

17 $(x - 2)(2x + 1)$

18 $(2x - 3)(x + 2)$

19 $(3a + b)(2a - 2b)$

20 $(4a - b)(a + 2b)$

21 $(3a - 2b)(2a - 3b)$

22 $(4a - 3b)(2a - 3b)$

23 $(4 - 3b)(5 + 2b)$

24 $(2a - b)(3a - b)$

25 $(7a + 3b)(2a + b)$

26 $(4x - 3y)^2$

27 $(3x - y)^2$

28 $(a - 2)(a + 2)$

29 $(3a + b)(3a - b)$

30 $(5x - 2y)(5x + 2y)$

31 $(4a + 3b)(a - b)$

32 $(5a + 4b)(2a - b)$

EXERCISE 18.1B

Multiply out the brackets.

1 $(x + 1)(x + 3)$

2 $(a + 3)(a + 3)$

3 $(a + 2)(a + 1)$

4 $(x - 2)(x + 1)$

5 $(p + 4)(p - 2)$

Exercise 18.1B cont'd

6 $(a + 7)(a + 8)$

7 $(x - 6)(x + 4)$

8 $(x - 9)(x - 3)$

9 $(x + 10)(x - 1)$

10 $(x - 10)^2$

11 $(x + 8)^2$

12 $(b - 7)^2$

13 $(x + 1)(x - 1)$

14 $(x + 10)(x - 10)$

15 $(x + 4)^2$

16 $(x + 7)(x - 7)$

Extension material

17 $(5x - 3y)(x + 2y)$

18 $(3a + b)(a - 2b)$

19 $(a - b)(3a + 2b)$

20 $(5a - 2)(a - 3)$

21 $(7 - 3b)(1 - 3b)$

22 $(a - 3b)(2a + b)$

23 $(6a - b)(3a - 2b)$

24 $(a + 3b)(2a + b)$

25 $(a - b)^2$

26 $(2x - 1)^2$

27 $(a - 5)(a + 5)$

28 $(2a + b)(2a - b)$

29 $(3x - 2y)(3x + 2y)$

30 $(5a + 4b)(2a - b)$

31 $(7a - 5b)(a - b)$

32 For each diagram write down the length and width and then multiply them to find the total area.

a)

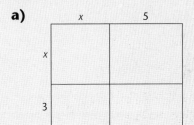

b)

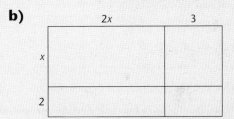

33 Find the values of the letters in the following expressions.

a) $(3x - 1)(x + 2) + x(x - 3)$
$= ax^2 + bx + c$

b) $(2x + 1)^2 + 5 = dx^2 + ex + 6$

Factorising expressions of the type $x^2 + ax + b$

Expressions where the last sign is positive

The expression $(x + 2)(x + 3)$ can be simplified to give $x^2 + 5x + 6$.
Therefore, $x^2 + 5x + 6$ can be factorised as a product of two brackets, by reversing the process.

EXAMPLE 5

Factorise $x^2 + 7x + 12$.

This will factorise into two brackets with x as the first term in each.

$x^2 + 7x + 12 = (x \qquad)(x \qquad)$

As both the signs are positive, both the numbers will be positive.

You need to find two numbers that multiply to give 12 and add to give 7.

These will be +3 and +4.

So $x^2 + 7x + 12 = (x + 3)(x + 4)$ or

$x^2 + 7x + 12 = (x + 4)(x + 3)$

Exam tip

If the last sign is positive (+), both the signs in the brackets must be the same as the sign before the x-term.

The order in which you write the brackets does not matter.

If the middle sign is negative and the last sign is positive, the two numbers will be negative.

EXAMPLE 6

Factorise $x^2 - 3x + 2$.

You need to find two negative numbers that multiply to give +2 and add to ‾3. They are ‾2 and ‾1.

$x^2 - 3x + 2 = (x - 2)(x - 1)$.

ACTIVITY 1

Copy and multiply out these brackets. See if you can discover a relationship between the numbers in the brackets and the numbers in the final expression.

$(x + 1)(x + 2) = x^2 + 3x + 2$

$(x + 1)(x + 3) =$

$(x + 1)(x + 4) =$

$(x + 2)(x + 3) =$

$(x + 2)(x + 4) =$

Do more if you need to.

Do your rules work for negative numbers?

Try $(x - 1)(x - 2) =$

$(x - 1)(x - 3) =$

ACTIVITY 2

Some of these factors are correct and some are wrong. Can you find which?

$x^2 + 16x + 15 = (x + 5)(x + 3)$

$p^2 - 9p + 8 = (p - 1)(p - 8)$

$a^2 - 7a + 12 = (a - 4)(a - 3)$

$x^2 - 13x + 36 = (x + 4)(x + 9)$

Correct the wrong ones if you can.

EXERCISE 18.2A

Factorise these expressions.

1 $x^2 + 5x + 6$ **9** $y^2 - 9y + 14$

2 $x^2 + 6x + 5$ **10** $x^2 - 6x + 8$

3 $x^2 + 6x + 8$ **11** $a^2 + 8a + 12$

4 $x^2 + 5x + 4$ **12** $a^2 - 6a + 9$

5 $x^2 + 2x + 1$ **13** $b^2 - 12b + 32$

6 $x^2 - 7x + 6$ **14** $x^2 + 11x + 24$

7 $x^2 - 7x + 10$ **15** $x^2 - 9x + 20$

8 $x^2 - 4x + 3$

EXERCISE 18.2B

Factorise these expressions.

1 $x^2 + 7x + 10$ **9** $b^2 - 10b + 24$

2 $x^2 + 4x + 3$ **10** $c^2 - 4c + 3$

3 $x^2 + 8x + 15$ **11** $a^2 + 15a + 36$

4 $x^2 + 9x + 20$ **12** $x^2 - 12x + 27$

5 $x^2 + 7x + 6$ **13** $b^2 - 10b + 25$

6 $x^2 - 9x + 18$ **14** $x^2 + 14x + 24$

7 $x^2 - 7x + 12$ **15** $x^2 - 15x + 56$

8 $a^2 - 2a + 1$

Expressions where the last sign is negative

EXAMPLE 7

Factorise $x^2 - 3x - 10$.

As the last sign is negative, you need two numbers, with opposite signs, that multiply to give ⁻10 and add to give ⁻3. The numbers are ⁻5 and +2.

$x^2 - 3x - 10 = (x - 5)(x + 2)$

EXAMPLE 8

Factorise $x^2 + 4x - 12$.

The last sign is negative, so you need two numbers, with opposite signs, that multiply to give ⁻12 and add to give +4. The numbers are +6 and ⁻2.

$x^2 + 4x - 12 = (x + 6)(x - 2)$

EXERCISE 18.3A

Factorise these expressions.

1 $x^2 - 2x - 8$ **9** $y^2 + 9y - 22$

2 $x^2 + 4x - 5$ **10** $x^2 + x - 12$

3 $x^2 - x - 6$ **11** $a^2 + 8a - 20$

4 $x^2 + 5x - 6$ **12** $a^2 - 6a - 27$

5 $x^2 + 2x - 3$ **13** $b^2 + 12b + 20$

6 $x^2 - 3x - 18$ **14** $x^2 + 11x - 26$

7 $x^2 - 9x - 10$ **15** $x^2 - 9x + 18$

8 $x^2 + 9x + 14$

Exam tip

Remember that if the last sign is negative the two numbers have different signs and the larger number has the sign of the *x*-term.

It is easy to make a mistake when factorising. Always check by multiplying out the brackets.

EXERCISE 18.3B

Factorise these expressions.

1 $x^2 + 2x - 3$ 6 $x^2 - 3x - 28$ 11 $y^2 + 19y + 48$

2 $x^2 + 3x - 10$ 7 $x^2 - 17x + 30$ 12 $a^2 - 6a - 16$

3 $x^2 - x - 12$ 8 $x^2 + 4x - 32$ 13 $b^2 - 15b + 36$

4 $x^2 + 5x - 14$ 9 $a^2 + 9a - 36$ 14 $x^2 + 7x - 30$

5 $x^2 - 2x - 15$ 10 $x^2 + x - 20$ 15 $x^2 - 3x - 40$

Factorising expressions of the form $x^2 - b^2$

Multiplying out $(x - 4)(x + 4)$ gives
$x^2 + 4x - 4x - 16$. This is $x^2 - 16$ when
simplified. The x terms disappear.

Similarly, $(x - 3)(x + 3) = x^2 - 9$.

So, following this pattern we see that

$x^2 - b^2$ factorises to $(x - b)(x + b)$

Exam tip

It is worth learning this so that you
recognise it when you see it!

EXERCISE 18.4A

Factorise these expressions.

1 $x^2 - 4$ 5 $y^2 - 400$

2 $x^2 - 25$ 6 $y^2 - 121$

3 $x^2 - 49$ 7 $a^2 - 289$

4 $y^2 - 100$

EXERCISE 18.4B

Factorise these expressions.

1 $x^2 - 1$ 5 $a^2 - 169$

2 $x^2 - 36$ 6 $b^2 - 225$

3 $x^2 - 81$ 7 $p^2 - q^2$

4 $m^2 - 144$

Key ideas

● When multiplying two brackets, multiply every term in the first bracket by every
  term in the second.

● To factorise $x^2 + ax + b$:

  If b is positive find two numbers that multiply to give b and add up to a

  If b is negative find two numbers that multiply to give b and have a difference of b.

● The difference of two squares factorises $x^2 - a^2 = (x + a)(x - a)$.

19 Prisms

You should already know

- common metric units for length, area and volume
- how to find the area of a rectangle, triangle, parallelogram and trapezium
- how to find the circumference and area of a circle
- how to find lengths using Pythagoras and trigonometry
- how to round answers to a suitable degree of accuracy.

Volume of a prism

You should remember how to find the volume of a cuboid.

volume of a cuboid = length × width × height

It may also be thought of as:

volume of a cuboid = area of cross-section × height

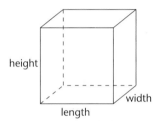

This is an example of a general formula for the volume of a prism. When laid on its side, along its length:

volume of a prism = area of cross-section × length

Another important prism is the cylinder. Its cross-section is a circle, which has area πr^2.

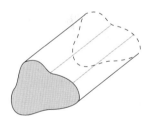

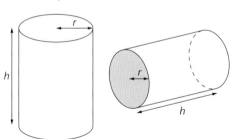

volume of a cylinder = $\pi r^2 h$

EXAMPLE 1

Calculate the volume of a cylinder with base diameter 15 cm and height 10 cm.

radius of base $\frac{15}{2}$ = 7·5 cm

volume of a cylinder = $\pi r^2 h$

$\qquad = \pi \times 7\cdot5^2 \times 10 \, cm^3$

$\qquad = 1770 \, cm^3$ to three significant figures

EXAMPLE 2

A chocolate box is a prism with a trapezium as cross-section, as shown. Calculate the volume of the prism.

area of a trapezium $= \frac{1}{2}(a + b)h$

$\qquad = \frac{1}{2}(20 + 16) \times 6 \, cm^2$

$\qquad = 108 \, cm^2$

volume of a prism $=$ area of cross-section $\times$ length

$\qquad = 108 \times 25 \, cm^3$

$\qquad = 2700 \, cm^3$

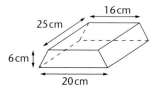

EXAMPLE 3

A cylinder has volume $100 \, cm^3$ and is $4.2 \, cm$ high. Find the radius of its base. Give your answer to the nearest millimetre.

Volume of cylinder $= \pi r^2 h$

$\qquad 100 = \pi \times r^2 \times 4.2$

$\qquad r^2 = \dfrac{100}{\pi \times 4.2}$

$\qquad = 7.578\ldots$

$\qquad r = \sqrt{7.578\ldots}$

$\qquad = 2.8 \, cm$ to the nearest mm

EXERCISE 19.1A

1   Calculate the volume of a cylinder with base radius $5.6 \, cm$ and height $8.5 \, cm$.

2   A cylindrical stick of rock is $12 \, cm$ long and has radius $2.4 \, cm$. Find its volume.

3   A cylinder has diameter $8 \, cm$ and height $8 \, cm$. Calculate its volume.

4   Calculate the volume of prisms each $15 \, cm$ long, with these cross-sections.

a)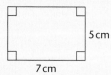

b)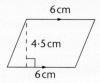

c)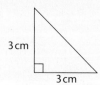

5   A chocolate bar is in the shape of a triangular prism. Calculate its volume.

Exercise 19.1A cont'd

6 A pencil-box is a prism with a trapezium as its cross-section, as shown. Calculate the volume of the box.

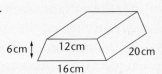

7 The area of cross-section of a prism is 75 cm². Its volume is 1200 cm³. Calculate its length.

8 The volume of a cylinder is 800 cm³. Its radius is 5·3 cm. Calculate its length.

9 A cylinder has volume 570 cm³ and height 7 cm. Find its base radius. Give your answer to the nearest millimetre.

10 The volume of a cylindrical tank is 600 m³. Its height is 4·6 m. Calculate the radius of its base.

EXERCISE 19.1B

1 Calculate the volume of a cylinder with base radius 4·3 cm and height 9·7 cm.

2 A cylindrical water tank is 4·2 m high and has radius 3·6 m. Find its volume.

3 A cylinder has diameter 9 cm and height 12 cm. Calculate its volume.

4 Calculate the volume of prisms each 12 cm long, with these cross-sections.

a)

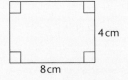

b)

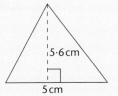

c)

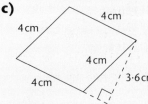

5 A gift box is a prism with a triangular base. Calculate its volume.

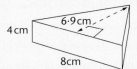

6 A vase is a prism with a trapezium as its base. The internal measurements are as shown. How much water can the vase hold? Give your answer in litres. (1 litre = 1000 cm³)

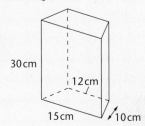

Chapter 19 *Prisms*

Exercise 19.1B cont'd

7 The area of cross-section of a prism is $90\,cm^2$. Its volume is $1503\,cm^3$. Calculate its length.

8 The volume of a cylinder is $1500\,cm^3$. Its radius is $7{\cdot}5\,cm$. Calculate its length. Give your answer to the nearest millimetre.

9 A cylinder has volume $620\,cm^3$ and height $8\,cm$. Find its base radius. Give your answer to the nearest millimetre.

10 The volume of a cylinder is $1100\,cm^3$. Its length is $10{\cdot}8\,cm$. Calculate its radius, giving your answer to the nearest millimetre.

Surface area of a prism

To find the total surface area of a prism simply add up the surface area of all the individual surfaces.

EXAMPLE 4

Find the total surface area of this prism.

area of end	$= \frac{1}{2} \times 12 \times 5$	$= 30\,cm^2$
area of other end		$= 30\,cm^2$
area of base	$= 12 \times 15$	$= 180\,cm^2$
area of top	$= 13 \times 15$	$= 195\,cm^2$
area of back	$= 5 \times 15$	$= 75\,cm^2$
total surface area		$= 510\,cm^2$

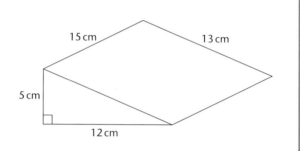

For a cylinder there are three surfaces.

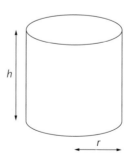

The two ends each have area = πr^2.

If the cylinder were made out of paper the curved surface would open out to a rectangle.

the length of the rectangle = the circumference of the cylinder = $2\pi r$

the curved surface area is therefore $2\pi r \times h = 2\pi rh$

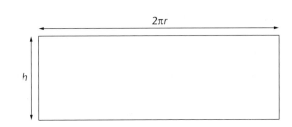

The total surface area of a cylinder = $2\pi rh + 2\pi r^2$

EXAMPLE 5

Calculate the total surface area of a cylinder with base diameter 15 cm and height 10 cm.

radius of base = $15 \div 2 = 7 \cdot 5$ cm

area of two ends = $2 \times \pi r^2 = 2 \times \pi \times 7 \cdot 5^2 = 353 \cdot 4$ cm^2

curved surface area = $2\pi rh = 2 \times \pi \times 7 \cdot 5 \times 10 = 471 \cdot 2$ cm^2

Total surface area = $353 \cdot 4 + 471 \cdot 2 = 825$ cm^2 to three significant figures.

Exam tip

Before calculating the surface area of a prism, it may be useful to make a rough sketch of the net of the prism. This should stop you missing out a side.

EXERCISE 19.2A

1 Find the total surface area of the cylinder in Exercise 19.1a question 1.
2 Find the total surface area of the cylinder in Exercise 19.1a question 2.
3 Find the total surface area of the cylinder in Exercise 19.1a question 3.
4 Find the total surface area of the prism in Exercise 19.1a question 4 a).
5 Find the total surface area of this prism. (You may wish to sketch the net of the prism first.)

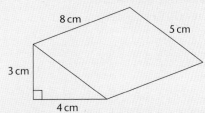

In questions 6 to 8 you will need your answers to Exercise 19.1a.

6 Find the total surface area of the cylinder in Exercise 19.1a question 8.
7 Find the total surface area of the cylinder in Exercise 19.1a question 9.
8 Find the total surface area of the cylinder in Exercise 19.1a question 10.

EXERCISE 19.2B

1 Find the total surface area of the cylinder in Exercise 19.1b question 1.

2 Find the total surface area of the cylinder in Exercise 19.1b question 2.

3 Find the total surface area of the cylinder in Exercise 19.1b question 3.

4 Find the total surface area of the prism in Exercise 19.1b question 4 a).

5 Find the total surface area of this prism. (You may wish to sketch the net of the prism first.)

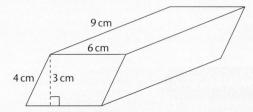

In questions 6 to 8 you will need your answers to Exercise 19.1b.

6 Find the total surface area of the cylinder in Exercise 19.1b question 8.

7 Find the total surface area of the cylinder in Exercise 19.1b question 9.

8 Find the total surface area of the cylinder in Exercise 19.1b question 10.

9 A prism has a cross-section which is an equilateral triangle of side 6 cm. The length of the prism is 10 cm. Find the total surface area of the prism.

10 A prism has a cross-section which is an isosceles triangle with sloping sides 10 cm and base 16 cm. The length of the prism is 4·5 cm. Find the total surface area of the prism.

Dimensions

You can tell whether a formula gives length, area or volume by looking at its dimensions.

number × length = length	(1 dimension)
length + length = length	(1 dimension)
length × length = area	(2 dimensions)
length × length × length = volume	(3 dimensions)

So which circle formula is for area?

Remember π is a number and has no dimensions.

$2\pi r$ = number × length = length   (the circumference of a circle)

πr^2 = number × length × length

    = length × length

    = area   (the area of a circle)

Thinking about the number of dimensions also helps you to sort out what units you should be using. For example:

length = m (1 dimension)
area = m^2 (2 dimensions)
volume = m^3 (3 dimensions)

Exam tip

For practice, check the dimensions of formulae you know.

EXAMPLE 6

If a, b and h are lengths, does the expression $\frac{1}{2}(a + b)h$ represent a length, area or volume, or none of these?

$a + b$ = length

so $\frac{1}{2}(a + b)h$ = number × length × length
= length × length = area

Exam tip

When adding and subtracting dimensions they must be all the same.
length + length = length   (1 dimension)
area + area = area   (2 dimensions)
volume + volume = volume
(3 dimensions)
Adding unlike quantities like area + length or area + volume is nonsense.

EXERCISE 19.3A

Throughout this exercise, letters in algebraic expressions represent lengths.

1 State whether each of these expressions represents a length, area or volume.

a) $r + h$ **b)** rh **c)** $2\pi rh$

Exercise 19.3A cont'd

2 Which of these expressions represents a length?

   a) $\frac{1}{2}bh$ **b)** $3b$ **c)** $b + 2h$

3 Which of these expressions represents an area?

   a) xy **b)** xy^2 **c)** $x(x + y)$

4 Which of these expressions represents a volume?

   a) r^3 **b)** $\pi r^2 h$ **c)** $r^2(r + h)$

5 State whether each expression represents length, area, volume or none of these.

   a) $r(r^2 + h)$ **b)** $(3 + \pi)h$

   c) $4\pi r^2$

6 What do these formulas represent? Some of them could be nonsense. (Assume that r, h, x and y are all lengths.)

   a) $2\pi r + \pi r^2$ **b)** $2\pi rh + 2\pi r^2$

   c) $\frac{4r^3}{3} + 2\pi rh$ **d)** $xy^2 + x^3$

EXERCISE 19.3B

Throughout this exercise, letters in algebraic expressions represent lengths.

1 State whether each of these expressions represents a length, area or volume.

   a) $a + 2b$ **b)** $2ab$

   c) a^2b

2 Which of these expressions represents a length?

   a) $a + 2b + c$ **b)** $3a + 2a^2$

   c) $a(2a + b)$

3 Which of these expressions represents an area?

   a) $4a^2$ **b)** $x(x + 2y)$

   c) $\pi r^2 + 2\pi rh$

4 Which of these expressions represents a volume?

   a) πab **b)** $\frac{4}{3}\pi r^3$

   c) $h^2(a + b)$

5 State whether each expression represents length, area, volume or none of these.

   a) $\frac{1}{3}\pi r^2 h$ **b)** $2a^2b(a + b)$

   c) $a(3 + \pi)$

6 What do these formulas represent? Some of them could be nonsense. (Assume that r, a, b, c, d, h, x, y and I are lengths.)

   a) $\frac{4}{3}\pi r^2 + 2abh$ **b)** $3xy + 5x^2$

   c) $5abc + 3a^2b$ **d)** $\frac{1}{2}bhl + r^3$

   e) $\pi d + 3(a + b)$

Converting metric units

$1000\,mm = 100\,cm = 1$ metre

This square has an area of $1\,cm^2$

What is its area in square millimetres?

area $= 100\,mm^2$

Similarly, $1\,m^2 = 100^2\,cm^2 = 10\,000\,cm^2$
$= 1000^2\,mm^2 = 1\,000\,000\,mm^2$

This cube has volume $1\,cm^3$.

What is its volume in cubic millimetres?

volume $= 1000\,mm^3$
Similarly $1\,m^3 = 100^3\,cm^3 = 1\,000\,000\,cm^3$.

Exam tip

1 litre $= 1000\,cm^3$

EXERCISE 19.4A

1 This carton holds 1 litre. How high is it?

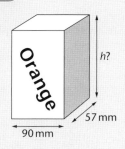

Orange

h?

57 mm

90 mm

The length of the guttering is 2·4 m. How many litres can it hold?

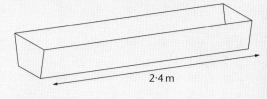

2·4 m

2 How many litres are there in 1 cubic metre?

3 The cross-section of this piece of guttering is a trapezium.

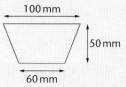

100 mm

50 mm

60 mm

EXERCISE 19.4B

1 This barrel is a cylinder and it holds 500 litres.
It is 1·5 m high.
Work out its diameter.

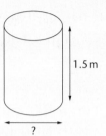

1.5 m

?

2 1 hectare = $10\,000\,\text{m}^2$.
How many hectares are there in $1\,\text{km}^2$?

3 A sugar cube has side 15 mm.
Find how many will fit in a box measuring 11 cm by 11 cm by 5 cm.

Key ideas

● The volume of a prism = the area of the end × the length.

● The total surface area of a solid is the total area of all the faces.

● To check a formula look at the dimensions. Length × length always gives area.
Length × length × length always gives volume. Remember numbers like π have no dimensions.

● $1\,\text{m}^2 = 10\,000\,\text{cm}^2 = 1\,000\,000\,\text{mm}^2$.

● $1\,\text{m}^3 = 1000$ litres $= 1\,000\,000\,\text{cm}^3$.

Time series and moving averages

Time series

The table shows the value, in thousands of pounds, of an ice-cream company's quarterly sales for 1995 to 1998.

	1st quarter	2nd quarter	3rd quarter	4th quarter
1995	145	256	328	258
1996	189	244	365	262
1997	190	266	359	250
1998	201	259	401	265

The graph illustrates these figures.

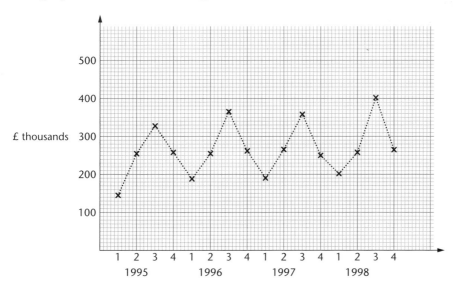

Note that the points have been joined up by dotted lines. Points on graphs should, really, only be joined up when it makes sense to read off in between the points. Here, since the figures are total sales it does not make sense to do so. Often, however, it is useful to join up with dotted lines to show the trend.

The figures and graphs are an example of a time series. You can see that there are 'peaks' at each 3rd quarter and 'troughs' at each 1st quarter. When you have a repeating pattern or 'cyclical' effect like this it is sometimes difficult to see trends.

Other examples of figures which may be 'cyclical' are monthly or seasonal rainfall, or monthly or seasonal unemployment figures in certain areas.

Moving averages

Moving averages give you a way of seeing trends in figures that are 'cyclical'. They are calculated as shown here.

Look at the figures for the first four quarters in the table.

The mean = $(145 + 256 + 328 + 258) \div 4 = 246 \cdot 75$.

Then find the mean for the second group of consecutive quarters, that is $(256 + 328 + 258 + 189) \div 4 = 257 \cdot 75$

Notice for this second group that 1995 quarter 1 is omitted and 1996 quarter 1 is included.

Now find the next mean by omitting the 256 and including the next quarter, 244, that is $(328 + 258 + 189 + 244) \div 4 = 254 \cdot 75$.

The next mean is $(258 + 189 + 244 + 365) \div 4 = 264$

This is continued until the last quarter is included, each time omitting the first figure and 'picking up' the next one in the table.

If all the quarters' figures are put in order and numbered as below, the lines underneath move along one each time and indicate the numbers which should be used.

1	2	3	4	5	6	7	8	9	10	11	12	13	14	15	16
145	256	328	258	189	244	365	262	190	266	359	250	201	259	401	265

and so on.

Check that you agree with this complete list.

Quarters	1–4	2–5	3–6	4–7	5–8	6–9	7–10	8–11	9–12	10–13	11–14	12–15	13–16
Moving average	246·75	257·75	254·75	264	265	265·25	270·75	269·25	266·25	269	267·25	277·75	281·5

These points are now plotted on the graph. They are plotted at the middle of the intervals of points. That is at 2·5 for quarters 1 to 4, at 3·5 for the next 4 quarters and so on.

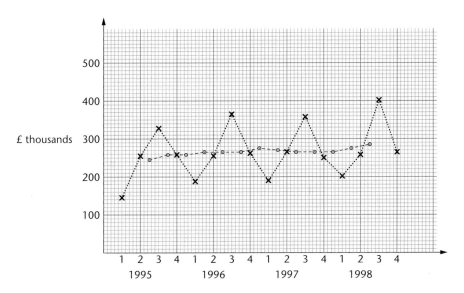

You can see that plotting the moving averages flattens out the peaks and troughs and shows a fairly flat graph with possibly a slight overall increase.

> When four figures are used to find a moving average as is the case in quarterly figures then this is called a 'four-quarter moving average'.

If the figures vary monthly then 12-month moving averages may be found using the means of 12 consecutive months.

EXERCISE 20.1A

1   The table shows the gross Accident & Health insurance premiums paid in the Netherlands for the 4 quarters of 1997 to 1999. The figures are in millions of euros.

	1st quarter	2nd quarter	3rd quarter	4th quarter
1997	43	17	15	15
1998	47	19	18	18
1999	57	26	22	13

  a) Plot these figures in a graph. Use a scale of 1 cm to each quarter on the horizontal axis and 2 cm to 10 million euros on the vertical axis.
  b) Calculate the four-quarter moving averages.
  c) Plot the moving averages on your graph.
  d) Comment on the general trend and the quarterly variation.

2   The table shows the total sales in megawatts of Danish wind turbines in the years 1995 to 1998.

	1st quarter	2nd quarter	3rd quarter	4th quarter
1995	96·6	125·8	122·9	229·1
1996	74·1	143·1	173·0	335·9
1997	216·2	234·2	234·5	282·6
1998	168·8	239·7	282·1	525·4

  a) Plot these figures in a graph. Use a scale of 1 cm to each quarter on the horizontal axis and 2 cm to 100 megawatts on the vertical axis.
  b) Calculate the four-quarter moving averages.
  c) Plot the moving averages on your graph.
  d) Comment on the general trend and the quarterly variation.

3   The table shows a company's quarterly sales of raincoats in the years 1996 to 1999. The figures are in thousands of pounds.

	1st quarter	2nd quarter	3rd quarter	4th quarter
1996	154	121	63	134
1997	132	106	72	108
1998	115	111	58	97
1999	110	93	47	82

Exercise 20.1A cont'd

    a) Plot these figures in a graph. Use a scale of 1 cm to each quarter on the horizontal axis and 2 cm to 20 thousand pounds on the vertical axis.

    b) Calculate the four-quarter moving averages.

    c) Plot the moving averages on your graph.

    d) Comment on the general trend and the quarterly variation.

4 The table shows the daily audiences for a 4 week Christmas pantomime season.

	Monday	Tuesday	Wednesday	Thursday	Friday	Saturday
Week 1	256	312	324	452	600	580
Week 2	297	367	382	538	600	600
Week 3	248	327	325	495	570	583
Week 4	192	219	287	306	490	572

    a) Plot these figures in a graph. Use a scale of 1 cm to each day on the horizontal axis and 2 cm to 100 people on the vertical axis. You will need to have your graph paper 'long ways'.

    b) Calculate the six-day moving averages.

    c) Plot the moving averages on your graph.

    d) Comment on the general trend and the daily variation.

EXERCISE 20.1B

1 The table shows a household's quarterly expenditure on fuel and light in the years 1995 to 1998. The figures are in pounds.

	1st quarter	2nd quarter	3rd quarter	4th quarter
1995	380	272	264	371
1996	432	285	207	272
1997	298	192	158	285
1998	310	208	182	291

    a) Plot these figures in a graph. Use a scale of 1 cm to each quarter on the horizontal axis and 2 cm to 100 pounds on the vertical axis.

    b) Calculate the four quarter moving averages.

    c) Plot the moving averages on your graph.

Exercise 20.1B cont'd

    d) Comment on the general trend and the quarterly variation.

    e) During this period, major insulation work was carried out on the house. When do you think that was?

2 The table shows the number of bankruptcies in Auckland by quarters from 1995 to 1998.

	1st quarter	2nd quarter	3rd quarter	4th quarter
1995	60	61	72	57
1996	83	75	90	66
1997	62	96	99	79
1998	72	63	79	65

    a) Plot these figures in a graph. Use a scale of 1 cm to each quarter on the horizontal axis and 2 cm to 20 bankruptcies on the vertical axis.

    b) Calculate the four-quarter moving averages.

    c) Plot the moving averages on your graph.

    d) Comment on the general trend and the quarterly variation.

3 The table shows the daily sales of a shop over a 3-week period. The figures are in thousands of pounds.

	Monday	Tuesday	Wednesday	Thursday	Friday	Saturday	Sunday
Week 1	7·3	8·8	9·2	10·3	15·5	16·2	12·8
Week 2	6·7	7·8	10·1	11·8	14·7	17·9	11·3
Week 3	7·1	6·3	8·2	10·9	12·9	16·6	11·6

    a) Plot these figures in a graph. Use a scale of 1 cm to each day on the horizontal axis and 2 cm to 2 thousand pounds on the vertical axis. You will need to have your graph paper 'long ways'.

    b) Calculate the 7-day moving averages.

    c) Plot the moving averages on your graph.

    d) Comment on the general trend and the daily variation.

Exercise 20.1B cont'd

4 The table shows the monthly number of U.S. Citizens flying to Europe from 1997 to 1999. The figures are in 100 thousands.

	Jan	Feb	Mar	Apr	May	Jun	Jul	Aug	Sep	Oct	Nov	Dec
1997	5·8	5·4	7·6	7·5	10·3	11·8	10·9	9·9	10·2	8·0	6·8	7·0
1998	6·3	5·9	8·9	8·5	11·0	12·8	12·0	10·3	10·8	8·8	7·1	7·4
1999	6·4	6·2	10·3	9·3	11·5	13·2	12·5	11·0	11·1	9·4	8·2	7·5

    a) Plot these figures in a graph. Use a scale of 1 cm to two months on the horizontal axis and 1 cm to 100 thousand citizens on the vertical axis.

    b) Calculate the 12-month moving averages.

    c) Plot the moving averages on your graph.

    d) Comment on the general trend and the monthly variation.

Key ideas

- A time series shows the variation of sets of figures over periods of time. These periods can be quarterly, daily, monthly and so on. These are usually displayed on a graph.

- To calculate a moving average, for example for quarterly figures, first calculate the mean for the first four quarters. Then omit the first quarter and include the fifth quarter and find the new mean. Then omit the second quarter and include the sixth and so on.

- The moving averages are plotted at the middle of the interval.

Chapter 20 *Time series and moving averages*

21 Equations and formulae

You should already know

- how to factorise quadratic expressions of the form $x^2 + ax + b$, $x^2 + ax$ and $x^2 - a^2$
- how to rearrange simple formulas to change the subject.

Solving quadratic equations

For any two numbers, if $A \times B = 0$, then either $A = 0$ or $B = 0$.

If $(x - 3)(x - 2) = 0$ then either $(x - 3) = 0$ or $(x - 2) = 0$.

To solve a quadratic equation, factorise it into two brackets and then use this fact.

Remember, to factorise $x^2 + ax + b$:
- if b is positive find two numbers with product b and sum a; the signs in the bracket are both the same as a;
- if b is negative find two numbers with product b and difference a;
  the signs in the bracket are different;
  the bigger number in the bracket has the same sign as a.

EXAMPLE 1

Solve the equation $x^2 - 4x + 3 = 0$.

$(x - 3)(x - 1) = 0$

$x - 3 = 0$ or $x - 1 = 0$

The solution is $x = 3$ or $x = 1$.

Factorising: both signs are negative, $1 \times 3 = 3$ and $1 + 3 = 4$.

EXAMPLE 2

Solve the equation $x^2 + 5x + 6 = 0$.

$(x + 3)(x + 2) = 0$

$x + 3 + 0$ or $x + 2 = 0$

The solution is $x = -3$ or $x = -2$.

Factorising: both signs are positive, $2 \times 3 = 6$ and $2 + 3 = 5$.

EXAMPLE 3

Solve the equation $x^2 - 3x - 10 = 0$.

$(x - 5)(x + 2) = 0$

$x - 5 = 0$ or $x + 2 = 0$

The solution is $x = 5$ or $x = {^-}2$.

Factorising: the signs are different, $5 \times 2 = 10$ and $5 - 2 = 3$.

If an equation is written as $x^2 - 2x = 15$ or $x^2 = 2x - 15$, first rearrange it so that all three terms are on the same side.

EXAMPLE 4

Solve the equation $x^2 = 4x - 4$ by factorisation.

$x^2 - 4x + 4 = 0$

$(x - 2)(x - 2) = 0$

$x - 2 = 0$ or $x - 2 = 0$

The solution is $x = 2$ (twice).

There are always two answers, so if they are both the same write 'twice'.

Rearrange so that all three terms are on the same side.

Factorising; the signs are both negative, $2 \times 2 = 4$, $2 + 2 = 4$.

EXAMPLE 5

Solve the equation $x^2 + 5x = 0$.

$x(x + 5) = 0$

$x = 0$ or $x + 5 = 0$

The solution is $x = 0$ or $x = {^-}5$.

Factorising with x as a common factor.

EXAMPLE 6

Solve the equation $x^2 - 49 = 0$

$(x + 7)(x - 7) = 0$ | Factorising by 'difference of two squares'.

$x + 7 = 0$ or $x - 7 = 0$

The solution is $x = {}^-7$ or $x = 7$ | This can be written $x = \pm7$.

An alternative method is

$x^2 - 49 = 0$

$x^2 = 49$ | Adding 49 to both sides.

$x = \pm7$ | Taking the square root of both sides, remembering that this can give 7 or $^-7$.

This method is perhaps simpler but it is easy to forget the negative solution.

EXERCISE 21.1A

Solve these equations by factorisation.

1 $x^2 - 5x + 6 = 0$

2 $x^2 - 6x + 5 = 0$

3 $x^2 - 16 = 0$

4 $x^2 + 6x + 8 = 0$

5 $x^2 + 5x + 4 = 0$

6 $x^2 - 7x = 0$

7 $x^2 + 2x + 1 = 0$

8 $x^2 - 7x + 6 = 0$

9 $x^2 - 1 = 0$

10 $x^2 - 7x + 10 = 0$

11 $x^2 - 4x + 3 = 0$

12 $x^2 + 3x = 0$

13 $x^2 - 9x + 14 = 0$

14 $x^2 - 6x + 8 = 0$

15 $x^2 - 169 = 0$

16 $x^2 - 2x - 8 = 0$

17 $x^2 + 4x - 5 = 0$

18 $x^2 = 10x$

19 $x^2 - x - 6 = 0$

20 $x^2 + 5x - 6 = 0$

21 $x^2 = x$

22 $x^2 + 2x = 3$

23 $x^2 - 3x = 18$

24 $x^2 - 9x = 10$

25 $x^2 + 9x + 14 = 0$

26 $x^2 + 9x - 22 = 0$

27 $x^2 + x - 12 = 0$

EXERCISE 21.1B

Solve these equations by factorisation.

1 $x^2 - 7x + 10 = 0$

2 $x^2 - 4x + 3 = 0$

3 $x^2 - 100 = 0$

4 $x^2 - 8x + 15 = 0$

5 $x^2 + 9x + 20 = 0$

6 $x^2 - 25 = 0$

7 $x^2 + 7x + 6 = 0$

8 $x^2 - 9x + 18 = 0$

9 $x^2 - 8x = 0$

Exercise 21.1B cont'd

10 $x^2 + 7x + 12 = 0$ **16** $x^2 + 2x - 3 = 0$ **22** $x^2 - 2x - 15 = 0$

11 $x^2 - 2x + 1 = 0$ **17** $x^2 + 3x - 10 = 0$ **23** $x^2 - 3x - 28 = 0$

12 $x^2 + 6x = 0$ **18** $x^2 = 5x$ **24** $x^2 - 17x + 30 = 0$

13 $x^2 - 10x + 24 = 0$ **19** $x^2 - x - 12 = 0$ **25** $x^2 + 4x = 32$

14 $x^2 + 4x + 3 = 0$ **20** $x^2 + 5x - 14 = 0$ **26** $x^2 + 9x = 36$

15 $x^2 - 225 = 0$ **21** $x^2 = 3x$ **27** $x^2 + x = 20$

Rearranging formulae

All the formulae that you have rearranged previously contained the new subject only once, and also the subject was not raised to a power. This is now extended in the following examples.

EXAMPLE 7

Rearrange the formula $A = \pi r^2$ to make r the subject.

$A = \pi r^2$

$\dfrac{A}{\pi} = r^2$ — Divide both sides by r.

$r^2 = \dfrac{A}{\pi}$ — Rearrange to get all terms involving r on the left hand side.

$r = \sqrt{\dfrac{A}{\pi}}$ — Take the square root of both sides.

EXAMPLE 8

Rearrange the formula $V = \frac{4}{3}\pi r^3$ to make r the subject.

$3V = 4\pi r^3$ — Multiply both sides by 3.

$4\pi r^3 = 3V$ — Rearrange to get all terms involving r on the left hand side.

$r^3 = \dfrac{3V}{4\pi}$ — Divide both sides by 4π.

$r = \sqrt[3]{\dfrac{3V}{4\pi}}$ — Take the cube root of both sides.

Chapter 21 *Equations and formulae*

EXAMPLE 9

Rearrange the formula $a = x + \dfrac{cx}{d}$ to make x the subject.

$ad = dx + cx$	Multiply both sides by d.
$dx + cx = ad$	Rearrange to get all terms involving x (the subject) on the left-hand side.
$x(d + c) = ad$	Factorise the left-hand side taking out the factor x.
$x = \dfrac{ad}{d + c}$	Divide both sides by the bracket $(d + c)$.

EXAMPLE 10

Rearrange the equation $ax + by = cy - ad$ to make a the subject.

$ax + ad = cy - by$	Rearrange to get all terms involving a on the left-hand side and all the other terms on the right-hand side. This is done by adding ad to both sides and subtracting by from both sides.
$a(x + d) = cy - by$	Factorise the left-hand side taking out the factor a.
$a = \dfrac{cy - by}{x + d}$	Divide both sides by the bracket $(x + d)$.

EXERCISE 21.2A

For each question make the letter shown afterwards in brackets the subject.

1   $s = at + 2bt$ $\qquad$ (t)

2   $P = t - \dfrac{at}{b}$ $\qquad$ (t)

3   $A = 4\pi r^2$ $\qquad$ (r)

4   $ab - cd = ac$ $\qquad$ (a)

5   $ab - cd = ac$ $\qquad$ (c)

6   $s - 2ax = b(x - s)$ $\qquad$ (s)

7   $s - 2ax = b(x - s)$ $\qquad$ (x)

8   $a = \dfrac{t}{b} - st$ $\qquad$ (t)

9   $a = b + c^2$ $\qquad$ (c)

10 $A = P + \dfrac{PRT}{100}$ $\qquad$ (P)

EXERCISE 21.2B

For each question make the letter shown afterwards in brackets the subject.

1 $s = ab - bc$ (*b*)

2 $v^2 = u^2 + 2as$ (*u*)

3 $3(a + y) = by + 7$ (*y*)

4 $2(a - 1) = b(1 - 2a)$ (*a*)

5 $\dfrac{a}{b} - 2a = b$ (*a*)

6 $s = 2r^2 - 1$ (*r*)

7 $a(b + d) = c(b - d)$ (*d*)

8 $a(b + d) = c(b - d)$ (*b*)

9 $V = 5ab^2 + 3c^3$ (*c*)

10 $s = \dfrac{uv}{u + v}$ (*v*)

Key ideas

- To solve quadratic equations first rearrange the equation so that all the terms are on the left, leaving 0 on the right-hand side.

- Then factorise the left-hand side and put each factor equal to zero.

- To rearrange a formula where the subject occurs twice, first rearrange the formula so that all the terms containing the subject are on one side and all the other terms are on the other. Then take the subject out as a common factor. Finally divide by the other factor.

- To rearrange a formula where the subject (r) is squared, first make r^2 the subject, then find the square root of both sides. If the subject is cubed then the cube root is used.

Revision exercise

1 Simplify, without using your calculator.

a) $\sqrt{32}$ **b)** $\sqrt{150}$ **c)** $\sqrt{128}$
d) $\sqrt{54}$ **e)** $\sqrt{60}$ **f)** $\sqrt{80}$
g) $\sqrt{500}$ **h)** $\sqrt{98}$

2 Simplify, without using your calculator.

a) $\sqrt{12} \times \sqrt{75}$ **b)** $\sqrt{10} \times \sqrt{18}$
c) $\sqrt{72} \div 3$ **d)** $\sqrt{288} \times \sqrt{48}$

3 Without using your calculator, find the area of these shapes. Leave your answers in terms of π.

a)   **b)**

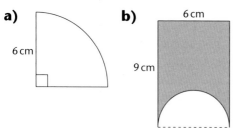

4 Multiply out these brackets and simplify your answers.

a) $(x + 6)(x + 3)$ **b)** $(x + 7)(x - 4)$
c) $(a - 6)(a + 5)$ **d)** $(b - 3)^2$
e) $(x - 5)(x - 8)$ **f)** $(p + 3)(p - 3)$
g) $(a + 8)^2$ **h)** $(x + 8)(x - 8)$

5 Factorise these.

a) $x^2 + 5x + 4$ **b)** $x^2 - 6x + 8$
c) $x^2 - 10x + 16$ **d)** $x^2 + 8x + 15$
e) $x^2 - 6x - 7$ **f)** $x^2 - 3x - 10$
g) $x^2 - 8x + 12$ **h)** $x^2 - 2x - 15$
i) $x^2 - 3x - 70$ **j)** $x^2 + 16x + 48$
k) $x^2 - 7x - 18$ **l)** $x^2 + 8x - 20$

6 Factorise these.

a) $a^2 - 64$ **b)** $x^2 - 9$
c) $p^2 - 100$ **d)** $x^2 - 196$

7 A prism 25 cm long has this L-shape as its cross-section. Calculate the volume of the prism.

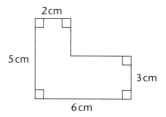

8 A cylindrical vase has internal radius 5·6 cm and height 22·5 cm. Calculate how many litres of water this vase can hold.

9 The diagram shows a full-size net for a triangular prism. Use measurements from the drawing to calculate

a) the surface area
b) the volume of the prism.

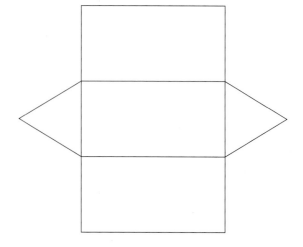

10 In these expressions, r and h are lengths. State which of length, area and volume is represented by each of these expressions.

  a) $\pi rh + \pi r^2$
  b) $\frac{1}{2}(r + h)$
  c) $3r^2h$

11 Find the missing powers in these formulae.

  a) volume $= \frac{1}{3}\pi^? h$
  b) area $= 6r^?$
  c) length $= \dfrac{r^?}{h^2}$

12 The diagram shows the cross-section of a prism which is 8 cm long. Calculate

  a) the height of the trapezium
  b) the volume of the prism.
  c) the total surface area of the prism.

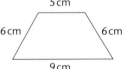

13 The table shows the number of unemployed people at the end of each quarter in Devon to the nearest 100. The months indicate the end of the quarter for which the figures are given.

	January	April	July	October
1996	41 700	38 300	35 600	33 100
1997	33 800	28 500	24 600	23 500
1998	26 600	24 000	22 200	21 100
1999	23 800	20 900	18 900	17 700

  a) Plot these figures in a graph. Use a scale of 1 cm to each quarter on the horizontal axis and 2 cm to 10 000 people on the vertical axis.
  b) Calculate the four-quarter moving averages.
  c) Plot the moving averages on your graph.
  d) Comment on the general trend and the quarterly variation.

14 Solve the quadratic equations.

  a) $x^2 - 6x + 8 = 0$
  b) $x^2 + 5x + 6 = 0$
  c) $x^2 - 2x - 3 = 0$
  d) $x^2 - 3x - 10 = 0$
  e) $x^2 - 5x + 4 = 0$
  f) $x^2 + 7x + 10 = 0$
  g) $x^2 - 5x - 14 = 0$
  h) $x^2 + 17x + 30 = 0$
  i) $x^2 - 9x + 20 = 0$
  j) $x^2 + 4x + 3 = 0$
  k) $x^2 - 9x - 36 = 0$
  l) $x^2 + 7x - 18 = 0$

15 Solve these quadratic equations.

  a) $x^2 + 8x = 0$ **b)** $x^2 - 5x = 0$
  c) $x^2 = 64$ **d)** $x^2 - 100 = 0$
  e) $x^2 = 10x$ **f)** $x^2 - 4x = 5$
  g) $x^2 + 2x = 8$ **h)** $x^2 = 8x + 9$

16 Make the letter shown afterwards in brackets the subject of these formulae.

  a) $x = by + a^2$ (a)
  b) $y = x + ay$ (y)
  c) $ab - cd = bx$ (b)
  d) $ab + cd = ac - bd$ (b)
  e) $A = b^3 + 3c^2d$ (b)

INDEX